VIOLENCE
THROUGH A
FORENSIC LENS

Ann Wolbert Burgess
University of Pennsylvania
School of Nursing

A Nursing Spectrum Publication
King of Prussia, PA
2000

Cover Design by Julie Juern, Nursing Spectrum

Nursing Spectrum is a media company that promotes the recognition and support of the nursing community. Our regionally targeted magazines, Career Fitness® website, and our recruitment and career management services are the foundation of our business. Through our RN-led staff, we provide timely, relevant, and compelling information, while offering cost-effective, innovative services, events, and products.

Nursing Spectrum
Division of Continuing Education
2002 Renaissance Blvd., Ste. 120
King of Prussia, PA 19406
(610) 275-4100
(800) 866-0919
ce@nursingspectrum.com
www.nursingspectrum.com

Printed and bound in the United States of America.

First edition

ISBN: 1-930745-00-1

Library of Congress Card Number: 00-102943

CONTENTS

Preface

Crime and criminals exert a certain fascination over our society. Crime sells books and newspapers and captures our attention on television. The interest seems to focus on what makes people commit the crimes they commit and the way they commit them.

A series of institutions – hospitals, law enforcement agencies, and courts – deal with crime and its victims. When a crime is reported, these institutions go into motion to process both the victim and offender. Studies on the course of the criminal through this institutional maze are numerous, but less scientific attention has been given to how the victim proceeds through the same labyrinth. Burgess and a colleague, Holmstrom, attempted to correct this oversight in 1979 (and updated in 1983) with the publication of a study of rape victims.

Following this study, over a 15 year period, Burgess teamed with several supervisory special agents at the FBI Academy in Quantico, Virginia – John Douglas, Robert Hazelwood, Ken Lanning, and Bob Ressler – to study sexual homicide, autoerotic fatalities, child pornography, and infant abduction, and to devise a classification system for violent crime.

Concurrent with the study of offenders, Boston College Professor Carol Hartman joined Burgess to develop a model of the way trauma was perceived and processed. This research expanded into studying some of the indirect aspects of victimization – threats and stalking.

Much of the research was funded through federal agencies, including the National Center on Child Abuse and Neglect, the National Institute of Justice, the Office of Juvenile Justice and Delinquency Prevention, and the National Institutes of Health. The National Center for Missing and Exploited Children published a series of monographs and Cases-in-Point from the serial offender study. This book is a clinical primer and includes research findings adapted from the various scientific papers and publications that are reprinted with permission.

Introduction

Violence in our society is documented statistically in the FBI Crime Reports and National Crime Surveys and clinically in the number of victims admitted to emergency departments of trauma centers and hospitals. While substantial literature addresses the perpetrator of the crime, it has only been in the last quarter of the 20th century that publication focusing on the victim has increased.

When a crime victim is admitted to a hospital for trauma care, emergency nurses become involved. As the patient recovers, additional specialty nurses, such as psychiatric, community health, home care, and rehabilitation nurses, may become involved. If an offender is arrested, the case will go into the judicial system, or if a civil suit is filed, the nurse may be called as a testifying or expert witness. Thus, all nurses need to be aware of the manner in which they document their assessments of injury, how they assist in the collection and preservation of evidence, and how coordinate critical data with law enforcement and crime scene officers.[1] This book serves as a primer for nurses who care for victims, their families, and, on occasion, offenders.

Forensic

The term "forensic" is derived from the Latin *forens(is)*: Of or belonging to the forum of public. By extension it also came to mean argumentative, rhetorical, belonging to debate or discussion. In contemporary terms, forensic means pertaining to, connected with, or used in courts of judicature or public discussion and debate. Thus the forensic sciences include the application of specialized scientific and/or technical knowledge to questions of criminal and civil law, especially in court proceedings.

There are many specialty areas that practice within a legal arena and employ the principles of forensic science. It is the interface of the specialty and law that produces a forensic case. Such specialties include forensic pathology, forensic medicine, forensic nursing, forensic dentistry, forensic radiology, forensic photography, forensic social work, and forensic accounting, to name a few.

Historically, the term forensic was connected with death and homicide. And until the second half of the 20th century, one kind of forensic science dominated – forensic pathology, which is mainly concerned with the scientific investigation of death. Clinical forensic practice, on the other hand, is a contemporary forensic science, and it's primarily concerned with the survivor of violent crime or liability-related trauma. It is the clinician rather than the pathologist who concerns him or herself with investigating injuries. The sexual assault examiner is one such contemporary clinician.[2]

Healthcare practice can embrace a large number of legal issues, for example, age determination, assault, inheritance, larceny, malpractice, parentage, personal injury, genetics, product liability, organ transplants, sexual offenses, virginity, and wrongful birth or death. Evidence of the origin of forensic practice is medicine, traced to records of ancient people thousands of years ago whenever a law appeared to influence medicine. The Egyptian, Imhotep, is believed to be one of the first to apply both the law and medicine to his surroundings. In about 2200 BC Hammurabi was said to have codified medical law, and medicolegal issues were covered in early Jewish law. Later, other civilizations evolved jurisprudential standards involving medical fact or opinion.[3,4]

History tells us that early cultures recognized the importance of controlling the organization, duties, and liabilities of the medical profession. These cultures were also aware of the importance of the knowledge and opinions of the medical person in the legal consideration of issues, such as the use of poisons, the duration of pregnancy, superfetation (conception during pregnancy), the prognosis of wounds in different body locations (a physician determined that only one of Caesar's 23 stab wounds was fatal), sterility and impotence, sexual deviations, and suspicious death.[5]

The first separate discipline of forensic medicine began early in the 16th century. New codes of law required expert testimony in trials of certain types of crime or civil action. The first medicolegal books appeared in the late 16th and early 17th centuries, and after 1650, lectures on legal medicine were given in Germany and France. The first book on medical jurisprudence in the English language appeared in 1788. The English coroner's system was imported to the colonies in 1607, and in 1871, Massachusetts established a medical examiner system.

Forensic nursing's history has been traced to the 18th century when midwives were called into court on issues pertaining to virginity, pregnancy, and rape. The contemporary role of forensic nurses has become steadily visible since the 1970s and includes practice as death investigators and sexual assault nurse examiners.

Advanced practice forensic nurses work with crime victims and their families as well as individuals with liability-related injuries resulting from automobile or pedestrian accidents, occupation-related injuries, disputed paternity, and malpractice and resulting injuries. The forensic nurse has a vital role in cases resulting from intentional or unintentional acts involving criminality or civil action. In this medicolegal arena, practice requires a knowledge of where human behavior interfaces with the law.[2]

References

1. Schram C. Forensic medicine: what the perioperative nurse needs to know. *Am Operating Room Nurs J.* 1991;53:3.
2. Lynch VA, Burgess AW. Forensic nursing. In: Burgess AW, ed. *Advanced Practice Psychiatric Nursing.* Stamford, CT: Appleton Lange;1998:473-457.
3. Camps FE, ed. *Gradwohl's Legal Medicine.* 3rd ed. Chicago, IL: Yearbook; 1976.
4. Wecht CH. Forensic use of medical information. In: *Legal Medicine: Legal Dynamics of Medical Encounter.* 2nd ed. St. Louis, MO: Mosby-Yearbook; 1991:chap 47.
5. Brogdon BG. *Forensic Radiology.* Boca Raton, FL: CRC Press; 1998.

Part 1
Crime and Homicide

Chapter 1 – Anatomy of a Crime

Crime scenes tell an important story of the crime. The analysis of the crime scene seeks out those messages that will lead to the answers needed to solve the crime: How it happened, why it happened, and to whom it happened. In addition, the analyst requires a clear mental image of the total picture formed by these details.

An understanding of the dynamics of human behavior is required in analyzing a crime. Patterns of behavior encompass personality, and these individualistic patterns usually remains consistent, whether it concerns running a household, selecting a wardrobe, or committing a rape or murder.

The commission of a violent crime involves all the same dynamics of "normal" human behavior. The same forces that influence normal everyday conduct also influence the subject's actions during an offense. Thus, the crime scene usually reflects these behavior patterns or gestures.

Behavior reflects personality. Although each crime is different, behavior fits into certain patterns. Picking out the significant pieces of those patterns translates to figure out what is going on and more importantly, answers the question "Why?" And that leads to the ultimate answer: "Who."

Let's look at two relatively straight forward crimes. On the surface they look similar, but they are really very different.

Crime 1: A young woman returns to her apartment and finds several items missing – a stereo, VCR, TV, and cash.

Crime 2: A young woman returns to her apartment and notices that although it has been broken into, apparently all that is missing is some of her underwear. She calls the police and they investigate. They locate the window that was broken into and find evidence that someone had been masturbating outside the window.

Both crimes are burglaries. Is the offender in one more dangerous than the other? How do we know?

The difference is motive. How do we know? Because of research and experience. The first offender, a criminal enterprise burglar, steals with a profit in mind, and because he wants merchandise. The second offender did not take women's underwear to fence it or because he could not buy his own. His motive has to do with fantasy. And his crime has probably advanced from voyeurism to breaking and entering.

Similar burglaries but vastly different burglars.

Indirect Criminal Acts

A crime is generally composed of two types of acts: direct and indirect. The direct act is quite clear to the victim. He or she is robbed, burglarized, abducted, assaulted, raped, molested, mutilated, or murdered. Direct criminal acts are designed to physically control and injure. Criminal statutes identify the act in specific detail.

However, indirect acts are less visible because there is no physical contact. Criminals use them in specific ways either to heighten a fantasy, for sexual gratification, to give courage to act, or to deliberately weaken the victim. Examples of indirect sexual acts include obscene telephone calls, exhibitionism, and voyeurism. Statutes for these indirect acts are difficult to enforce because there is no physical contact between the victim and offender. Law enforcement often labels these acts as nuisance offenses. Two other types of indirect act, threats and stalking, will be discussed in a separate chapter.

Nuisance Offenses

The *Crime Classification Manual* describes four separate categories for nuisance offenses.[1] The offense occurs for sexual gratification and the offender has no physical contact with the victim.

Isolated/Opportunistic Offenses: These offenses are isolated incidents of individuals who take an opportunity or something presents itself. For example, they call someone and get a wrong number and blurt out an obscenity. Or they are in a public place after having too much to drink, and they urinate as a woman walks by or

4

turn and expose themselves. Another example is an offender who walks down a street and takes advantage of an opportunity to look into a window at something sexually stimulating.

Preferential Offenses: Preferential offenses relate to the psychiatric diagnoses termed the *paraphilias*. The acts are the individual's preferred sexual acts. This is the true voyeur or the true exhibitionist. Sexual gratification is intended from the act. These are the individuals for whom this has been a long-term pattern of compulsive behavior. The individual may have regular routes for window peeping or elaborate procedures covering such behavior, such as walking a dog. In some cases, the offender carries a video camera to record his sexual interest.

The key to this case is for the investigator to have the time to discover the evidence. There will be rigid, ritual patterns of behavior. The offenders return to specific areas over and over for peeping, or they expose themselves in certain places. They repeatedly make telephone calls, which makes them easy to trace.

Transition Offenses: The transition offender may be caught in a peeping act, but he is trying to find out if the act is capable of producing sexual gratification. He is exploring his arousal patterns, building confidence, and improving his ability to commit crime. This offender is often a younger individual, such as a teenager who is exploring his sexuality and starts out peeping. However, this is just an early step in his criminal sexual development. Although not all nuisance sex offenders progress to more serious offenses, some do.

Preliminary Offenses: A preliminary offender is an individual whose nuisance offense is a preliminary aspect to contact sexual offenses. He may be a fetish burglar who cases a home before returning to commit a rape. This noncontact offense is a prelude to other serious sex offenses.

A key question to ask about nuisance offenders is whether or not they are dangerous. Two points to evaluate: focus and escalation.

Do the crimes have a focus? Is there a pattern occurring over and over? Anything that indicates there is a pattern, such as an offender calling the same number repeatedly or exposing himself at the same location, should be evaluated carefully. The most important aspect of focus to evaluate is victim focus. Are victims being selected at random, or is a specific individual being targeted?

Is there escalation? Has this individual escalated his behavior from peeping outside to burglarizing an indoor location? Is he progressing to more serious invasive activity over time?

Two additional indirect acts are threats and stalking. Each dangerous behavior is discussed in a separate chapter.

Assessing For Motive

There are three manifestations of offender behavior at a crime scene: modus operandi, personation, and staging. All are analyzed in determining motive.

Modus Operandi: The offender's actions during the commission of a crime form the modus operandi (MO). The offender develops and uses an MO over time because it works, but it also continuously evolves. The MO is very dynamic and malleable. During a subject's criminal career, an offender usually modifies the MO as the he gains experience. The burglar refines his breaking and entering techniques to lower his risk of apprehension and increase his profit. Experience and confidence will reshape an offender's MO. Incarceration usually impacts on the future MO of a subject, especially the career criminal. He refines the MO as he learns from the mistakes that led to his arrest. MO is a learned behavior.

The victim's response can also significantly influence the evolution of an MO. If the rapist has problems controlling a victim, he will modify his MO to accommodate resistance. He may bring duct tape or other ligatures, he may use a weapon, or he may blitz the victim and immediately incapacitate her. If such measures are ineffective, he may resort to greater violence or kill the victim. Thus, the MO will evolve to meet the demands of the crime. In one case, a rapist described how he would run up to women and put his hands around their breasts. One woman laughed at him and struck him with an umbrella. He carried a knife when he attacked his next victim. He learned how to control a woman's response.

Personation: Unusual behavior by an offender, beyond that necessary to commit the crime is called personation. The offender invests intimate meaning into the crime scene, for example, by body positioning, mutilation, items removed or left, or other symbolic gestures involving the crime scene. Only the offender knows the meaning of these acts. When a serial offender demonstrates repetitive ritualistic behavior from crime to crime, it is called the signature. The signature aspect of a crime is simply repetitive personation.

6

Most violent crime careers have a secret, isolated beginning within the offender's imagination. The subject daydreams about raping, torturing, killing, building bombs, setting fires, or any combination of these violent acts. When the offender translates these daydreams into action, his needs compel him to exhibit unusual behavior during the crime.

Police found a 26-year-old white female on the roof of her apartment in New York City. She had died of ligature strangulation. The offender left her body face up and positioned to resemble a Jewish religious medal. He had carefully removed her earrings and placed them on either side of her head. He had cut her nipples off and placed them on her chest. The offender also had inserted her umbrella into her vagina and placed her comb into her pubic hair. He then placed the victim's nylons around her wrists and ankles. He scrawled a derogatory message to the police on her body using her pen. Finally, he left a pile of his own feces, covered with her clothing, a few feet from the body. The team assessed all of this activity as being postmortem. A few inexpensive articles of jewelry were missing, including the Jewish religious medal that resembled the body's positioning.

This crime scene displayed some unusual input by this offender. The perpetration of this crime did not require the positioning of the body, the postmortem mutilation, insertion, removal of items, and use of postmortem ligatures. The significance of this behavior was not readily apparent to the investigator. The act of sexual assault and murder had little to do with most of this subject's behavior at the crime scene. His behavior went far beyond the actions necessary to carry out this offense (the MO), because assault and murder alone would not satisfy his needs.

"Undoing" represents a form of personation with more obvious meaning. Undoing frequently occurs at the crime scene when there is a close association between the offender and victim, or the victim represents someone of significance to the offender. The following case exemplifies undoing.

A son stabbed his mother to death during a fierce argument. After calming down, the full impact of the son's actions hit him. First, he changed her bloodied shirt, then placed the body on the couch with the head on a pillow. He covered her with a blanket and folded her hands over her chest, so she appeared to be sleeping peacefully. He displayed his remorse by attempting to emotionally "undo" the murder.

Other forms of undoing include the offender washing up, cleaning the body up, covering the victim's face, or completely covering the body with something.

Signature: Another element of criminal behavior is the signature aspect or "calling card." This pattern of behavior is a specific and integral part of the offender's behavior while committing the offense.

A subject's fantasies generally underlie violent crime. As the offender broods and daydreams, he develops a need to express these violent fantasies. When he finally acts out, some aspect of the crime will demonstrate a unique, personal expression or ritual based on these fantasies. Committing the crime does not satisfy the offender's needs. This insufficiency compels him to go beyond the scope of perpetration and perform his ritual. When the subject displays this ritual at the crime scene, he has left his "calling card."

How does the crime scene manifest this "calling card" or signature aspect? The subject introduces an aspect of his personality into the scene through this ritual. The crime scene displays this aspect by peculiar crime scene characteristics or unusual offender input during the perpetration of the crime. A rapist demonstrates his signature by engaging in acts of domination, manipulation, or control, during the verbal, physical, and/or sexual phase of the assault. Exceptionally vulgar and/or abusive language or scripting represents a verbal signature. When the offender scripts a victim, he dictates a particular verbal response from her, for example, "Tell me how much you enjoy sex with me" or "Tell me how good I am." The use of excessive physical force exemplifies another aspect of a subject's signature. One example of signature sexual behavior involved an offender who repeatedly engaged in a specific order of sexual activity with different victims. Another rapist was noted by several victims to turn his back when redressing.

The core of the offender's ritual will never change. Unlike the MO, it remains a constant and enduring part of the offender. However, signature aspects may evolve, for example, the lust murderer, who performs greater postmortem mutilation as he progresses from crime to crime. Elements of the original ritual become more fully developed. In addition, the signature doesn't always show up in every crime because of contingencies arising, like interruptions or an unexpected victim response.

The signature aspect cannot always be determined. Violent offenses often involve high-risk victims or decomposition from outdoor body disposal that interferes with the recognition of the signature.

Modus Operandi or Signature Crime?

A rapist entered a residence and captured a woman and her husband. The offender ordered the husband to lie on his stomach on the floor. He then placed a cup and saucer on the husband's back. "If I hear that cup move or hit the floor, your wife dies," he told the husband. He then took the wife into the next room and raped her.

In another situation, a rapist entered the house and ordered the woman to phone her husband and use some ploy to get him home. Once the husband arrived, the offender tied the husband to a chair and forced him to witness the rape of his wife.

The rapist who used the cup and saucer had developed an effective MO to control the husband. The second rapist, however, had gone beyond the simple commission of rape. The full satisfaction of his fantasies not only required raping the wife, but humiliating and dominating the husband. His personal needs compelled him to perform this signature aspect of crime.

In Michigan, a certain bank robber made the tellers undress during the robbery. In Texas, another bank robber also forced the bank employees to undress, but then made them pose in sexually provocative positions as he snapped photographs. Do both these crimes demonstrate a signature aspect? The Michigan robber used a very effective means to increase his escape time (i.e., the tellers dressed before summoning the police). When interviewed, these employees offered vague, meager descriptions because their embarrassment had prevented eye contact with the perpetrator. This subject had developed a clever MO. The Texas robber, however, went beyond the required actions to successfully perpetrate his crime. He felt compelled to enact the ritual of posing the tellers and taking pictures, leaving his signature on the crime. The act of robbing the bank did not gratify his psychosexual needs.

Staging

Staging is when someone purposely alters the crime scene before the arrival of the police. There are two reasons why someone employs staging: to redirect the investigation away from the most logical suspect, or to protect the victim or victim's family.

When a crime is staged, the responsible person is not someone who just happens upon the victim. It is almost always someone who had some kind of association or relationship with the victim. This offender will further attempt to steer the investigation away from him by his conduct when in contact with law enforcement. Investigators should never eliminate a suspect solely on the grounds of the subject's overly cooperative or distraught behavior.

The second reason for staging, to protect the victim or victim's family, is employed most frequently with rape-murder crimes or autoerotic fatalities. One can hardly fault this behavior, but the investigator needs to obtain an accurate description of the body's condition when found and exactly what that person did to alter the crime scene. Forensics, victimology, and minute crime scene details become critical to the detection of staging.

Red Flags at the Crime Scene

Mistakes are made in staging because the criminal designs it the way he thinks a crime scene should look. While doing this, the offender experiences a great deal of stress and does not have time to logically fit all the pieces together. Inconsistencies will begin appearing at the crime scene, with forensics and with the overall picture of the offense. These contradictions will often serve as the "red flags" of staging.

Did the subject take inappropriate items from the crime scene, if burglary appears the motive? For example, a man is killed after returning home from work and interrupting a burglary in progress. The burglars had passed over items of worth (jewelry). Police soon discovered the wife (who was having an affair) had paid the offenders to stage the burglary and kill her husband.

Did the point of entry make sense, for example, entering a house through by a second-story window? Did the crime pose a high risk to the offender, such as occurring during daylight hours, in a populated area, with obvious signs of occupation at the house (lights on, vehicles in the driveway), and/or involving highly visible entry points? In one case, the ladder left no impressions in the yard and was positioned backwards with the rungs going in the wrong direction. In staged domestic murders, the offender escapes without injury or with a nonfatal injury.

There are forensic red flags and the question needs to be asked: Do the injuries fit the crime? If not, consider staging. Sexual and domestic homicides are usually committed at close range and are a personalized assault. The victim (not money or goods) is the primary focus of the offender. The offender prefers a quick, clean kill that reduces his time at the scene.

Does the witness/survivor's story conflict with the forensic findings. In one case, an estranged wife found her husband in the bathroom tub with the water running. Initially, it appeared as if he slipped in the tub, struck his head on a bathroom fixture, and drowned. However, the toxicology reports revealed a high level of diazepam (Valium) in the victim's blood stream at the time of death, and the autopsy revealed several concentrated areas of injury or impact points on the head, as if he had struck his head more than once. Later, investigators learned the wife had been with him the night of his death. The wife later confessed that she made dinner for her ex-husband and laced his salad with diazepam. After her husband passed out, she let three men in the house she had hired to kill him and make it look accidental.

References

1. Douglas JE, Ressler RK, Burgess AW, Burgess AG. *Crime Classification Manual.* San Francisco, CA: Jossey-Bass; 1995.

Chapter 2 – Crime Classification

This chapter includes a brief outline of the history of classifying crime and the assessment process adapted from the Crime Classification Manual that crime analysts use in determining motive for the crime and the resultant classification of that crime.

Historical Perspective

Understanding behavior and methodology has been a challenge to the civilized world. The term "dangerous classes" has been used throughout history to describe individuals who are deemed a threat to law and order. Initially the term described the environment in which one lived, or was found to be living in, versus the reality of any type of crime being committed. An example of this occurred in England at the end of the Hundred Years' War with France. The demobilization of thousands of soldiers coupled with the changing economic trade market saw the displacement of farmers increase the homeless population nationwide.[1] During the reign of England's King Henry the VIII, 72,000 major and minor thieves were hanged. Under his daughter Queen Elizabeth I, vagabonds were strung up in rows, as many as 300 and 400 at a time.[1]

The categorization of these individuals began to change in 1838 when the winning entry at the French *Academie des Sciences Morales et Politiques* was titled, *The Dangerous Classes of the Population in the Great Cities, and the Means of Making Them Better*.[1] The dangerous-class term was then used to describe individuals who were criminals or who had such potential. Initially these included the poor, homeless, and unemployed of the large cities.

Beginning classification of offenders began in the work of statistics. These early works permitted a comparison of the incidence of crime with factors, such as race, age, sex, education, and geography.[1] Cesare Lombrosos, the famed Italian physician, is generally credited with launching the scientific era in criminology. In 1872 he differentiated five types of criminals: the born criminal, the insane criminal, the criminal by passion, the habitual criminal, and the occasional criminal.[2]

This early classification system was based on Darwin's theory of evolution. Operational definitions for the five groups were developed, which allowed for subsequent investigators to test Lombrosos's formulations empirically. A majority of his hypotheses and theories proved to be invalid, but the fact that they were testable was an advancement for the science.[3]

Typologies of crime traditionally have been developed addressing the criminal offense. The psychiatric perspective to understanding crime has used two approaches: scrutiny of the inner (mental and moral) world of the criminal offender and examination of the external (social) world in which he lives.[4]

The investigation of the psychological motivations and social stresses that underlie crime has proved that those behavior patterns involved in criminal acts are not far removed from those of normal behavior. Studies indicate that criminal behavior, as is true of all behavior, is responsive to inner and outer stresses.

Crime is part of the human condition; the forces that make for crime are difficult to lay hold of or to control, but though they are widespread, elusive, and seemingly outside the scope of social coexistence, they are not beyond our conception. Criminal behavior is suggested to derive from three behavioral areas: (1) the aggressive tendency, both destructive and acquisitive; (2) passive, or subverted, aggression; and (3) psychological needs.[4]

Classification of criminal offenders has been and is currently an important component in correctional facilities throughout this country. In 1973 the National Advisory Commission called for criminal classification programs to be initiated throughout the criminal justice system.[3] This proved to be a difficult task to undertake. The correctional system is a complex, expanding, expensive operation that has accountability to society, individual communities, correctional staff, and to the inmates themselves. The current trend within the correctional system has been growth of the inmate population with a modest growth in facilities. As the population within the system is faced with economic and now medical issues (such as AIDS), classification is an cost-effective and efficient management and treatment tool.

In the 1980s, a research team at the Massachusetts Treatment Center in Bridgewater, MA, began a program of research to classify sexual offenders.[5] Their application of a programmatic approach to typology construction and validation has produced taxonomic systems for both child molesters and rapists. The former has demonstrated reasonable reliability and consistent ties to distinctive developmental antecedents. In addition, preliminary results of a 25-year recidivism study of child molesters indicates that aspects of the model have important prognostic implications.[6]

Contemporary Crime Classification

The work of investigative analysts at the FBI Academy with the large number of cases seen weekly has led to an expansion of these traditional crime categories. Over a 10-year period, FBI agents John Douglas and Robert Ressler worked with their team of special agents at the FBI Academy's National Center for the Analysis of Violent Crime in Quantico, VA, to develop a diagnostic system to standardize terminology of crime. They formally categorized the critical characteristics of the perpetrators and victims of three major crimes: murder, arson, and sexual assault. The data base for this project came from several research projects on serial offenders funded by the Department of Justice. The result of this project was the publication of a book, the *Crime Classification Manual (CCM)*.[7] The *CCM* is the first step to make explicit crime.

Crime Characteristics

To classify a crime using the *CCM*, questions about the defining characteristics of the crime need to be answered. These characteristics include information about the victim, the crime scene, and the nature of the victim-offender exchange.

Victimology

Victimology is the complete history of the victim and is the crucial part in the anatomy of a crime. The critical question is to evaluate why this particular person was targeted for a violent crime – the answer to which will lead to motive.

The relationship of the victim to the offender: Was the victim known to the offender and if so, was it through family, work, school, or the neighborhood?

Risk levels: Was the victim low-, medium-, or high-risk, that is, what were the victim's chances of becoming a target for violent crime? Low-risk victims are those whose personal, professional, and social lives would not normally expose them to crime-threatening situations. Such victims are usually sought out by the offender. Medium-risk victims have elevated their risk through employment, lifestyle, or personal habits. High-risk victims are those whose lifestyles or employment consistently expose them to danger from the criminal element (residential location, drug dealing, or sexual lifestyle).

Also relevant is what risk did the offender take in perpetrating this crime? Where did the crime occur and at what time? Were witnesses present?

Verbal Exchange: What was said between victim and offender. Were there threats and/or orders. Vulgar or abusive language, scripting, or apologetic language are common to a certain type of offender.

The nature of the confrontation between the victim and offender: Did the offender control the victim verbally? Are restraints present at the scene, or did the offender immediately blitz and incapacitate the victim?

Crime Scene Indicators

Number of Crime Scenes: There may be one site, as in a group-excitement homicide. In contrast, a product tamperer may taint the product at one location and then put it on shelves in several stores. The victim may consume the product in one location, but die in another. In this case, there are at least four crime scenes involved.

The use of several locales during the commission of an offense gives insight into the nature of the offender. One example is the disorganized sexual killer who may confront, assault, kill, and leave the body all in the same location. In contrast, the organized killer may abduct, assault, kill, and dispose of the victim using separate locations for each event.

Environment: The environment of a crime scene refers to the conditions or circumstances in which the offense occurs. Is it indoors or outside? Was it during daylight hours or in the middle of the night? Did it happen on a busy street or a deserted country road? Answering these questions not only assists in defining the classification of an offense, but provides an assessment of the offender risk.

How long did the offender stay at the scene? Generally, the length of time offenders spend at the scene is proportional to the degree of comfort they feel committing the offense at that particular location. Evidence of a lingering offender may point towards a suspect who lives or works near the crime scene, knows the neighborhood, and consequently, feels at ease there.

Offenders: How many offenders were involved in the crime? The answer to this question will help determine whether to place the offense into either the criminal enterprise category or the group cause category.

Organized or Disorganized: The overall condition of the crime scene is very important in classifying a crime. Is it like a group excitement offense – spontaneous and disarrayed with a great deal of physical evidence at the scene? Or does the crime scene reflect a methodical, well-organized subject who didn't leave a single print or piece of physical evidence behind? The latter may be seen with an organized crime hit, as in the criminal competition category.

The condition of the crime scene will suggest the offender's level of criminal sophistication. It will also demonstrate how well the offender was able to control the victim and how much premeditation was involved with the crime. The crime scene will rarely be completely organized or disorganized. It is more likely to be somewhere on a continuum between the two extremes of the orderly, "neat" crime scene and the disarrayed, sloppy one.

Weapon: Was a weapon used? Was it a weapon of choice, brought to the crime scene by the offender? Or was it a weapon of opportunity acquired at the scene? With rape, did the offender take a knife from the victim's kitchen? Is the weapon absent from the crime scene or has it been left behind? Was there evidence of multiple weapons and ammunition? Multiple weaponry doesn't always signify multiple offenders. Authority killing and nonspecific motive killing are examples of offenses that often involve the use of multiple firearms and ammunition by a lone offender.

Body Disposition: Was the body openly displayed or otherwise placed in a deliberate manner to ensure discovery? Or was the body concealed or buried to prevent discovery? Did the offender seem to have no concern as to whether the body would be discovered or not? Disorganized sexual homicide may involve the intentional arranging of the body in an unnatural or unusual position; in cult or drug murder, the body may be left in a degrading position or in a location to convey a message.

Items Left/Missing: The addition or absence of items at the crime scene can assist in classifying the offense. The presence of unusual artifacts, drawings, graffiti, or other items may be seen with offenses such as extremist murder or street gang murder. Offender communication (e.g., a ransom demand or extortion note) frequently will be associated with the crime scene of a kidnap murder or product tampering.

Items taken from the scene as a crime scene indicator is found in felony murder, breaking and entering, arson for crime concealment, and felony sexual assault. A victim's personal belongings may be taken from a rape victim as souvenirs (i.e., photos, driver's license, costume jewelry).

Other crime scene indicators include wounded victims, no escape plan, and witnesses.

Forensic Findings

Forensic findings include the analysis of physical evidence pertaining to a crime, evidence that is used toward legal proof that a crime occurred. This evidence is often called a silent witness, offering objective facts specific to the commission of a crime. The primary sources of physical evidence are the victim, the suspect, and the crime scene. Secondary sources include the home or work environment of a suspect; however, search warrants are necessary for the collection of such evidence.

Medical reports provide important evidence. These reports include toxicological results, X-ray films, and autopsy findings. In homicide cases, the forensic pathologist identifies and documents the postmortem findings present and interprets the findings within the context of the circumstances of death.[8]

Cause of Death: The mechanism of death is often a determining factor when attempting to classify a homicide. The victim of a street gang murder almost always dies from gunshot wounds. Explosive trauma is a frequent forensic finding with many criminal competition and extremist murder. Strangulation is common to the more personal crimes, such as domestic murder and the sexual homicide.

Trauma: The type, extent, and focus of injury sustained by the victim are additional critical factors used when classifying a crime. Overkill, facial battery, torture, bite marks, and mutilation are examples of forensic findings that will often lead to a specific homicide category and thus, a possible motive for the offense.

Sexual Assault: Evidence of assault to the victim's sexual organs or body cavities has great bearing on motive and classification. The type and sequence of the assault is important as well as the timing of the assault (before, during, or after death). The apparent absence of penetration with the penis does not mean the victim was not sexually assaulted. Sexual assault also includes insertion of foreign objects, regressive necrophilia, and many activities that target the breasts, buttocks, and genitals.

Type, Style, and Number of Victims

Crimes may be classified by type, style, and number of victims. Using the homicide classification as an example, a single homicide is one victim, one homicidal event. A double homicide is two victims, one event, and in one location. A triple homicide has three victims in one location during one event. Anything beyond three victims is classified as a mass murder, that is, a homicide involving four or more victims in one location, and within one event.

Two additional types of multiple murder are spree murder and serial murder. A spree murder involves killing at two or more locations with no emotional cooling-off period between murders. The killings are all the result of a single event, which can be of short or long duration. Serial murders are involved in three or more separate events with an emotional cooling-off period between homicides.

References
1. Rennie Y. The search for criminal man: the dangerous offender project. Lexington, MA: Lexington Books; 1977.
2. Lindesmith AR, Dunham HW. Some principles of criminal typology. *Social Forces*. 1941;10:307-14.
3. Megargee EI, Bohn MJ. Classifying criminal offenders: a new system based on the MMPI. London: Sage; 1979.
4. Bromberg W. *Crime and the Mind: A Psychiatric Analysis of Crime and Punishment*. New York, NY: Macmillan; 1965
5. Knight RA, Rosenberg R, Schneider BA. Classification of sexual offenders: perspectives, methods, and validation. In: Burgess AW, ed. *Rape and Sexual Assault*. New York, NY: Garland; 1985.
6. Knight RA, Prentky RA. Classifying sexual offenders: the development and corroboration of taxonomic models. In: Marshall WL, Laws DR, Barbaree HE, eds. *Handbook of Sexual Assault*. New York, NY: Plenum; 1990.
7. Douglas JE, Ressler RK, Burgess AW, Burgess AG. *Crime Classification Manual*. San Francisco, CA: Jossey-Bass; 1995.
8. Luke JL. The role of forensic pathology in criminal profiling. In: Ressler R, Burgess RA, Douglas J, eds. *Sexual Homicide*. Lexington, MA: Lexington Books; 1988.

Chapter 3 – Prosecuting a 20-Year-Old Sadistic Murder

Ann Wolbert Burgess and Robert D. Anderson

Old unsolved murders are difficult to prosecute due to limited forensic evidence and missing or reluctant witnesses. Such was the case in preparing for the Commonwealth of Virginia v. Melvin Shifflett pretrial hearing. Shifflett, already convicted of one homicide and two sexual assaults, had been an early suspect in the 1978 murder of Patricia Smith. In 1997, as the prosecution team was identifying witnesses, they learned that a prior victim of Shifflett's was too terrified to testify against him. A prison inmate who indicated that Shifflett told him that he urinated on the face of Patricia Smith after he killed her had refused to testify out of concern for his safety. Shifflett was obsessed with lifting weights to the extent that one of the bailiffs indicated that he could bench press close to 600 pounds. Another prison inmate who was willing to relate conversations he had with Shifflett about the Smith murder had credibility concerns from his convictions of various theft and embezzlement charges.

Because the case was almost 20 years old, there was no forensic evidence for a number of reasons. Analysis at the time of the murder showed "sperm heads" in the vaginal cavity, but no analysis had been done to identify the donor. If the sperm came from Shifflett, it was inconsistent with two living witnesses and an ex-wife's report of his inability to maintain an erection. But Smith had a boyfriend in 1978, and there was a question of whether or not to try to locate him to determine if he would testify as to sexual intercourse around the date of her murder.

The pretrial hearing allowed introducing evidence of other crimes and the case was successfully prosecuted. The case is presented to illustrate the linking of prior crimes to an unsolved crime by the killer's profile characteristics of sadistic ritual; the prosecution of a sexual homicide without forensic evidence; the prosecution of a case in which there are reluctant and intimidated witnesses, and the analysis of the crime by phases of murder.

Serial Sexual Assault and Murder

On August 2, 1978, Donna, age 21, was in the pub of a restaurant in northern Virginia when Melvin Shifflett, a young man she had met while both were washing their cars at a nearby park, joined a group who were talking. Shifflett kept interrupting Donna and asking her to go outside and talk with him. She agreed. Shifflett said he wanted to date her, and Donna said no, thinking that he was not her style. They returned to the pub, and Shifflett then changed the conversation to her car because Donna had been having brake problems telling her he could help. He said he needed to ride in the car to determine the problem and suggested she drop him off at a friend's house. He directed her to an apartment complex and when she asked him to get out, Shifflett told her she was not going anywhere. He knocked the car keys out of her hand with a knife, pushing her against the steering wheel and holding the knife to her throat. He threatened to cut her into little pieces and slit her throat. Although Donna was successful in getting him to put the knife down, he next ordered her to undo her belt, unzip his pants, and perform oral sodomy. She did; he was unable to maintain an erection. He then tied her hands behind her back, ordering her to look at him while he increased the tension on the bindings. He then took a wad of toilet paper and pushed it into her throat. She swallowed the first wad; he inserted a second wad that she used her tongue to hold; he inserted a third wad and she could not breathe until she was able push the wad into an area where wisdom teeth had been pulled. He knocked out her teeth and she almost swallowed her tongue. He would let her breathe and then relax and then shove more tissue into her mouth. In the meantime, she worked to get her hands untied but did not let him know. She coughed out the toilet paper and surprised him. He shoved her to the car floor and had her repeat the oral sodomy; he still failed to get an erection. While on the car floor she reached under the front seat, grabbed a bottle and hit him over the head. The bottle bounced off his head and he began stabbing at her. She managed to get out of the car and heard people yelling that distracted him. She ran for help. She was rushed to a hospital where she was in intensive care for 13 days with a punctured lung, deep wounds to her back, liver, heart, and abdomen, and multiple pinpoint pricks all over her body.

Approximately 90 days later, Shifflett was out on bond as a result of his attack on Donna. According to facts related by prison inmates of their conversations with Shifflett, he encountered Patricia Smith in a bar. He enticed her to ride with him from one bar to another and decided when she got in his car that he was going to kill her. He forced her to commit oral sodomy on him at which time she bit him in the genital area. He asphyxiated her using her denim jacket. According to one witness he said he urinated on her after she was dead. He said he enjoyed killing her and others.

It was in late October, 1978, that Patricia Smith, age 20, was found nude from the waist down lying face down in a small ravine alongside a dirt road some three weeks after she disappeared. She was wearing a knitted blouse which along with her bra was pulled up over her breasts. A denim jacket was tied around her neck. Death was by strangulation. A part of her left ear was eaten away apparently by animals. The body was decomposed to the extent that visual identification was not possible. Patricia Smith was last seen leaving a bar with Melvin Shifflett in his Chevrolet Camaro, which was an automobile he kept in top shape. ("It was his baby.")

On July 2, 1979, Shifflett was convicted in the attack on Donna and was sentenced to 18 years incarceration. He was released on February 27, 1989.

On November 19, 1994, Shifflett was arrested for an attack the night before on a 33-year old woman, Sally, who knew him through her boyfriend for about 1 1/2 years. She had had a fight with her boyfriend and had paged Shifflett to help her find him. She returned home, locked the door, and was in bed reading when she suddenly looked up to see him in her bedroom. He tried to kiss her; she refused; he became enraged; he called her derogatory names such as slut, whore, and bitch. He said she was worthless. He taped her hands, face, feet, and hair with duct tape. He forced her to perform oral sodomy, but was unable to obtain an erection. He urinated in her mouth twice and repeatedly choked off her airflow by placing a rag in her mouth until she was close to passing out. He was interrupted by two people who saw him. He then released her with threats. He later told the inmate witness that he intended to kill her, but he was afraid because he was seen with her.

On May 25, 1995, Shifflett was convicted of attacking Sally and sentenced to an 85-year sentence. During the preparation for that trial, he told a fellow inmate and others that he had killed Debra, who was last seen in May of 1994. Her body was discovered on May 22, 1994. Shifflett told an inmate that he had been with her at a bar the night he killed her, and they went down to the river. He said they watched fish eat and smoked a cigarette. He then asphyxiated her by crushing her larynx and threw her in the river. He knew the tides of the river from growing up in the area and knew the tides would take the body out to the Bay; he thought the crabs and fish would eat the body.

Expert Opinion Testimony: Classifying the Murder

Two opinions were offered at the pre-trial hearing.
    1. The death of Patricia Smith was a sexual murder committed by an organized killer. Organized murderers show evidence of planning, premeditation, malice, intent to kill, absence of accident, and conduct indicating feelings of hatred toward women.

2. Melvin Shifflett showed sadistic behavior in the murder of Debra, in the trial testimony of Donna and Sally, and in the interview with his ex-wife. His conversations with inmates were consistent with sadistic motive, premeditation, and intent to kill.

Basis for Opinion:

A crime can be analyzed in four phases: planning, the murderous act, escape, and post-crime behavior.

1. Premeditation, or the planning of an act beforehand, is noted by Shifflett's use of a confidence ploy to gain access to his victims. Shifflett is acquainted with his victims, has met them before, e.g., worked at a gas station where Smith bought gas; met Donna at the park washing cars and then saw her at a bar; Sally was the girl friend of his friend; and met Debra at a bar and claimed to know her as the town whore.

Shifflett has his sadist's kit in his truck: knife, duct tape, toilet paper. He uses a knife to control his victim and if the killing was circumvented. His intent is to kill the women in a stylistic way that fits his sadistic fantasy, that is, to render them as close to death as possible through asphyxiation. He prefers the victim half alive and half dead and that is when the arousal and sexual excitement is released. The knife is present to orchestrate this or if his control is challenged or to cut the body. And he strategically isolates the victims by taking them outside or to a pier or in his truck to have them totally under his control.

2. The murderous act. Malice is the intent to commit an unlawful act; a wish to cause suffering; and pleasure at other's suffering. He ties up the victims; urinates on them; and knows how to kill by strangling or breaking the windpipe, thereby asphyxiating them.

Motive is that which is internal to the individual rather than external that prompts action. Surviving victims of Shifflett describe that he is a sexual sadist, e.g., there is a persistent pattern of his becoming sexually excited in response to their suffering.

3. Escape. He is afraid of being caught; thus two women survive because others come on the scene or the victim is able to escape. He evades police initially with Smith because he cleans his car, even finds a fingernail of hers. He plans to bury Smith, but then decides the Bobcat would attract attention and make too much noise. He discards Debra's body in the river.

4. Post-crime behavior. He returns at lease once to Smith's crime scene, calling on a nearby resident to ask if he has seen the female mannequin in the ditch off the

road. He may have moved the body or otherwise touched her and continued his sadistic fantasy.

Profiling and Patterns

Profile Characteristics

Reviewing all four crime scenes, the following characteristics make up Shifflett's profile: victim is known; same age and race as victims; isolates and abducts the victim; maintains control with weapon or physical strength; gains victim's trust; degrades women calling them bitches and whores; enforces his sexual sadistic ritual of encapsulating them in a vehicle, sitting them on his lap, forcing oral sex, urinating on them; he is impotent and blames the women; degrades and asphyxiates them.

Sadistic Rape Pattern

Shifflett targets acquaintances, a profile characteristic that speaks to a strong psychological component that is linked into his early history with mother and females in family. We learn that he is fearful of his mother and duty bound. His wife tells him to come home for dinner, that his mother wants him and he says he will be there in a minute. But not for the wife. The mother has control over him by making sure all the women pass muster and take care of him. The mother blames the wife for his problems. This supports his notion that women are there to do his bidding. He is attached to his mother; has to phone her on his wedding night and then is impotent with his wife.

Shifflett's ex-wife testified that they were married in February 1989 upon his release from prison and were divorced in November 1989. Shifflett was unable to perform sexually unless he was the aggressor or performing a forcible act such as anal sodomy. On one occasion he attempted to force oral sex and tried to urinate in her mouth. When she refused to cooperate, he urinated on her and raped her.

Shifflett is not interested in consenting sex with women. He would demand sex from his wife when she did not want it. He tried to force anal sex on his wife despite her protests. He has no regard toward women. Patricia Smith's body is dumped; left partially clothed. The body is not carefully covered; rather he leaves her breasts exposed.

We learn from a witness that his fourth victim, Debra, tries to initiate sex. This turns Shifflett off. It is a well-established pattern through testimony of his ex-wife. He doesn't want the women to be comfortable or enjoy sex. He makes sure nothing is pleasurable. Everything is inflicting pain and degradation and speaks to his hatred of women.

Elements of his sadistic fantasy include domination and control. He uses aggression beyond what is needed to control the victim. He induces fear, helplessness, humiliation, and pleading. He tells Donna, "I'll cut you in pieces; cut your face; your jugular." It feeds his need to have control and punish the woman; it excites him. He thrives on pain; injury; and death. Psychological suffering is noted by bindings and sexual bondage. He tied his wife with pantyhose. He gags and holds his victims captive. There is an elaborate use of duct tape, e.g., tapes Sally's hair to door. He restrains victims in variety of positions; he uses Donna's purse to restrain her arms.

At the 1997 trial for the murder of Patricia Smith, Melvin Shifflett was convicted and given a life sentence. In 1998 the Court of Appeals upheld allowing evidence of prior crimes and currently the case is pending Virginia's Superior Court ruling on the use of prior bad acts.

Chapter 4 – Hospital Communication Threats and Intervention

Ann W. Burgess, John E. Douglas, Allen G. Burgess, Timothy Baker, Herb Sauve, and Katherine Gariti

On July 26, 1996, an Atlanta 911 operator received a call saying, "There will be a bomb in Centennial Park. You have 30 minutes." This telephonic threat to a crowded public setting, preceded by 18 minutes a terrorist act of bombing, triggered great fear for millions of Americans.

Offenders have been taught that fear is a power tactic. They know that if they can generate fear in some form of a threat they can manipulate and achieve whatever they want. Threat analysis is one strategy to identify and intervene with a threat subject and counter terrorist fear. The brief empirical literature on targets of threat communication has been on unknown subjects, including psychotic visitors to government offices,[1] White House visitors,[2] members of the United States Congress,[3] and Hollywood celebrities.[4] To contribute to the threat assessment literature, this paper will focus on communication threats within a hospital setting.

Data was collected from two large urban hospital facilities, one a Veterans Administration (VA) hospital and one a private hospital. Three research questions guided the study. Who are the targets and threateners or offenders in hospital communication threats? What is the hospital's response to communication threats? What are the implications for nursing, security, and hospital administration

Threat Communication Analysis

A threat is defined for this paper as an attempt to inflict harm by a threat subject. Threat analysis seeks to assess the genuineness, viability, and potential impending danger of the threat. As with all investigations, the forensic analyst has priorities that are followed in concert with law enforcement as well as institutional goals and objectives. Threat analysis goals are –

- To save lives by attempting to evaluate the level of danger for physical assault or harm

- To evaluate threat potential (hoax vs. non-hoax) in order to reduce unnecessary panic and to better utilize security resources

- To develop investigative techniques/strategies by providing advice on how to communicate with the offender and/or how to cause him or her to surface during the investigation

- To help identify and apprehend the offender by attempting to provide general characteristics of the threatener and his or her motive in order to focus the investigation

- To recover money and/or property, if a ransom has been paid prior to police involvement.

Threat Motive

The WHY of the threat, or motive, is critical to analyze. Threats are made for a variety of reasons and are driven by an assortment of often complex motives. Some of the reasons why individuals threaten include –

- To warn: If you don't stop what you are doing, you will regret it.

- To harass: You'll never escape me.

- To intimidate: If you don't do what I say, you'll be sorry.

- To manipulate: If you don't do what I say, your child will be hurt.

- To frighten: You're a dead man.

- To alarm: A heavy breathing phone call late at night..

Threats may be targeted to terrorize a particular person, building, industry, or institution. The motivation for a threat might also include a desire on the part of the subject to force an action, e.g., inmates threatening a specific violent act if their demands for better conditions within a correctional facility are not met.

The motives that underlie various forms of threats are very similar to other types of criminal acts. The motivations may be conflict, sex, love, hate, vengeance, or guilt. In addition the need for excitement, recognition, or attention, or wish to inflict punishment on another may also be underlying motives of the offender. Another obvious and more frequent motive might be an offender whose primary motive is criminal enterprise. This offender's aim is for financial gain through illegal means (extortion, kidnapping, etc.).

Intent of the Threat

Threats cover a wide variety of criminal behavior. Ten categories have been developed for purposes of assessing the intent of the threat communication and include intent to: physically harm, extort, kidnap, bomb, damage property, disrupt events, intimidate, product tamper, sabotage, or falsely threaten.

1. Threats to physically assault or harm are directed toward elected or appointed officials, judges, movie stars, rock singers, spouses, exspouses, police officers, former employers, or hospital staff (e.g., to gain admission or certain prescription medication). For example, a mental health patient arrived at an institution to see the on-call psychiatrist. The patient was seeking admission and apparently believed that the small ax he brought with him would ensure the psychiatrist's compliance with his demand for admission.

2. Threats to extort money are often directed toward chief executive officers, bank officials, prominent or wealthy individuals, or members of the entertainment industry. In hospitals, threats may be directed toward staff, visitors, and/or patients to extort money for food, transportation, or illicit substances by patients or unknown subjects.

3. Threats to kidnap are directed to elected or appointed officials, members of their families, dignitaries, prominent individuals, or corporate officials.

4. Threats to bomb are directed toward individuals at all levels, schools, churches, synagogues, abortion clinics, courthouses, government buildings, nuclear facilities, military bases, casinos, etc.

5. Threats to deface or damage property are directed toward schools, churches, synagogues, abortion clinics, animal research facilities, utility plants, military bases, or nuclear facilities.

6. Threats to disrupt events are made to disrupt municipal functions, political rallies, parades, marches, ceremonies, public events, rock shows, or civil rights rallies.

7. Threats to taunt, harass, and intimidate are made by agitated or terminated employees, disgruntled consumers, competitors, ex-lovers, ex-spouses, unfriendly neighbors, unknown enemies, substance abusers and mentally unstable persons, or individuals intent on expressing unsolicited attention or affection.

8. Threats to product tamper are related to poisoning or contamination of foods, medicines, cosmetics, water or blood supplies, hygienic products, or tampering with sensitive manufacturing equipment.

9. Threats to sabotage are directed to military bases, ammunitions manufacturers/shippers, aircraft plants, nuclear facilities, manufacturer of scientific equipment, research and development centers, product technologies, or marketing strategies.

10. Hoaxes are a fabricated threat created by pseudovictims alleging the receipt of obscene phone calls and/or letters from non-existent offenders.

Threat Delivery Classification

Additional valuable information can be derived about the threatener and his or her motive(s), by a consideration of how the threatening message was delivered. This classification is by visual, verbal, written, symbolic, or physical mode.

Visual threats may include a drawing, a gesture, or a body movement. One example involved a nurse being greeted in the following manner by a known "behavior management problem" patient each time he saw her: He makes eye contact, then pretends to shoot her with a hand motion imitating the firing of a pistol; he never speaks a word to her.

Verbal threats made during personal encounters with targeted individuals often involve offenders suffering from some degree of mental illness and/or emotional instability. In these types of cases the offender's identity is known, and certain intervention strategies are recommended in conjunction with a dangerousness assessment in order to prevent a potential violent confrontation.

Often a verbal threat will be delivered by telephone. Telephone threats maybe short, succinct messages or may involve long complex schemes. Occasionally the caller may disguise his or her voice and may demand to speak with only the targeted victim. Some offenders may use prerecorded tape messages over the phone, and the calls may be made locally, long distance, or collect. Other investigative considerations would include possible background noises, foreign accents, local dialects, and a consideration of specific calling patterns.

Verbal threats may be tape recorded. Tape-recorded threats may be short and succinct or involve long complex schemes. The other important considerations would include determining if the caller attempts to disguise his or her voice, or whether or not background noises are detectable, and whether or not the tape was mailed or played over the phone. Tape-recorded messages often reflect extensive criminal sophistication, especially in elaborate extortion, kidnapping, or product tampering cases.

Written threats are usually delivered by letter or e-mail. The great majority of threat cases that are analyzed by a threat analyst are those in which the identity of the subject is unknown. In seeking to identify the unknown perpetrator, the method of delivery used by the subject must be carefully assessed.

Letter threats are often hand written and may be in block print, or otherwise disguised format; they also may be prepared on a typewriter or word processor. In some instances, they are fabricated in the "cut and paste" method, and on rare occasions, may be printed by use of a template or constructed with a "dymo-type" embossing tool. In all instances, they must be evaluated for both content and stylistic characteristics. An advantage of the letter threat is that it provides law enforcement with valuable documentary evidence for further comparison to other letters and for other forensic tests customarily conducted in the crime lab.

Symbolic threats involve an item with a frightening connotation, often positioned clearly in the threat subjects view. One example of a symbolic threat involved an employee who reported arriving at his desk each morning for a week to find a broken pencil placed visibly on his appointment book.

Physical threats may involve the threatener's hand or a weapon. One example involved an angry patient who was denied a weekend pass. He broke a glass and holding it to a staff member's throat, demanded his pass.

Physical threat delivery can compound when there is direct confrontation. A 49-year-old patient and two elderly women were waiting for a bus when approached for money at a hospital bus stop. The patient said to the robber, "You are not going to ask for money?" To which the robber said he was and subsequently opened his jacket to display a large knife in his pocket. The patient became agitated and struck the robber, breaking his nose. The perpetrator pressed charges, but the patient was successful in arguing it was self-defense.

Content and Style

Threats must be examined for both content and style characteristics.

Content analysis includes an examination of words, syntax, semantics, structure, symbols, phrases, essential meanings, and the overall substance of the threatening message. Stylistic analysis includes an examination of the writing instrument, paper type, envelope, writing style, margins, indentations, spacing, punctuation, and overall grammatical ability.

There also involves examining the manner of expression, such as implied emotional tone, construction and design of the message, the way words are used to express thoughts, and an evaluation of the author's overall artistic expression. The verbal threat, "I'm going to get you back," implies a prior event, anger, and revenge.

Threats, actual or perceived, may be subdivided into types based in part on the verbiage or content contained within the threat. The types include direct, indirect, conditional, or a nonspecific threat.

Direct threats leave no room for misinterpretation on the part of the recipient. The threat is aimed at a specific target (person or institution). Direct threats offer no conditions, exemptions, or options. Often the wording is blunt, straightforward, candid, and/or explicit, as in the Atlanta Centennial Park opening example.

Indirect threats are either spoken or written in a very vague manner. They usually contain very wordy language that is not forthright or candid. The message or intended theme is often times circuitous and maybe buried within oblique wording or symbolic passages.

Conditional threats are threats that insist upon the acquiescence of the targeted victim, to the terms being dictated by the threatened. Conditional threats imply that they are contingent, tentative, restrictive, and/or provisional depending upon the victim's response to the demands being made. The threatened generally outlines a set of prescribed behaviors that must be met in order for the victim to avoid possible harm. They will most often include words or phraseology such as "if, unless, or, until, if you want to avoid, unless you follow my instructions," etc. For example, a walk-in patient demanded of the on-call psychiatrist, "If you don't give me a prescription for Xanax, I'm going to tear this office apart."

Nonspecific threats are those which are aimed at a larger collective group or the institution. They do not name a particular individual. In this case, targets of nonspecific threats included members of the federal judiciary, members of the medical profession, members of the US Congress, or the White House.

Victim Risk

The most critical classification is the level of victim risk. Risk level can be categorized from low, moderate, high, or the most serious level – imminent danger. Assessment of the threat is made as to whether the person making the threat has the knowledge, ability, motivation, and access to any weapons that would give him the opportunity to go through with the violent act.

Method of Study

The study of hospital communication threats took the form of a pilot study in 1995-1996 among the members of a forensic analysis group. Two large institutions provided cases of threat communications for testing of a Workplace Threat Communication Short Form (WTC-SF). Coders were trained to enter data onto the WTC-SF. This form contains 13 variables: threatener-target relationship; target age, gender, and race; threatener age, gender, and race; threats duration, number of threats, threat delivery; target risk; and intervention.

The VA hospital data sample included 22 cases collected over a four-month period and the private hospital data included 66 cases collected over a one-year period. Both samples are used to describe the findings and provide case examples. To protect confidentiality of the institutions and victims, identifying data is not provided. Permission to analyze the threat communications was secured in each institution.

Data were entered into SPSS for Windows Version 6.0 and were cleaned and verified against the WTC-SF. The demographic characteristics of each sample were first determined and the frequency counts computed for each of the threat variables. A Pearson correlation coefficient was then computed for all the variables.

Findings

Sample

In the VA hospital sample of 22 threats, the majority of threateners were male (91%) and black (68%) with an age range of 26 to 73 and a mean 44 years. The targets of the threats were evenly split between males and females and between black and Caucasian races.

In the private hospital sample of 66 threats, the majority of threateners were male (84.8%) and white (62.1%) with 19.7% being black, 6.1% being Hispanic, and the race of 12.1% threateners not known. The age range of threateners was 23 to 52 with a mean of 35. The majority of victim targets were female (86%) and white (74%). The majority of cases involved target and threatener of the same race (65%), but only 18% of the targets and threateners were of the same sex.

Motive

The motive for threats was determined by analyzing the threat intent and the target-threatener relationship. Threats made by one staff member to another staff member who knew each other either as a spouse or significant other, past or present was classified as domestic. This motive occurred in one VA hospital case and 24 private hospital cases. For example, an employee had been stalked by an exsignificant other, who also worked at the hospital. Although there was a restraining order against him, he would pass by her department and leave unsigned harassing notes for her.

The motive in patient to staff threats included communications of love and/or wish for sex in psychotherapy cases involving positive transference, dissatisfaction with treatment from ex-patients, and irrational thoughts in emotionally disturbed persons. In the VA hospital sample, 17 threats were made by patients to staff as compared to 14 in the private hospital sample.

In one case, a patient sent his therapist of two years flowers, gifts, and cards via the mail. He called her on several occasions and left messages using a pseudonym on her answering machine. In another case, shortly after terminating three months of treatment, the patient appeared at the therapist's office acting bizarre. Over several months, he hand delivered letters of poetry, small gifts, and notes, and one time, a bunch of dead flowers.

One woman wrote to the hospital that bad medicine she received as a patient caused her to get sicker at home. The hospital wrote back denying her claim. When she retaliated by writing to a US Senator, he responded by siding with the hospital. She then wrote to the US Attorney General's office accusing conspiracy between the hospital and the Senator. In another example, a patient wrote letters threatening to kill his wife, the mayor, his doctor, and the President of the United States.

The motive in cases of staff-to-staff threat included argument conflicts. The private hospital had 17 cases as compared to no cases in the VA hospital sample. In one case, an older employee subject threatened a younger employee over territorial issues. A background check indicated the older employee did have a criminal record.

In cases of threats against the hospital, the motive was an angry family member or a disgruntled former employee. This type of threat was noted in one VA hospital case and four private hospital cases. The threatener was either an exemployee or former patient. For example, in a case where a father died following surgery, two brothers wrote a letter saying, "Your butchers killed him and we will get you." An investigation revealed both brothers had criminal records for assault and battery.

The threatener was unknown in three VA hospital cases and seven cases in the private hospital sample.

Threat Intent

Three of the 10 threat intent categories were classified in the combined hospital samples.

Threats to physically assault or harm were directed toward expartners and former employers.

Threats to deface or damage property were directed toward hospital walls and grounds. In one case, the threatened wrote sexual graffiti on the walls adjacent to his expartner's office. In another case, an employees name was written on a wall with the notation that she was a drug dealer.

Threats to taunt, harass, and intimidate were made by agitated or terminated employees, disgruntled family members or expartners, and patients intent on expressing unsolicited attention and affection.

Threat Duration and Number

The duration of threats ranged from under a month to three years. The number of threats ranged from one to 20. Almost half of the private hospital threats (45%) occurred a second time.

Threat delivery

In the VA hospital sample, there were nine verbal threats with an additional four being telephone threats. There were no written threats. Staff were physically threatened six times. In the private hospital sample, 20 threats were verbal with an additional 16 being telephonic threats. There were 11 written threats and 14 staff were physically threatened. Five were threatened with a weapon or received a symbolic threat. In one case, a pig's head was fastened to a staff member's automobile.

Interventions

In the VA hospital sample, several interventions were used directly with threateners. Threateners were escorted back to their room, placed in restraints, ordered off the grounds, transferred to a psychiatric unit, discharged, or arrested. One case was referred to local police for further investigation and one case to the hospital administrator.

In the private hospital sample, the most frequently used intervention was to meet with the target victim (59%). In 27% of the cases a restraining order was issued. Other interventions included writing or telephoning the threatener and recommending treatment. In only one case was no action taken. In 26% of the cases, interventions included arrest and/or civil action.

Statistical testing of the target-threatener demographics with type of intervention revealed the following significant findings –

- When there is domestic abuse between employee and employee, the authorities will more likely meet with the victim and assist or support the implementation of a restraining order.

- The threatener was more likely to be telephoned if the threatener and target are in an employee/significant other relationship.

- The greater number of threats, the higher the probability that the threatener will be placed in treatment. If the target is male, there is greater likelihood that the threatener will be placed in treatment. So, too, if the threat was symbolic. And there was less likelihood of a male threatener being placed in treatment.

Discussion

In this hospital sample, communication threats were made by persons usually known to the target. Because of the relationship, threat intent and motive could be quickly determined and an intervention implemented. The VA hospital had older, predominately male veterans who made threats to staff significantly more than subjects in the private hospital sample.

The similarities of the two samples included that both were large East coast institutions in a large city. The differences included the VA hospital had predominately older, male patients and lower staff and patient turnover, and the private hospital had high numbers of female patients and ethnic and cultural representation. For both hospitals, it is not known the percentage of threats not being reported to security staff. Although little empirical research exists on hospital workplace violence, Lanza has studied patient assault in VA hospital settings and recommends prompt reporting as well as primary intervention strategies to lower staff risk.[5]

Continuum of Dangerous Behavior

Threats are indirect acts that are secretive, critical to planning a crime, and may be invisible to the target or victim. Law enforcement may be unable to arrest an individual because no criminal act, *per se*, has been committed. While these indirect acts are often motivated by the intent to weaken the victim, they also are acts of revenge, anger, power, and control. Indirect acts include obscene phone calls, voyeurism, stalking, and threats; the offender may remain unknown to the victim. Indirect acts may so diminish the victim's power that the offender is satisfied his mission has been accomplished. Or the victim's behavior may challenge the control of the offender and motivate him to move into a direct act of robbery, assault, arson, bombing, sexual assault, or murder. There is a continuum to these direct acts that move from a distant presence to the victim to personal contact. Crimes may be classified as to this contact continuum.

It is noteworthy in this sample that security staff intervened before any further escalation beyond their notification. One reason is that security in both samples addressed threats with priority security attention. In fact, the average response time of the security staff at the private hospital was three minutes. In one case, security responded in 80 seconds to a call and were able to apprehend the offender. The case began as a harassing telephone call, followed by a telephone threat. On the third call, the employee, using caller identification, notified security of the extension where the call originated and the caller was apprehended.

Intervention

The question, What do I do? is the most frequently asked question by targets of a threat. What one should do depends upon each individual's specific situation, the nature of the threat, and whether or not the threatener is capable of carrying out the threat. In cases where the threatener is unknown, an assessment is made based upon the victimology and an analysis of the threat itself.

Target Risk Level Assessment

Target risk level is calibrated as to the authenticity of the threat and the potential of the threatened to move into a direct action. The most critical classification is the level of victim risk. The risk level can be categorized from low, moderate, high, or the most serious level, imminent danger.

In this study, upon notification of a threat and an interview of the target, the initial level of intervention was to provide escort service to the victim while in the workplace and to and from his or her vehicle. A medium risk level required security staff to identify and contact the threatener. Often, hospital security arranged a visit to the threatener with local law enforcement to emphasize that multiple agencies knew of the threats and that they must stop. High-risk level involves posting the threatener's photograph at all hospital security stations and notification of both local law enforcement and law enforcement in the town where the threatener resides.

The process recommended to assess target risk level is as follows –

1. Treat each threat initially as high level of risk. A universal principle in threat management is that threats should not be ignored with the hope they will disappear.

In some cases this may be true; however, if a threat is not addressed head-on, the risk of physical harm to the target may be potentially present. If the target is harmed, the question of liability will be an issue.

2. Assess victimology. When analyzing any threat against a target, the first question to answer is, Why is this person being threatened? The target may be an individual, i.e., "I'm going to kill Dr. S," or the threat may be against an institution or hospital, i.e., "I'm going to blow up Community Hospital." A complete and thorough analysis of the target should provide clues as to who is possibly responsible for making the threats.

A target who, for example, is separated from her husband, and has been physically abused in the past, would be a high risk. If the target's husband is a substance abuser, has access to weapons, and has made a threat, the target's life is in danger. A hospital employee who has received threats and is living alone and working nights has an elevated risk level. However, if the employee works and lives in an environment where security is provided, the risk level may be reduced.

Assessment questions include: Is the target an individual, hospital, or other. What is the relationship with the threatener: partner, patient, employee. What is the motive: domestic, argument, competition, anger, conflict, retaliation, etc.

3. Assess the known threatener's level of dangerousness by checking prior history for direct violence and indirect acts of threats, stalking, etc.

3a. Profile the unknown subject. The threatener's potential for action is determined by a content analysis of the threat and whether it is direct, indirect, conditional, or nonspecific. Other investigative techniques include tracing telephone calls, staking out hospital areas, surveilling a target's residence, and working with local law enforcement authorities.

4. Assign level of risk and implement intervention. See Table 1.

5. Computerize threats for internal review, analysis, and follow-up.

Many threats continue for months and a system for follow-up needs to be implemented whereby information from the target-victim is reviewed.

In summary, threat communication analysis is a viable tool in the assessment of same if the person(s) doing the assessment has the research and experience base to properly guide the target through a potentially dangerous encounter. This article describes categories for a target risk threat communication classification system. It is hoped that hospitals and institutions concerned with primary and secondary prevention develop threat assessment analysis skills and use a multidisciplinary advisory committee. This study combines investigative, clinical, and methodological expertise in confronting a contemporary issue of hospital safety and security.

References
1. Hoffman JL. Psychotic visitors to government offices in the national capital. *Am J Psychiatry*. 1943;99:571-575.
2. Sebastiani JA, Foy JL Psychotic visitors to the White House. *Am J Psychiatry*. 1965;122:679-686.
3. Dietz PE, Matthews DR, Martell DA, Stewart TM, Hrouda DR, Warren J. Threatening and otherwise inappropriate letters to members of the United States Congress. *J Forensic Sci*. 1991;36:1445-1468.
4. Dietz PE, Matthews DB, Van Duyne C, et al. Threatening and otherwise inappropriate letters to Hollywood celebrities. *J Forensic Sci*. 1991;36:185-209.
5. Lanza M. Patient assault. In: Lion, Dubin & Futrell, eds. *Hospital Security*. Chicago, IL: American Hospital Corporation; 1996

Table 1: A Continuum of Target Risk Level	
Fact:	**Intervention:**
1. Low Risk Level of Harm to Target*	
Obscene telephone call Nonspecific threat No individual named Nondomestic	Meet with target Reassure target Offer escort services
2. Medium Risk of Danger to Target *	
Harassing calls Indirect threat Target named Threatener identified Domestic threat but target refuses to file restraining order	Notify local law enforcement Meet with threat target
3. High Risk of Danger to Target *	

Direct threat to a named individual
Conditional threat involving
  additional victims
Threatener known and has prior
  criminal background
	Apprehend and arrest
	Notify local law enforcement

4. Imminent Risk of Danger to Target *	
Bomb threat Hostage situation Person with weapon	Notify of all security by code name Mobilize special response team Apprehend and arrest
*Note: Risk level is reassessed with new information.	

Reprinted with permission from the *Journal of Psychosocial Nursing*, Slack, Inc.
Burgess AW, Douglas JE, Burgess AG, Baker T, Sauve H, Gariti K. Hospital communication threats and intervention. *J Psychosoc Nurs*. 1997;35(8):9-16.

Chapter 5 – Investigating Stalking Crimes

James A. Wright, Allen G. Burgess, Ann W. Burgess, Gregg O. McCrary, and John E. Douglas

Consider this case: A 21-year-old, blonde, attractive woman began receiving a series of hang-up calls and greeting cards in her mailbox signed, "I love you." She reported these occurrences to law enforcement, who provided advice and within several weeks were able to identify the stalker as a 24-year-old man living in the apartment complex adjacent to hers. As part of the court proceedings, the man was sent for examination to a female forensic psychiatrist. Days after the examination, the blonde psychiatrist began receiving hang-up phone calls on her office answering machine and greeting cards in her mail.

With increasing frequency, women and men of all ages are finding themselves the focus of unwanted attention. This chapter presents a descriptive classification of interpersonal stalking.

Definition and Motivation

Stalking is the act of following, viewing, communicating with, or moving threateningly or menacingly toward another person. Stalking may, in some cases, result in threats to injure, actual injuries, and/or homicide. Stalker crimes are primarily motivated by interpersonal aggression, rather than by material gain or sex. The purpose of stalking resides in the mind of stalkers, who are compulsive individuals with a misperceived fixation. Stalking is the result of an underlying emotional conflict that propels the offender to stalk and/or harass a target. Targets of stalkers often feel trapped in an environment filled with anxiety, stress, and fear that often results in their having to make drastic adjustments in how they live their lives.

Stalking can be conceptualized as occurring on a continuum from nondelusional to delusional behavior. Delusional behavior indicates the presence of a mental disorder (psychosis). Nondelusional behavior, while reflecting a gross disturbance in a

43

particular relationship, does not necessarily indicate a detachment from reality. This distinction is significant because of the potential legal implications, i.e., pleas of insanity, etc. What most readily distinguishes the behavior on this spectrum is the type and nature of the relationship an offender has had with his target.

On the extreme delusional end of this spectrum there is usually no actual relationship; a relationship exits only in the mind of the offender. On the nondelusional end of the spectrum, there is usually a historical relationship between the offender victim. These tend to be multidimensional relationships, such as marriage or common-law relationships replete with a history of close interpersonal involvement. In between these two poles are relationships of varied dimensions and stalkers who exhibit a mix of behavior. The offender may have dated his target once, twice, or not at all. The target may only have smiled and said hello in passing or may in some way be socially or vocationally acquainted. For the purpose of classification, we divide this spectrum of stalking behavior into three general types by relationship: domestic, nondomestic, and erotomania (delusional).

For purposes of this chapter the terms "target" and "victim" are not necessarily interchangeable. The term "target" is used to describe the primary recipient of the stalker's attention. However, in many cases, those people around a stalker's target become victims of the stalker's behavior.

Domestic Stalker

Domestic stalking occurs when a former boy/girlfriend, family, or household member threatens or harasses another member of the household. This definition includes common-law relationships as well as long-term acquaintance relationships. The domestic stalker is initially motivated by a desire to continue or reestablish a relationship that can evolve into an attitude of "If I can't have her no one can."

Victimology

The target knows the stalker as an acquaintance or may have a familial or common-law relationship that the target has attempted to terminate. The target is aware of the stalking and may have requested a restraining order or assistance from law enforcement on prior occasions. In addition, there is a history of prior abuse or conflict with the stalker. The target may report a sense of being "smothered" in the prior relationship.

Crime Scene Indicators

The domestic stalking case often culminates in a violent attack directed at the target. Usually the scene of this attack involves only one crime scene, and it is commonly the target and/or stalker's residence or place of employment. The crime scene reflects disorder and the impetuous nature of the stalker. A weapon will be brought to the scene. There could be signs of little or no forced entry and no sign of theft. The crime scene may also reflect an escalation of violence, (e.g., the confrontation starts as an argument, intensifies into hitting or throwing things, and could culminate in the target's death, and would then be classified as domestic homicide. Others, such as family members and boy/girlfriends, may be involved in an assault. If the target has taken steps to keep the stalker away (changed phone number, changed residence, restraining order, etc.), the only access the stalker may have is at the target's place of employment. In such cases, coworkers, security personnel, customers, etc., may become victims. In some instances, the stalker will abduct his target in an attempt to convince her to stay with him.

The stalker may be at the scene when law enforcement and/or emergency medical personnel arrive or may commit suicide. The stalker may make incriminating statements.

Common Forensic Findings

Alcohol/drugs may be involved. There usually are forensic findings consistent with a personal type of assault. Depersonalization, evidenced by facial battery and a focused area of injury indicative of anger, are examples of a personal assault.

Investigative Considerations

If the crime occurs in the target's residence, domestic stalking should be considered. When other family members are contacted, they often describe a history of domestic violence involving the target and stalker. This is often supported by police reports. A history of conflict due to external stressors (financial, vocational, alcohol, etc.) are common elements of domestic stalking. The stalker may have demonstrated personalized aggression in the past as well as a change in attitude after the triggering event.

Case Study – Domestic Stalker

Earl, a 22-year-old nightclub bouncer who gunned down his exgirlfriend on a busy street, had previously beaten and stalked her, and violated a court order to stay away from her. At the time, he was also on probation in connection with the stalking and abuse of another former girl friend. Following the shooting, the gunman returned to his apartment and killed himself.

Earl had been placed in a foster home by his mother at age seven and was later moved into a boy's home. He became addicted to drugs and had several aliases and jail sentences by age 20. His violent temper was known to his friends. He punished his newly purchased kitten, who had soiled a carpet, by shaving it and putting it under hot water. A few days later he killed the cat by throwing it through a third story window.

At age 18, Earl was charged with disturbing the peace, being a disorderly person, trespassing, and malicious destruction of property. At age 20, he was charged with possession of a hypodermic needle and syringe in connection with putting something in somebody's food. At age 22, he attacked his former girlfriend, while riding public transportation, cutting her hair and punching her in the face.

Two weeks prior to the killing, Earl was fired from his job for irregular work attendance. He was described as quiet and a loner and sported tattoos of a castle on his neck and a skull on his arm. The shooting occurred as his exgirlfriend exited her work place.

Nondomestic Stalker

The target and stalker are not in any type of domestic partnership. The relationship in the non-domestic stalker classification has been initiated through visual contact between the victim and offender. For example, the victim may be a waitress or waiter or living in the same apartment complex. The target has seen the target somewhere and interacts with the victim through hang-up, obscene, or harassing telephone calls; unsigned letters and other anonymous communications; or continuous physical appearance at the target's residence, place of employment, shopping mall, or school campus. At some point, the individual may make his identity known through continuous physical appearances at the victim's residence, place of employment, or other location. It is unlikely the victim will become aware of being stalked prior to the initial communication or contact. Only after the stalker has chosen to make personal or written contact will the target realize the problem.

Victimology

The target, usually a female, has often crossed paths with the stalker, most likely without her noticing. She will, therefore, have no knowledge of the stalker's identity. The relationship between the stalker and target is one way. The target will eventually become aware of the physically presence of the stalker. Other potential victims are spouses, boy/girlfriends, or any who are viewed as an obstacle coming between the stalker and his target.

Crime Scene Indicators

Stalking is an ongoing, usually long-term, crime without a traditional crime scene. The stalking will occur at the target's residence, place of employment, shopping mall, school campus, or other public place. There will be a number of aborted or obscene phone calls and/or anonymous letters addressed to the target, professing love or knowledge of the target's movements. Written communications are often left on vehicle windows or placed in mailboxes or under doors by the stalker. The tone of communications may progress from protestations of adoration, to love, to annoyance at not being able to make personal contact, to eventually threats and menace.

The stalker may place him/herself in a position to make casual contact with the target at which time verbal communication may occur. A description of this contact may be used in a later communication to terrorize and/or impress upon the target that the stalker is capable of carrying out any threats.

Investigative Considerations

Trace telephone calls and perform threat analysis of the written or phone communications. Careful analysis of early communications may provide leads for identifying the stalker. Observe target's places of employment, residence, mall, or campus for stalker. Since communications are often left on or in a target's vehicle, observation of vehicles can often lead to the identity of the stalker. The target should be interviewed about any suspicious "accidental" contacts she may have had in the recent past, such as being bumped into while shopping, door-to-door salesmen, telephone solicitations, a stranger asking to use the telephone or asking for directions, etc.

Case Study – Nondomestic Stalker

A man who stalked a woman was arrested outside her house carrying weapons, a stocking mask, and other items.

The woman told police she recently found her bathing suit taped to the windshield of her car. On one other occasion she found some of her undergarments draped on the car's mirror. Police sources revealed that one week prior, the victim found cartridge casings from a handgun taped to the car's window.

On the night of the arrest of the stalker, the victim saw a man outside her apartment and called the police. Minutes later the police arrested the stalker, who months prior to this incident had been acquitted of burglarizing the woman's home.

The stalker was found sitting in his vehicle less than 100 yards from the victim's apartment. Officers searched the stalker, and found a knife and a key to the victim's residence.

In his vehicle they found a .22 caliber pistol and ammunition, a stun gun, Mace, a camera and film, two sets of binoculars, two tape recorders, two flashlights, pictures of the victim's residence and car, rubber gloves, cotton gloves, a stocking mask, a large nylon bag, a bag with a change of clothes, several condoms, a book of nude pictures, a gun cleaning kit, and a cooler filled with ice and beer.

Erotomania Stalker

Erotomania-related stalking is motivated by an offender-target relationship that is based on the stalker's fixation. This fantasy is commonly expressed in such forms as fusion (the stalker blends his personality into his target's) or erotomania (a fantasy-based, idealized romantic love or spiritual union of a person [rather than sexual attraction]). The stalker can also be motivated by religious fantasies or voices directing him to target a particular individual. This preoccupation with the target becomes consuming and ultimately could lead to the target's death. The drive to stalk arises from a variety of motives, ranging from rebuffed advances to internal conflicts stemming from the stalker's fusion of identity with the target. The target almost always is perceived by the stalker as someone of higher status. Targets often include political figures, entertainers, and high-media visibility individuals, but they do not have to be public figures. They can even be supervisors at work or even complete strangers. Sometimes the victim becomes someone who is perceived by the stalker as an obstruction.

When erotomania is involved and the target is a highly visible media personality (usually someone unattainable to the stalker), the target becomes the imagined lover of the stalker through hidden messages known only to the stalker. The stalker builds an elaborate fantasy revolving around this imagined love. Male erotomaniacs tend to act out this fantasy with greater force than do female.

Victimology

The target is aware of the stalker through many prior encounters or communications (letters or phone calls). The target often has high media visibility. Many times the initial contact with a public figure will be in the form of "fan mail."

Crime Scene Indicators

As with other classifications of stalking, the activity of the erotomania stalker is often long-term with written and telephonic communications, surveillance, attempts to approach the target, etc. With the passage of time, the activity becomes more intense with the stalker's attitude shifting to one of "If I can't have her, no one can."

The majority of erotomania-motivated attacks are at close range and confrontational. The stalker may even remain at the scene. These close-range encounters tend to be more spontaneous, as reflected by a more haphazard approach to the target: Evidence is left, and there are likely to be witnesses. This does not mean the stalker did not fantasize, premeditate, and plan the stalking; all of these elements characterize this crime. Rather, the actual act is usually an opportunistic one. The stalker takes advantage of opportunity to interact with the target as it is presented to him.

Common Forensic Findings

Firearms are the most common weapon carried by stalkers, especially with a distance stalking. Occasionally, the will use a sharp edge weapon, such as a knife. The sophistication and type of weapon will help establish the degree of stalker sophistication.

If the target of the stalker is killed, the vital organs, especially the head and chest, are most frequently targeted.

Investigative Considerations

The stalker almost always surveys and/or stalks the target preceding the encounter with the target. Therefore, the availability of the target's itinerary and who may have access to it is one investigative consideration. There is a likelihood of preoffense attempts by the stalker to contact the target through telephone calls, letters, gifts, or visits to the target's home or place of employment. There may even be an incident involving law enforcement or security officers having to remove the stalker from the target's residence or work place.

The stalker's conversation often will reflect this preoccupation and/or fantasy life with the target. When those associated with the stalker are interviewed, they will most likely recall that much of the stalker's conversation focused on the target. He or she may have claimed to have had a relationship with the target and may have invented stories to support this encounter.

Assistance should be requested from FBI's Investigative Support Unit or mental health professionals experienced with these complicated cases.

Case Study – Erotomania Stalker

On the morning of March 15, 1982, Arthur Richard Jackson, 47, was waiting near Theresa Saldana's West Hollywood apartment house. As Saldana, 27, rushed out to a music class at Los Angeles City College Jackson approached. When Saldana paused to unlock her car, Jackson asked, "Excuse me, are you Theresa Saldana?" Saldana replied, "Yes".

Her identity confirmed, Jackson began stabbing Saldana with a hunting knife. He stabbed and slashed her so hard and so often that the knife bent. Hearing Saldana's screams, a delivery man rushed to her aid and wrested the weapon away from Jackson. The intervention of the delivery man, heart-lung surgery, and 26 pints of blood saved Saldana's life. Jackson, convicted of attempted murder and inflicting great bodily injury, was given the maximum sentence of 12 years in prison.

Arthur Jackson was born in Aberdeen, Scotland, in 1935 to an alcoholic father and a mother whom investigators believe may have been schizophrenic; he was an odd and fanatical child who often became lost in fantasy. In an 89-page autobiographical letter addressed to Saldana written in 1982 shortly after his arrest, Jackson wrote that at 10, he became fixated on a neighbor girl called Fiona. At 13 he described a sexual encounter with an older boy.

It was also this letter to Saldana where he expressed his "torturous love sickness in my soul to you combined with a desperate desire to escape into a beautiful world I have always dreamed of (the palaces of gardens of sweet paradise), whereby the plan was for you, Theresa, to go ahead first, then I would join you in a few months...I swear on the ashes of my dead mother and on the scars of Theresa Saldana that neither God nor I will rest in peace until this special request and my solemn petition has been granted."

At 17, he suffered his first nervous breakdown. It took a full year before Jackson was released from a Scottish psychiatric hospital where he sought treatment. After his release, he began a trip across two continents, working in London as a kitchen porter, in Toronto as a zoo helper, and in New York as a jack-of-all menial trades.

In 1955 he joined the US Army. While in the army he fell in love with a fellow soldier and suffered another nervous breakdown. He was sent to Walter Reed Hospital in Washington, DC, for psychiatric treatment. While in the hospital he was given a weekend pass in honor of his 21st birthday in 1956. Jackson celebrated his birthday by going to New York. While in New York, he attempted suicide with an overdose of sleeping pills.

Discharged from the Army, he continued to wander the US. In 1961, the US Secret Service arrested Jackson for threatening President John F. Kennedy. Later that year he was deported to Scotland where he occasionally lived with his widowed mother. During this time period he was a vagrant on the dole and seldom stayed in one place for more than a few months. In 1966, Jackson reentered the US through Miami and was given a six-month visitor's visa. He was again deported when he overstayed the six months.

He first became aware of Saldana in 1979, when he sat in an Aberdeen theater and watched *I Want to Hold Your Hand*, a film about Beatlemania. Movies were Jackson's only reality. Jackson conceived mad passions for women in movies whom he thought of as stars.

Two years later he saw Saldana in *Defiance*, a movie in which she plays a girl trying to make a life for herself in a crime-ridden slum. When costar Jan-Michael Vincent was attacked in the movie by a street gang, the scene provoked vivid memories of his 1956 suicide attempt. Focusing his macabre excitement on Theresa, Jackson convinced himself he could win the actress by "sending her into eternity."

Jackson began stalking Saldana in early 1982, the year he illegally returned to the US. Jackson would make several cross country bus trips in this single-minded quest. He initially went to New York City where he tried to contact Saldana's relatives and business associates. The ruse used was pretending to be an agent with a hot script. He was unable to locate Saldana. A trip to Los Angeles also yielded nothing. Only after he had returned to New York from California did he manage to trick one of Saldana's relatives into telling him the actress lived in Hollywood. While he stalked Saldana, he tried to purchase a gun in many different states, but was prevented by state laws requiring a minimum of a driver's license for identification. The only weapon available to Jackson was a hunting knife.

After returning to Hollywood, he hired a private detective who provided Saldana's address. During questioning by the police he was asked why he had tried to kill Saldana. Jackson replied, "Read my diary. It's all in there." Jackson had kept a dairy of his quest in his knapsack. While in custody Jackson confessed to the murder of two people during a robbery of a London bank in 1962. Jackson continues to write to Saldana as well as reporters about his quest for Saldana. Jackson became eligible for parole in 1991.

In summary, the nondomestic stalker may know the target through social contact (business, school, etc) or from a random meeting in a public place (store, mall, sporting event, etc.). Targets of the nondomestic and erotomania stalkers are selected by the stalker for love, hate, religion, or voices heard by the stalker. The selection process may only be known to the stalker. These targets are unaware of the initial reason for their selection. The domestic stalker is known to the target and had a close personal relationship with the target. These cases are the most likely to end in a violent confrontation. The erotomania stalker's target is typically a public figure. Television appears to be the most probable source because it provides visual and auditory material for the fantasy being developed by the stalker. The stalker is usually unable to develop meaningful relationships with others and is classed as a loner. They often have prior involvement with law enforcement (arrests, trespass complaints, etc.) and with psychiatric facilities. They may have attempted suicide in the past. The stalker may have engaged in similar activity on prior occasions.

Reprinted with permission from the *Journal of Psychosocial Nursing*, Slack, Inc. Wright JA, Burgess AG, Burgess AW, McCrary G, Douglas JE. Investigating stalking crimes. *J Psychosoc Nurs*. 1995;33(9):38-43.

Chapter 6 – Workplace Violence

Ann Wolbert Burgess, Allen G. Burgess, and John E. Douglas

A study of workplace violence using a convenience sample of news wire cases was employed to develop implications for patient care, workplace security, and individual safety. In 132 cases of workplace violence, 206 people were wounded, and 90 offenders killed 303 victims. Eighty-four percent of the victims were male, and 16% were female. Twenty-six of the 90 offenders committed suicide, and seven were killed at the crime scene. Only three of the offenders were female. Six homicide classifications or motives were identified: nonspecific or random killings (18 offenders killed 105 and wounded 103), authority killings (35 offenders killed 86 people and wounded 69), revenge killings (nine offenders killed 42 persons and wounded 22), domestic violence (nine offenders killed 21 family members and wounded eight others), felony murder (nine offenders killed 34 people) and argument/conflict (seven offenders killed 15 people and wounded four).

As violence in America increases, it has moved from the home to the community and into the workplace exacting a staggering toll of victims. Violence is occurring even in such formerly protected and sacrosanct environments as schools, hospitals, and places of worship. Morale and productivity of tens of thousands of employees, the vicarious victims of violence, are affected.

FBI statistics tell us that although stranger murders dominate the media, people are three to four times more likely to be killed by known persons. Firearms are used in two-thirds of homicides, and half the persons arrested are under 25 and 90% are male.[1]

Statistics from The National Institute for Occupational Safety and Health (NIOSH)[2] found that homicide was the cause of a surprisingly high proportion of all traumatic workplace deaths. Although accidents in general still cause the greatest number of workplace fatalities for males, 12% of these fatalities, or about 750 people, were due to criminal assault. For females, the percentage of work-related fatalities was higher.

Although known to have a low mortality rate from occupational injury, women are more likely to die as victims of assault than from any other manner of workplace injury. The NIOSH study revealed that 42% of all women who died in work-related incidents were victims of homicide.

Violence is expensive. It has surpassed automobile accidents as causation for spinal cord injury and often brain injury. In Los Angeles county, in a one year period, $53 million was spent on gun shot wounds. At one county medical center, 686 patients were admitted for torso bullet wounds. They spent 4,666 days in the hospital. Just 30 had private health insurance, and nearly half had no coverage.[3]

Violence has expanded into the hospital setting. Mahoney's study of 124 Pennsylvania acute care hospitals noted that emergency department nurses are at higher risk for victimization than either the general public or other human service workers. The study cites 67.3% of emergency room nurses reported at least one assault during their careers, and 36.3% of nurses had been assaulted at least once during the previous year.[4]

Nursing is called upon to manage both the victim and the victimizer in the healthcare setting. Stories of gun fights in patient rooms and areas do not cause much of a reaction anymore among experienced rehabilitation team members. In the large, urban nonpsychiatric hospitals with rehabilitation units and free-standing rehabilitation facilities, the healthcare team members tell of violence within the facility involving patients, families, and guests.[5] The violence is not just seen in the disabilities of clients who are victims of violence, but this is situational throughout facilities because of the cultures of many of their patients and the areas in which facilities are located. These nurses deal with the results of domestic, criminal, and gang-related violence. It is not only a cause of their patients' disabilities, but it is a daily threat to the safety of the rehabilitation team members. One nursing administrator in Detroit said she found herself consciously wondering on an almost daily basis, if the colors she put on in the morning would provoke gang-related violence. She feared she might get "blown away" in the hallway for wearing colors associated with a particular gang, since the families for many rehabilitation patients are violent gang members.[6]

Method

Since its inception in 1985, the FBI's National Center for the Analysis of Violent Crime has been evaluating postcritical incidents regarding violent crime investigative matters. The recent increase in requests specific to workplace violence prompted one of the authors (JED) to initiate a survey of violent crime with multiple victims using the

LEXIS/NEXIS news and information service. The first case reported over the national wire services was in 1949 when 13 people were fatally shot in 12 minutes. Howard Unruh, age 28, who told police, "I'd have killed a thousand if I'd had enough bullets," was found legally insane. The second reported case was in 1966 in which 16 people were killed by Charles Whitman, 25, after he climbed to the top of a campus tower at the University of Texas. Whitman was killed by police; an autopsy revealed a small brain tumor. The third case was in 1975 and involved 11 victims, including eight children. A relative, James Ruppert, age 40, was convicted of two killings and found innocent by reason of insanity in the others. In 1978, six employees were herded into a walk-in freezer and shot to death during a robbery. Surveying violent crime in the workplace between 1978 and 1989, 40 cases made the national wire service. Between 1990 and 1993, a four-year period, that number more than doubled as 92 cases were identified.

Given this dramatic increase in nationally reported cases, an analysis of the 132 cases of workplace violence was undertaken by the authors to answer the research questions: Could these workplace crimes be classified using the FBI *Crime Classification Manual* (*CCM*) and if so, what types of crimes were being committed in the workplace.

Data for the study was obtained from two sources. First, the 132 cases represent a wide geographical convenience sample identified through national wire service reporting. Second, telephone consultation with local law enforcement verified specific facts of the study cases.

For the analysis of data, the cases were first classified using the 33 categories of homicide identified in the *CCM*.[7] Second, statistical tests (Pearson correlation and cross-tabulations) were employed.

The findings include six types of homicide, and each one will be discussed separately by number and profile characteristics of offenders, number of victims killed and/or wounded, and offenders who suicided or were killed at the workplace. Implications for patient care, workplace security, and individual safety are discussed. All cases used for examples are from the study database.

Type of Homicide

Nonspecific Homicide

Eighteen offenders of non-specific homicide killed 105 people and wounded 103 victims. Five of the offenders suicided and two were killed on-site. This type of killing appears irrational and is committed for a reason known only to the offender. The offender could be psychotic and in some cases determined to be legally insane. The victims are random, with no direct relationship between victim and offender. Victims generally are targeted by gender, race, position, age, religion, or they can be at the wrong place at the wrong time.

The crime is usually committed during the daytime and in a public place as the offender wants as many victims as possible. The crime scene poses a high risk of capture to the offender. It is a disorganized crime scene with no effort having been made to conceal the victim. A firearm, the weapon of choice for this type of offender, is brought to the scene. This crime often becomes a massacre reflected by use of weapons that offer optimal lethality, by multiple weapons, and by an abundance of ammunition.

Profile characteristics of such offenders suggest they may have a distinctive appearance, are socially isolated, demonstrate a flat affect, or possibly exhibit erratic behavior. Such offenders may have a history of psychiatric problems or be previously undiagnosed. The firearm may be concealed in a canvas bag until the shooting begins. Typically, the offender has no escape plan and intends to suicide or be killed by police.

A case of victim targeting by race was in 1989 in Stockton, CA, when Patrick Purdy, 26, an embittered drifter, dressed in military attire and seemingly obsessed with war, rampaged through a school yard, killing five Asian-American children and wounding 30 others before he fatally shot himself with a pistol. His weapons included an AK-47 style assault rifle and a 9mm pistol.

A case of victim targeting by position occurred in 1993, in Los Angeles, CA. A disgruntled patient opened fire in the emergency room, wounding three doctors. He took two women hostage before surrendering. He told police he had AIDS and was a "victim of a medical conspiracy."

Authority Homicide

Thirty-five offenders committed authority homicide and killed 86 persons and wounded 69. Ten of the offenders suicided; 9 offenders were killed at the site, and one was wounded.

An authority killing involves a subject who kills persons that have an authority relationship or symbolic authority relationship by which the killer perceives he or she has been wronged. The target of the assault may be a person(s) or a building,

56

structure, or institution symbolizing the authority. Random victims are often wounded and/or killed during the assault as a result of their actual or perceived association with the authority figure or the institution being attacked.

The offender is mission-oriented, and he is at the crime scene with his mission having ultimate priority. He has little or no intention to abort his plan and escape from the scene or from responsibility for the act. He may desire to die at the scene, either by suicide or police bullets, and thereby attain martyrdom for his actions and cause. There is always a direct and planned confrontation between the offender and victim.

Because of his obsession of being wronged over a period of time, the offender gathers and collects weapons and usually brings multiple weapons to the scene of his confrontation. The assault may develop into a mass or spree killing.

The offender will have a history of paranoid behavior and will openly voice dissatisfaction with general or specific circumstances in his life. There are usually long-term precipitating and predisposing factors in the development of this state, and a likely result is untreated emotional or mental illness. The mental disorders commonly found among authority killers are depressive reactions, paranoia, or paranoid psychosis. Another result of this developmental situation is interpersonal failures and conflicts, such as separation, divorce, job loss, failure in school, or other such personal stressful events that will precipitate the acting out against authority. Frustration accompanied by the inability to handle or resolve such situations are often precipitating events. Suicide attempts prior to the killing are common.

In 1986 in Edmund, OK, US Postal employee Pat Sherrill, who was about to be fired, killed 14 coworkers and wounded six before he killed himself.

On December 7, 1987, David Burke, after recently being fired from a major airline company, used his credentials to board a commuter flight and with a smuggled .44 magnum pistol shot and killed his supervisor and the members of the flight crew. He and all persons on board died in the plane crash that followed.

On January 1, 1989, in Verona, MS, a police chief died after being shot 15 times while serving an arrest warrant in a church parking lot. A couple later arrested for the crime had been wanted for threatening an employer who fired them.

Revenge Homicide

Twelve men committed revenge homicides killing 42 persons and wounding 22. Three of the offenders killed themselves.

Revenge killing involves the murder of another person in retaliation for perceived wrongs, real or imagined, committed against the offender or a significant other. The victim may not personally know the offender, but something in the victim's life is related directly to the actions of the offender. There is a significant event or interaction that links the offender to the victim. Multiple victims may be involved, depending on the nature of the event that triggered the act of revenge.

There are often several crime scene locations involved with the offense. For example, the precipitating event may happen at one site, but the revenge is acted out later at another location.

An offender who has brooded over the victim's affront very often demonstrates a less spontaneous crime than is reflected by a well-ordered crime scene. However, the mission-oriented offender may not be experienced with criminal activity. Some offenders are often in a highly charged emotional state due to excessive fantasizing about the act of vengeance. The crime scene may reflect this inexperience, with a clear shift from organized to disorganized behavior. The weapon may be left at the scene. Because the act of vengeance was the priority and an end in itself, there may be no escape plan.

Preoffense behavior by the offender often will follow a pattern in which he or she is at first very verbal about the incident that involves the victim's injustice. As the offender formulates a plan for vengeance, he or she may become preoccupied and less vocal in general. After the offense, there is often as sense of relief on the part of the offender. The mission has been accomplished. He or she may even stay at the scene to savor the achievement and may make no attempt to conceal his or her identity. The death of the victim is justified in the eyes of the offender; it is restitution.

On December 6, 1989, a 25-year-old man wearing hunting attire and using a rifle killed 14 women and wounded 12 other people before killing himself at the University of Montreal engineering school. The gunman singled out his victims at seven different sites in the building. A suicide note said that women, in particular feminists, had ruined his life. The note contained a list of 15 prominent Quebec women as objects of special hostility, and he wrote that he had been rejected for enlistment in the army because he was "antisocial." He had also once sought admission to the engineering school.

Non ovember 2, 1991, a brilliant former graduate student in physics stood up during a scheduled meeting in his department and began, without a word, to methodically extinguish six victims. In a melee of no more than 10 minutes, Gang Lu swiftly moved through two university buildings. Four male professors in the department of physics and astronomy, the female associate vice president of academic affairs, and her female receptionist were shot and killed. The student, armed with two handguns, believed he had been wronged by the university when his doctoral dissertation did not win the prestigious academic award and $1,000. He killed himself.

Domestic Homicide

Nine offenders killed 21 family members and wounded eight others. Seven offenders committed suicide.

Domestic homicide occurs when a family or household member kills another member of the household. This definition includes common-law relationships.

Prior domestic violence can often be supported by police reports. A history of conflict due to external sources (financial, vocational, alcohol, etc.) are common elements of domestic homicide.

The domestic offender is mission-oriented, e.g., to get his ex-partner. He is preoccupied with her, he checks up on her through hang-up telephone calls, and he stalks her. He believes he owns her; he idolizes or has an obsession about losing her. He may have made threats to kill her; he may have described how he would kill her. He has weapons in his residence or car; he has threatened suicide and has a plan; he abuses alcohol and/or drugs; he isolates himself from family and friends.

On August 9, 1991 in Odessa, TX, a 23-year-old man was released from a state psychiatric facility after threatening to kill himself over his separation from his wife. One day later he bought a .38-caliber pistol and used it to kill his estranged wife, his stepdaughter, his two sons, and himself. After buying the gun, the man asked a friend to go out and buy him cigarettes. The friend found the bodies when he returned.

In August 6, 1992, at Elgin Air Force Base, FL, Raymond Baker, 38, fired on five to 10 security police officers when he came into the base hospital with his son. The officers killed him in return fire, the child was not injured. The civilian gun man's exwife, an Air Force nurse on duty at the hospital, was not injured.

Felony Homicide

Nine offenders committed felony homicides killing 34 people and wounding none.

Property crime (robbery, burglary) is the primary motivation for felony murder, with murder the secondary motivation. During the commission of a violent crime, a homicide occurs. In an indiscriminate felony murder, a homicide is planned in advance of committing the felony without a specific victim in mind. In a situational felony murder, the murder is unplanned prior to the commission of the felony; the homicide is committed out of panic, confusion, or impulse.

The victim is one of opportunity: walking into a store or house at the wrong time or having a work shift coincide with a robbery. There are occupations, shifts, and environments that elevate a victim's risk factor. Working the night shift alone at a 24-hour gas station or convenience store is one example. Environmental factors include working in high-crime areas or in poorly lit areas with no alarms or intercom systems and where cash is easily available. It is also possible for a victim to elevate his or her risk by attitude and behavior. A careless, naive, or flippant approach to personal safety heightens the chance of being targeted for robbery.

Offenders of felony homicide are usually in the middle stage of their criminal career. They often have a history of alcohol/drug abuse that increases their already volatile nature. Some outside influence will often trigger the killing (e.g., an alarm sound, a spouse coming home, a victim screams).

On February 19, 1983, 13 people were shot dead during a gambling club robbery in Seattle's Chinatown section. Two men were convicted of felony murder. On July 17, 1992, in a Tulsa restaurant, four young restaurant workers were ordered into a walk-in refrigerator, made to kneel down, and shot in the head by robbers. Four men, one former employee, were charged with first-degree murder and armed robbery.

Argument/Conflict Homicide

Seven offenders committed an argument/conflict homicide killing 15 persons and wounding four. Two offenders killed themselves; one was killed by police and one was wounded.

Argument/conflict murder is death that results from a dispute between persons, excluding family or household members. The victim and offender are known to each other and the victim commonly has a history of assaultive behavior and of using violence to resolve his problems.

An exception to this victimology is the person who has the misfortune to cross paths and ignite the volatile, impulsive offender, predisposed to violent eruptions. The precipitating event may even be a trivial incident such as pulling in front of someone in traffic or flashing car lights from behind.

The precipitating event, e.g., the argument or conflict, is the cause of the death. The killing can be a spontaneous or delayed reaction to this event. The offender will have a history of assaultive behavior and of using violence to resolve problems. He will have access to weapons and bring them to the confrontation. He has a specific target.

In October 1992, at Fort Campbell, KY, a soldier shot and killed two sergeants after returning from a field exercise and then fatally shot himself. Gregory Radcliffe, 25, was upset over an argument that occurred during military maneuvers.

Implications

Patient Care

For the families of homicide victims, Grief Assistance Programs offer support and counseling. Such programs may be private or publicly funded and operate out of mental health clinics, prosecutors' offices, or a medical examiner's office, as in the City of Philadelphia.

For survivors of violence, patient care includes six steps.

1. **Crisis response:** Victims and victimizers of violence are admitted into acute care settings, such as hospital emergency departments or trauma centers. The majority of cases will be gunshot or knife wounds and require acute trauma care. Hospitalization will be required for moderate to severe injuries.

2. **Injury Assessment:** While many hospitals have their own assessment protocols, routine questions to screen for violence need to address both victim and victimizers. Key areas for assessment include: patient transportation to trauma center; stated cause of injury; body area of injury focus; assessment for serious injury; assessment for moderate injury; person who inflicted injury to others or to self; location where

injury occurred; interpersonal violence classification; prior injury or abuse history; and discharge plan.

3. **Intervention and treatment:** Interventions will vary according to the nature of the injury, its impact on the patient, whether the patient is the victim or victimizer, other health issues of the patient, and the patient's motivation and resources to deal with the abuse. Rehabilitation nursing will be needed for those with long-term injuries, such as spinal cord or head injuries.

A safety plan must be developed with the patient, both in the hospital, the home and at work. Exploration of where and how the patient feels safe and what resources are needed to strengthen safety is critical. The patient needs to know the nature of violence and that it is in the mind of the victimizer. Violence represents a basic disregard for human life.

4. **Recording and reporting:** Nurses need to carefully document each patient's history and assessment of injury. Healthcare records are official documents and may be used as forensic evidence as well as within the healthcare system to follow a patient. State laws require the reporting of certain crimes, e.g., gunshot wounds and stalking.

5. **Directing outpatient referrals:** Referrals are of two types: additional nursing services and community resources. Nursing services include advance practice nurses, such as nurse practitioners, primary care nurses, clinical specialists in psychiatric mental health nursing, rehabilitation nurse specialists, community health, and visiting nurses. This requires nurses to know community nursing services and resources that can assist with victims. Advocacy services, when available, are critical with domestic violence victims. Encouraging the input of the victim in deciding what kinds of referrals is important.

6. **Follow-up care:** Violence is often a pattern of coercive behaviors. Subsequent abuse and injury need to be checked at each healthcare contact. The follow-up should be done by each nurse practitioner seeing the patient. These follow-up inquiries can be brief and to the point.

Workplace Environments

The safety and security of the workplace environment can be strengthened through policy development and implementation, inservice training, and consultation in the following areas.

1. **Reporting and reviewing workplace violence:** While most hospitals have incident-reporting forms for threats and aggressive acts, it is the fast review and knowledgeable disposition that communicates hospital administration's view of violence.

Administrators or executives that allow violent actions, words, or threats to go unnoticed without discipline are sanctioning violence. Failure to set limits on aggression in the workplace provides people not prone to committing violent acts a model. Hospitals that fail to meet acceptable standards of security could be held liable for violent acts committed on their premises. Condoning or ignoring violent and/or aggressive behavior may set the scene for future employee violence. Managers need to secure consultation on the definition, assessment, and management of threatening and dangerous behavior.

2. **Management of workplace violence: Code Violence:** Hospitals need a plan of action for what to do if a violent situation occurs, and they need to rehearse their plan. There needs to be a routine Code Violence practice similar to fire drills. For example, when a violent subject enters the workplace, silent alarms need to alert the security department and fire or escape doors need to be activated. Routine review of all security measures needs to be implemented, including the testing of video-monitoring systems and unit security, as well as patient and visitor areas.

3. **Copy cat alert:** Hospitals need to be on high alert whenever the media reports on workplace violence. Some subjects mimic violent acts after reading of a local occurrence.

4. **Security department:** The security department is critical to the operation of a safe hospital environment. Policy needs to be reviewed on issues such as weapons and victimizers. There should be no tolerance of weapons in the work place unless by prior authorization. Weapon screening may be necessary at visitor areas. It is important that a hospital be able to stop a subject who violently enters the workplace. The use of electronic door locks or armed security guards are two ways to prevent entry by armed persons. Workplace policy is critical on whether or not they permit security guards to carry weapons. Although not always a deterrent, weapons can prevent or deter a subject from lethal action. Security guards without weapons must have access to a secure area and ways to notify local authorities that do not compromise their safety. Security personnel are at high risk because the subject may incorporate the security guard into his obsessional system that everyone associated

within the institution needs to be killed. In such a situation, the security guard will not be able to deter the subject.

5. **Identifying suspicious persons:** Two types of suspicious persons need to be identified in hospital settings. The first type is identified by appearance of a flat or angry demeanor, an agitated mood, or unkempt clothing. The second type is the subject who has previewed the workplace. This person is seeking to become familiar with the location and to get the "lay of the land" or case the facility. For example, in felonies, the bank robber often asks the teller for an inconsequential act, such buying a roll of quarters, but he is really looking around at the security system. In hospitals, women preparing to abduct an infant will be noticed loitering around nurseries or birthing centers.

However, it is the getting familiar with the setting that is also the subject's downfall. If nurses are alert, they will notice the person is acting suspicious, is casing the place, and seems preoccupied with the environment. Security must be notified for both types of suspicious persons.

6. **Red flags regarding employee behavior:** Sometimes the violent action is taken by an employee. Behaviors that should place managers on alert include an employee who is obsessed with weapons; compulsive reader and collector of gun magazines; excessive discussion of weapons; makes direct or veiled threats; intimidates or instill fear in others; obsessive involvement with their job; little involvement with coworkers; unwanted romantic interest in coworker; paranoid behavior; unaccepting of criticism; holds a grudge; recent family, financial, academic, social, legal, or other personal problems; interest in recently publicized violent acts; tests limits of acceptable behavior; and extreme change in behavior or stated beliefs.

Red flags for stress in the workplace include layoffs, reductions-in-force (RIFs), and labor disputes. Managers need to be trained so they can properly discuss these realities with employees.

7. **Career advancement:** Managers need training in how to handle employees who are passed over for promotion for how to provide additional incentives in the workplace to promotion.

8. **Employee grievances:** Personnel department, human resources division, employee assistance, and security need to work as a team in the handling of grievances and problems. When there is conflict between an employee and a manager, the manager should not be part of the negotiations; rather, the employer

should bring in another supervisor. Personnel departments need to have resources to manage grievances as they occur and not to encourage them to build up in the employees mind.

9. Terminating employees: Employees need warning before they are terminated. Acts such as escorting the employee to their car ("instant parking lot"), removing their parking sticker, or changing office door locks will increase anger, hostility, and resentment. A pink slip in the last pay envelope is inflammatory; human concern and regard for employees must be given as violence prevention policy.

Employers must realize terminated employees need outplacement counseling on how to handle being out of the institution. They are high risk because of loss of structure from the workplace, loss of predictable safety, and inability to function alone. Vocational counseling, not called mental health counseling, must be part of benefits package for employees. Economic concerns to review with the employee include loss of job, loss of income, loss of benefits, and possible loss of housing. Exit interviews should not include the problem manager.

Summary

This study answered the research question by identifying only six out of a possible 33 homicide classifications for workplace violent crime. As expected, the largest number of offenders represented authority killings. Half that number, however, had the largest number of victims and were classified as nonspecific homicide. It was interesting to note the high number of domestic homicides occurring in the workplace. One can speculate as families break up, addresses and telephone numbers can be changed, but not necessarily employment. Victims are sought out at their places of employment and killed there. Argument/conflict homicides, which were expected to be high, accounted for only seven homicides. The other important finding was the large number of suicides in this offender group.

Individual Safety

A basic human instinct is survival and preservation of life. The neurobiology of the limbic system alerts and prepares an individual to respond defensively to threat of danger. The four activated neurocircuits of fear, flight, fight, and freeze translate into personal safety behaviors of alert, escape, defend, and hostage.

Fear/alert: The body is alerted to danger through the sensory system: hearing gunshots, seeing a weapon, smelling smoke, feeling a building rock. If time is available, call for assistance and security. Calm yourself; take deep breaths; think rationally.

Flight/escape: If you can escape, leave quietly, calmly, and unobtrusively and seek help. If escape is not possible, lock yourself into a secure area, such as an office or room and place a barrier between yourself and the door.

Fight/defend: If unable to escape and the subject is in your immediate presence, position yourself out of the subject's range. Do not become a perceived barrier to his mission. Do not talk to him, do not try to block his path, do not attract his attention. Drop to the floor, try to get behind strong furniture for protection. Prepare to defend yourself with materials within the room, such as chair, desk supplies, scissors. Rehearsal of defense behavior will be critical for you to feel empowered in a dangerous situation when it's your life or the subject's life. Remain calm to keep your thinking clear.

Freeze/hostage: When there is no warning and a subject comes into a setting firing a weapon, people often freeze; they do not know what to do. One action to take is to feign being shot; do not move. The subject does not know whom he hit or missed; he is more likely than not to track and shoot at a moving target.

If taken hostage, body position needs to be below the subject. The subject needs to feel superior and dominant. A tall male victim will be the most intimidating to the subject. Maintain eye level below the subject's eye level. Stall for time because the subject has high emotion during a criminal act. Time helps decrease the emotional intensity. Maintain eye contact but do not stare; look occasionally at the subject. Do not turn your back or exit a room because that is a depersonalizing act that enables the subject to kill. If there is any conversation, because of the high emotion, and the subject is agitated and/or irrational, try to paraphrase what is being said and restate the content. Try to allow the subject to hear his own words. If he hears his words through restated content, the subject may begins to think he is being understood. He hears back his message. The goal is to stall for time and allow the explosive aggression to begin to wane.

Personalize yourself to the subject. It is important to let the subject know something about yourself. Hostage situations can go on for hours, and it will be difficult for the subject to kill you if he knows your name, that you have children, or have an illness or problems of your own. If you have no life problems, make some up. Talk of financial problems and conflicts with your partner. Give the subject a view that you have been a victim in life, because he feels he has been a victim in his life. If the

66

subject can identify with you, it will be difficult for him to kill you. In psychological terms, encourage transference of emotion to occur between you and the subject. Avoid telling the subject what to do or not to do. He has the weapon; he has control. Pleading for your life will not make him sympathetic. Telling him of your hypothetical mean boss may save your life.

References

1. Federal Bureau of Investigation: *Crime in the United States*. Washington, DC: US Department of Justice; 1992
2. National Institute for Occupational Safety and Health. Occupational homicides among women, 1980-1985. MMWR. 1990;39:514-522.
3. Los Angeles Times. October 3, 1993:1.
4. Mahoney BS. The extent, nature, and response to victimization of emergency nurses in Pennsylvania. *J Emerg Nurs*. 1991;17(5):282-91.
5. Prevention: A Prescription for Violence. Annual conference of Association of Rehabilitation Nurses; September 18, 1994; Orlando, FL.
6. Personal communication with Lunn S; 1994.
7. Douglas JE, Ressler RK, Burgess AW, Burgess AG. *Crime Classification Manual*. San Francisco, CA: Jossey-Bass; 1995.

Reprinted with permission from the *Journal of Psychosocial Nursing*, Slack, Inc. Burgess AW, Burgess AG, Douglas JE. Workplace violence. *J Psychosoc Nurs*. 1994;32(7):11-18.

Part 2
Rape and Sexual Assault

Chapter 7 – Sexual Trauma and Styles of Attack

Ann Wolbert Burgess and Lynda Lytle Holmstrom

Rape is a serious social issue that needs to be approached from many perspectives: social, cultural, legal, economic, political, and educational. What is to be addressed in this chapter, as well as the remainder of the book, is the clinical perspective and training implications for victim care. That does not mean it is the most important, but as a start, it is an essential component.

To provide some systematic way to help clinicians view rape from the victim's perspective, a clinical typology of sexual trauma was evolved. All persons admitted to the Boston City Hospital emergency department with the complaint of rape were seen by the authors. From this group of 146 people, three main types of victimizations were described. These categories of sexual trauma were made according to the criterion of consent and are described in this chapter: 1) rape-sex without consent; 2) accessory-to-sex-inability of the victim to consent; and 3) sex-stress situation-sex with initial consent.

Rape is an interactional process involving at least two persons. Rape also involves a control issue. One person must gain control over another person. It became clear in talking with rape victims that from their point of view, rape is an act initiated by the assailant; it is not primarily a sexual act, but an act of aggression, power, and violence. One factor of great importance to the victims was how the assailant gained access and control of them, i.e., his style of attack. Cases were analyzed – whether child, adolescent, or adult – and a typology of rape was based on how the assailant gained access to his victim. The two main styles of attack were the blitz rape and the confidence rape. These types are described below.

Rape: Sex Without the Victim's Consent

Control is a key ingredient of a rape. In practical terms, the assailant has two goals – physical and sexual control of the victim. In listening to victims describe assailants' styles of attack, it was clear that some rapists gained control in a direct physical action, such as a sudden surprise attack, while others used verbal ploys in an attack that has the qualities of a confidence game. In both types, the rapist gains sexual control of the victim by force and without her consent.

The Blitz Rape

The blitz rape occurs "out of the blue" and without any prior interaction between assailant and victim. The person is leading a normal everyday life. A split second later that lifestyle is shattered and that individual is a victim. As one 36-year-old victim said: "He came from behind. There was no way to get away. It happened so fast – like a shock of lightening going through you. [I] was so helpless at the time."

From the victim's point of view, there is no ready explanation for the man's presence. He suddenly appears, his presence is inappropriate, he is uninvited, and he forces himself into the situation. Often he selects an anonymous victim and tries to remain anonymous himself. He may wear a mask or gloves or cover the victim's face as he attacks.

The "mark," to use the language of the criminal world, is the person destined to become a victim of some form of illegal exploitation. The classic example of the blitz-type rape is a woman walking down the street and who, from the assailant's viewpoint, is the "right mark at the right time." He is looking for someone to capture and attack. She happens on the scene, and she becomes the target.

In the surprise attack, the victim is totally unaware of the assailant. She is literally surprised as she goes about her business. It is not unusual for the victims to be attacked while they are asleep in their own beds because the assailant has gained entry into the home.

A 62-year-old woman was brought to the hospital at 8:30 AM by the police. She had multiple bruises on her face, neck, chest, and back, as well as a two-inch stab wound in her abdomen. Her first words to the counselor were, "I thought I was going to be killed. I didn't want to die – I didn't think it was my time, but I remember thinking this is the way I was going to die."

The victim said that she had been in her bed sleeping – it was around 3AM – and she woke up to feel someone jumping on her. She said, "I started screaming, and he put a blanket over my head. I didn't have it off till he left. He said when he started, 'Let's see how you like this.' He started doing such crazy things. He was playing with my breasts and then he made me open my mouth and he put his thing in it. I never did such a thing. He made me keep my hands away from my mouth and he stuck it down so far I thought I would gag. It was just awful. Then he turned me over and tried my back end. He kept turning me this way and that. He raped me the regular way. At least he wasn't violent doing that; thank heaven, that wasn't crazy ... I remember thinking that I never thought such a thing could happen to me. I thought I would die, and his hand kept clamping my neck tighter and tighter. When he finished raping me, he told me to keep the blanket over my head for 20 minutes and said if I took the blanket off, he would finish me. I didn't hear him leave, but every now and then I would call out to see if he was still there. I hoped to get a view of him and kept peeking out of the blanket, but couldn't see anything. Finally I dared to take the blanket off, and I called the police. They came right away, and I called my daughter. The officer talked to my daughter and said I was lucky to be alive. I could hardly talk and was having a lot of trouble breathing..." The victim was unable to identify an assailant, although she did work with the police in hopes of finding a suspect. She definitely would have pressed charges against the assailant.

In the 43 blitz-type rapes in the 92-adult victim samples, 35% (15 rapes) were committed while the victim was outside. Victims would describe being jumped upon, grabbed, pushed, or shoved when the assailant approached them from behind. Other victims were in the process of entering their cars or apartments. One victim was stopped at a traffic light when a man approached her and opened the unlocked passenger side door. Other victims were pulled into cars or grabbed outside and taken to an indoor area, such as a hallway, building, or car. Of the victims raped in their own apartment or house, five were in bed sleeping; one woman had just stepped into her shower when the lights went out, and the man grabbed her and took her into a bedroom.

The children and adolescents who were victims of the blitz rape were often walking home from school, walking home from a friend's house, or playing with neighborhood friends when the attack occurred. The following report is a case in point:

A 13-year-old victim stated: "It was 9 PM, and I left my house to go to the corner store for a cupcake and a coke. I had my portable radio with me. As I was coming home, a guy grabbed me and dragged me down a hill that is in my own yard. He said a lot of nasty things to me and dirty things like was this the first time I'd fucked? And did I like it? And then he wanted my name and phone number." The assailant made her take her clothes off and then forced her to lie down on her coat, and he put a sleeve across her face so she could not see him. The girl said, "He did it three times and he made me kiss him. " The victim was noticeably upset with this part and looked as though she would vomit. She said she had tried to scream and struggle but no one heard her. She thought he was a "crazy man" and that "he will be looking for other girls to rape." The assailant ran off, and the girl ran into her home and told her parents, who immediately called the police. The family worked with the police, but a suspect was never found.

This was the first sexual experience for this young girl. The medical examination indicated lacerations of the hymen and bleeding.

The Confidence Rape

The confidence rape is a more subtle setup than the blitz style. The confidence rape is an attack in which the assailant obtains sex under false pretenses by using deceit, betrayal, and often violence. There is interaction between the assailant and the victim prior to the assault. He may know the victim from some other time and place, and thus, already may have developed some kind of relationship with her. Or, he may establish a relationship as a prelude to attack. Often there is quite a bit of conversation between victim and assailant. Like the confidence man, he encourages the victim to trust him, and then he betrays this trust. An analysis of rapists' talk during rape revealed a number of linguistic strategies that are used to control the victim before, during, and after the rape.

One of the linguistic strategies used by rapists is the confidence line. This line is used in various ways in terms of the rapist: offering or requesting assistance or the victim's company; promising information, material items, social activities, employment, business transactions; making reference to someone the victim knows; or trading on social pleasantries and niceties. There are variations of this sexual confidence game, and they are described below.

Capturing the victim: In this style, there is an effort to strike up a conversation with the victim and to use verbal means to capture her rather than physical force. The assailant establishes a kind of relationship with the victim, ostensibly for a reason acceptable to the victim. However, once he gains the person's confidence, he betrays that confidence. In the following situation, for example, the assailant presented himself to his victim as the person who could rescue her from danger:

A 21-year-old woman was walking home from work. She saw two men behind her, one on foot and one on a motorbike. The man on the motor-bike approached her and convinced her that the man on foot was following her and might try to attack her. She was convinced to accept a ride from him to the Square where she could get a cab. Instead of going to the Square, he made several turns on side streets and took her behind a restaurant where he pushed her down to the ground and took her clothes off. The woman said, "I cried all through it until he told me I had to stop or he'd hurt me." The police arrived on the scene as the man was trying to escape. They had received a call from someone who heard a girl screaming. The police chased the assailant down an alley and were able to get him at the end of the alley.

The victim testified at the district level court and at grand jury. The case came to trial four months following the assault. The defendant, age 21, pleaded guilty to the charges of rape and assault and battery. The judge accepted the assistant district attorney's recommendation of a prison sentence of not less than seven years and not more than 15 years. The charge of assault and battery was placed on file (no sentence given).

A number of people may be involved in this style of attack, either as assailants or as accomplices in the crime. Often another woman is an accomplice in the crime. This other woman is used as a decoy – as the person who deceives and entraps the victim. In cases involving hitchhiking victims, there may be a woman in the car sitting in a seat alone; the victim-to-be sees that she will get in next to a woman and thinks it will be a safe ride. Women have also deceived the victim in cases of gang rape by making the victim think she was going to a party. Once at the "party," the decoy woman disappears, and the victim very quickly realizes that she is the mark for sexual assault. The following case illustrates the gang-rape confidence approach:

A 29-year-old divorced woman was at a club where people were talking and mingling. The woman was with a group of several men and another woman when the talk focused on a party that was being held that evening. One man suggested they all go to the party. The two men and two women went in one car. They arrived at the apartment and the victim-to-be went in first, followed by one of the men. The minute she stepped into the apartment she realized something was wrong when she saw many men standing around with motorcycle jackets on and drinking beer. There were no other women there, and she suddenly realized the other woman had disappeared. She panicked and said, "This isn't what I expected. I do not wish to stay. Please let me out."

The men did not listen to her. She was pushed into a bathroom where a man was urinating. When he finished, he forced her to have oral sex, and then she was pushed back out into the room with the other men. Over a two-day period she was held captive and forced to comply with the sexual demands of nine men and was assaulted if she refused. The sexual demands were for oral sex, during which time the men ejaculated in her mouth, and anal and vaginal sex, with several men demanding sexual acts simultaneously. The victim feared that she might be murdered. She was taken by car to a second apartment in another town during part of the orgy. She was released when her purse was examined, and it was learned she worked for a local personality. The police were notified, and the victim worked with the police to identify the assailants. Within several weeks, four of the eight men were identified. The hearing for probable cause was held 14 days after the sexual assault. The trial was postponed for over 15 months at the request of the defense lawyers. Later the defense obtained dismissal prior to Superior Court trial.

Knowing the victim: There are many attacks where the assailant is known to the victim. The assailant is a neighbor, an acquaintance, a date, a friend, or a relative. The assailant uses his relationship with the victim to justify his being in the situation. He then deceives the person by not honoring the bounds of the relationship. He often gains entry in the situation by offering assistance, as in the following example:

A 19-year-old woman was brought to the emergency department by the police at 1:30 AM. She was tearful and said, "I am shocked that this happened. I cannot understand it; he has a girlfriend; how could he do such a thing?" The young woman went on to say that this had been her wedding day, and she and her husband were at their wedding reception. Her husband had become angry at one of the guests whom he felt was paying too much attention to her, and that prompted him to leave her. The bride then went looking for her husband. An invited guest, a friend of the groom, said he would help find the groom because he knew where he was. The bride left with the friend who said the groom was across the street, and as they headed toward the place, the friend forced the woman against the wall and held something to her throat that felt like a knife. The man said, "I want you, and I am going to have you." The victim said, "He tried to do it standing up, but couldn't. He then forced me to lie down on the ground, and he took off my pants and raped me lying down." When the man finished, he took off down the street. The victim said she became hysterical and ran into a stranger who asked what happened. He listened and then they went to a nearby restaurant and called the police.

This case went to the district level court, as the man was easily apprehended. Probable cause was found, and the case was sent to the grand jury. The victim and her husband received threatening telephone calls from the friends of the defendant that prompted the woman to request charges be dropped rather than to testify at grand jury.

A large number of assailants of adolescents and children know their victim prior to the attack, too. The assailant could be a school peer, known casually to the girl, who suddenly attacks her on the way home from school. Often this is a gang rape with several youths and one girl.

With the teenage girl, the youth often knows the girl from the neighborhood community or the school. He first acts like a friend, but then betrays her. The following is an illustration of this type of attack, tearfully reported by a 13-year-old victim:

"We were at the sub shop. There were four of us – my girlfriend and two boys we knew from school. The boys suggested going to this building to play games. I said yes; I thought it would be fun. I thought we would play pool. We went there, went up in the elevator and into the room through a sliding window. I thought it was a settlement house where all the kids go...In the room, he kissed me. I told him to stop, that I wasn't that kind of a girl. He used one hand to hold my arms together...He was undressing me with his other hand. We fought. He punched me, I punched him back in the mouth. I got a bruised finger because of it. He said to let him do it, or he'd stick it in hard. He said he wouldn't let me go till he checked to see if I was a virgin...Then he got on top of me. He attacked me."

This case was prosecuted at juvenile court before a judge. The boys, who were brothers, were found to be juvenile delinquents and were placed in the custody of their parents.

Controlling the victim over time: There are situations where the assailant uses rape as a means to control the woman, not just for one incident, but over a long period of time. The woman is usually an exgirlfriend of the assailant, who assumes he still has full sexual privileges with her. The victim is beaten as well as sexually assaulted. A 45-year-old woman was the victim in this situation:

The woman arrived at the emergency department at 3:30 AM accompanied by her boyfriend. She said the man who assaulted her had been a previous boyfriend of hers for a year and a half period, and that he had come to her apartment uninvited that evening. She said, "Men should not be allowed to get away with this kind of thing. Most women do not press charges. They are so frightened they will be killed if they

77

do tell. And many women end up dead in an apartment from such a thing, and no one knows what has happened to them. Well, I am going to tell on this guy. He gave me a shakedown. He knew where to hit me and how to get me scared, so I would do what he told me, and I did. You have to go along with what they say. At one point he said I was being too loud. But, you know, when that is happening to you, you don't care about noise...He messed me over the street way. I'm not supposed to tell. He said he'd beat me if I tell. And he gave me a sample tonight to show me. You know, they work you over – to control you – so they can have you sexually any time they want. He hit me on the ear, pulled my hair, hit me in the back by my kidneys – very strategic. But it's not the physical part that's the thing – it's mental to control you...I wonder how many women are beaten like this and never tell. But I'm not safe, I had to tell. Other women don't tell and then later they are found dead."

The woman went to the police station the next day to report the assault. She identified the man. The police never arrested the man, but suggested she file the complaint as a civil complaint. When she was asked how she felt about her experience with the legal process, the woman said: "I decided to relax on it. He said he would deny it and say he didn't do it. He said I'd be ashamed to bring such a thing out in the open – said what would my family and friends think. He just would deny the whole thing. But I have something on him and he will get what he deserves...I am just one more poor little victim who is helpless, and he is an untouchable because of who he is and who he works for. It is not so much outsmarting these men, but lucky to survive. As long as I know he is not bothering me, I feel OK. I have pointed him out to my friends so that they know him, and I am covered for future experiences."

Sometimes there is an adolescent or child victim who is controlled this way, too. The victim feels unable to tell family or anyone about the assaults. The assailant trades on this fear and continues to molest or assault the child. In such situations, the child or adolescent is manipulated by the assailant over time. An example follows:

A 17-year-old male babysitter terrorized six children in a family, both boys and girls, over a one-year period. The assailant would select one of the oldest children to sexually molest until that victim was able to physically resist him. He then would select the next oldest child. The oldest girl, age nine, was able to verbally fight off the assailant who said that he "didn't like girls." The assailant would threaten physical harm to the children if they told anyone what he was doing.

The babysitter enlisted in the Army and was away from the neighborhood for six months. He returned one weekend and stayed with the family and slept in the same bed as the six-year-old boy. The next day the boy complained to his parents that the babysitter had done "bad things" to him. He was quite emphatic, but his parents dismissed the accusation as a "story." On Sunday the parents went out, and the babysitter took the six-year-old boy into the parents' bedroom and molested him again. Some of the other children witnessed the assault and were thus able to corroborate the incident to the parents. The parents then became quite upset and brought the child to the hospital.

The assailant was AWOL from the Army at this time. He returned to the base and subsequently received a military discharge. He was arrested three months later when he returned home. The night before the hearing for probable cause, the assailant raped two 14-year-old girls at knife point. The girls were able to identify him because he was wearing his army jacket with his name on the pocket. He pleaded guilty to the rape charges and was sentenced to two consecutive eight-year terms. One year later he was returned to district level court in connection with the assault on the six-year-old boy. He pleaded guilty to the charge of indecent assault and battery to a child under age 14. He was given a suspended sentence of two years in the house of correction and placed on one-year probation following his release from his current prison sentence.

Accessory-to-Sex: Inability to Consent

In rape, the type of victimization discussed above, the victim, whether adult, adolescent, or child, clearly does not consent to the sexual activity. The sexual acts are against their will, and they are forced by the assailant to do them. In accessory-to-sex, the type of victimization discussed below, the victims aid or contribute in a secondary manner to the sexual activity. The victims' collaboration comes about because of their inability to consent or not consent due to their stage of personality or cognitive development. It should be noted that we do not define ability to consent arbitrarily by age. In all these cases, the primary person involved, the assailant, stands in a relationship of power over the secondary person, the victim, because of being older, being an authority figure, or for some other reason.

The assailant gains access to this victim by three methods: 1) pressures the victim to take material goods; 2) pressures the victim to accept human contact; and 3) pressures the victim to believe the sexual activity is appropriate and enjoyable. In each of these three approaches, the assailant makes sure the victim gets something out of the sexual encounter; thus at the time, the encounter is not a totally negative experience for the victim.

79

Pressure by Material Goods

In the child or adolescent victim situation, the assailant may apply pressure through the offer of money or candy. For example, one three-year-old boy was enticed away from his playmates by a man who offered him candy. In contrast to the case in which that victim was very upset at the time of sexual molesting, this three-year-old victim did not complain to his parents or show any signs of upset to his family. He simply walked into the house naked, carrying a paper bag. This prompted an outburst of emotion from his father, and then the child became upset.

In the case of a 12-year-old mentally retarded girl, the assailant offered her one dollar. The police testified at the district level court hearing for probable cause as follows:

"My partner and I responded to a call that a young girl had been brought into a house by a man. When we arrived we searched to no avail. We banged on the door, back and front, and no one answered. We observed a man on the staircase. He saw us and ran. We entered every room in the house and finally entered the kitchen and noticed there was another room off of it. We entered the room and found the child and the defendant naked in bed. The defendant was on top of the girl in the act of intercourse. We advised him of his rights at the scene and then placed him under arrest. We asked the child if he had enticed her with candy and she said no. Then we asked if he had enticed her with money and she said yes and gave us a dollar bill which we have here as evidence."

The defendant was a 73-year-old man and was tried before a judge at superior court level. He pleaded not guilty to two charges: assault and battery of a child under age 14 and abuse of a child under age 14. He was found guilty of both charges by the judge and sentenced to one year in the house of correction.

Pressure By Human Contact

Our sample included a few adult women who did not have the emotional development or cognitive development to be able to consent or not consent. Extremely impoverished socially and emotionally, they were enticed by men by their needs for minimal human contact. Having little contact with people in any other way, they were enticed by men with offers of human warmth, despite the violence and abusive manner in which it was given. Such a victim we call a "battered person." The following case illustrates this type:

The 28-year-old single woman was brought to the emergency department at 2:30 AM. She looked lonely and isolated, despite the many people who had been in to talk with her – the nurses, doctors, police, and counselors. Her clothes were an odd assortment and were oversized, emphasizing her unkempt look. She had nothing with her except the clothes she had on. She said, "I got dumped tonight. I was with two guys I had been living with the past week, but they left the Club we were at; they dumped me. I just can't go back to their place. I don't remember the number, just the street it was on...I was standing outside the Club when a car pulled up with four men in it. They pulled me into a car...Two of the men raped me and then they dumped me out. Someone passing by stopped and brought me in here." The victim described the past years as years of drifting around, never making any permanent ties and her past as being a failure. She said, "A psychiatrist told me I was trying to destroy myself. I get no enjoyment from sex, not even the men I stay with, but rather, feel guilty.

Later, in talking with the father of this victim, he said: "We haven't seen her since you saw her at the hospital. In fact, we have not seen her for 10 days before that. She had no visible means of support. I tried to get her to see a psychiatrist, but she wouldn't do it...I want her to get some help because she just drifts around. I am really afraid she will end up a statistic. I am working with the police department and have filed a missing person report, but even the detective said that a woman in that area of town is in trouble. Someone will get her and that will be the end."

This victim summed up her request well when she told us that she just wanted to find someone who would be kind to her and take care of her.

Misrepresenting Moral Standards

There are situations in which assailants will trade on the power they have in the relationship to put pressure on the victim, often a child, to believe certain sexual activity is acceptable. The victims are told that sex is all right to do and that they will enjoy it. The following case illustrates this type:

One adult rape victim was finally able to talk about her childhood and the fact that she was sexually molested by the same man over a six-year time period. She said, "He started when I was about six. I didn't know what he was doing, but it became more and more. He said it was OK and it felt good. He would rub me and kiss me where he was rubbing me. He would try to get me to kiss him the same way."

It is not uncommon for an assailant, once he has involved the victim in the sexual activity as an accessory, to pledge her to secrecy. Such a situation occurred in the same case as follows:

I have never been able to tell anyone. He wouldn't let me. I have had to guard myself so much. I was always watching what I said and scared that my mother or someone would find out.

Sex-Stress Situation: Sex with Initial Consent

Some cases in our sample showed a third type of victimization that we call a sex-stress situation, rather than rape or accessory-to-sex. They were not cases of the male's gaining access without the female's initial consent. Nor were they cases in which the victim, for personality or cognitive reasons, was incapable of making a decision of consent. Rather, as each story unfolded, it became clear that the case was one in which the male and female initially agreed to have sexual relations, but then something drastically "went wrong." Usually, what went wrong was that the male exploited this agreement in several ways. In some cases, what went wrong was that authorities – police or parents – came upon or found out about the consenting couples; and then these authorities themselves defined the situation as rape or caused the person to say it was rape as a way out of a dilemma of being caught. Also, in some of these sex-stress cases, the person who referred to the problem as rape, in reality wanted some service from the hospital and felt she could not directly ask for it. After all, given the prevailing attitudes, a young teenager cannot walk into a hospital and say that she and her boyfriend had sex the evening before, she is scared of getting pregnant, and she needs medication to prevent pregnancy. It should be emphasized that very few of these sex-stress victims took the case to court; they did not become "spite cases," that is, cases in which the female sought to "get the guy" on a rape charge simply out of spite.

It is important to understand sex-stress cases for several reasons. First, they greatly influence how the system deals with rape. Staff members tend to become obsessed with trying to determine if a case is a rape case or if it is one of the other types described here. A tremendous amount of energy goes into this "diagnosing" rather than helping the victim with the request for aid. Second, these sex-stress cases deserve counseling in their own right.

These females are victims in their own way and have many emotional concerns over what to them has been an upsetting experience. The two main types of sex-stress situations we identified – mutual agreement and contracting for sex – are discussed.

Mutual Agreement

In the sex-stress situation, both parties have agreed to have sex. Both are willing, but then something goes wrong. The male becomes perverted; the female becomes anxious; or the authorities – police or parents – intervene.

Violence and Perversion. In the sex-stress victim, what may have happened is that the man became violent or perverted in his approach and frightened the woman. Case 12 that follows is a case in point. It involves a 47-year-old woman who describes how she met the assailant in a lounge. They had considerable conversation leading up to the point where they left the lounge with the purpose of returning to his apartment to have sex there. He had offered to pay money for sex, but she said she was not interested in being paid. The woman described what happened after they left the lounge:

He had given me a good talk; he was a good con man, and I was looking forward to having sex with him. I was horny and was feeling neglected, and I love my sex. He took me outside and down an alley and threw me on the ground. I asked him what he was doing – told him he didn't have to do it there if all he wanted was a screw...I was on the ground 10 to 15 minutes. He just pulled everything off me – took all my clothes off. I couldn't believe what was happening. I told him I wasn't a slut or whore that did it in an alley. It didn't matter. He kept pulling at my clothes. He didn't take his clothes off; he just dropped his pants and then he started. First he tried natural sex; then he insisted on oral sex. I didn't want to but he forced me – it was choke or take it. He wanted to [put it] in my mouth. I said no. He started getting real mad. Then he said he was going to urinate on me...He rammed his fist up me twice and he bit my breasts. Then he stood up and piddled all over me and said, "I feel better." He told me not to leave – he hit me and said, "You will do what I say." Then he left. I didn't think he would come back. I started to get dressed, and then he was back. He had another guy with him. The guy who raped me asked the other guy if he wanted me, and the guy said, "I want no part of it." They both walked away.

The woman said she spent a few minutes trying to get composed. She looked around and saw a police precinct and so walked over to it. She said:

As I was going up the stairs I just let myself go. I just felt safe and let go. One plainclothesman and another officer came out and asked if I was OK. I said I had been raped. I felt so dirty. I called my mother and said I would be home shortly. My mother is in a wheelchair; she is all alone, but she said she would wait for me. The police wanted to see where it happened so I took them back there. The police advised that I come to a hospital. They said the guy might have a disease. The police brought me to the hospital, and they called the guy's description out over the radio, and they went right out after him after they left me at the hospital. They were very good to me.

The woman was in considerable conflict over pressing charges. She was fearful of repercussions from the man. She was also concerned that both had been drinking and that she had initially agreed to have sex. She did go to the district level court two weeks later with her mind made up. She told the judge she wished to drop charges, and she was allowed to do so.

Victim's Anxiety Over Sexuality. Occasionally, a female will get so anxious after having sexual relations, especially about getting pregnant, that she may say that a rape occurred. She may report the incident as rape so that she can get examined and receive medication. For example, a 14-year-old girl came to the hospital, accompanied by her girlfriend, and stated that she had been raped by two boys the previous evening. She said she came home, did not say anything to her parents, and went to her room. She described the rest of her night as follows:

I went to bed, but I didn't sleep. I banged on the mirror; I pulled my hair – I just went crazy. I finally lay down and went to sleep for a few hours. I woke at 6 PM and went right over to my girlfriend's house and woke her up. I got hysterical and told her she had to help me...I figured I could handle this myself if I had my friend to help me. We began reading a book, and we began to get scared I might get pregnant. I figured out I was midway in my period; I almost blacked out over that. My friend said we could go to a clinic and not have to give our names.

At the hospital, the girl was adamant that her parents or police not be notified. The hospital was unable to treat without parental permission, and after two hours of talking with all available hospital staff, the girl agreed to have her parents notified. Her mother immediately came to the hospital. The examination indicated no physical trauma, the hymen was still intact, and laboratory tests indicated no sperm present.

On follow-up, the mother revealed that the daughter later had been able to tell her that it was not a rape experience but rather, her first sexual contact; and that, plus the possibility of pregnancy, had frightened the girl. Counseling involved talking with the mother and daughter separately in order to help them deal with their feelings and reactions to the situation.

Parental anxiety over sexuality. Parents may become so overwhelmed with worry about their daughter's sexuality that they, too, may come to the hospital and claim that a rape has occurred in order to have the girl examined. The mother of a 14-year-old girl came to the emergency department of the hospital and took the nurse aside and said, "My girl was raped two days ago. Can you check without telling her you know?" A talk with the mother revealed some of her concerns:

About three weeks ago I noticed a change in her behavior. She was staying out late, and a male was calling her and identifying himself as "her man." She has been acting strange and suspicious; she doesn't talk to me. I suspect she is having sex. Why else would she be staying out so late? ...I don't feel a 14-year-old girl should be giving her body to those good-for-nothing boys. She knows I'm strictly against it. Boys just want one thing.

The gynecologist said that the girl had rights to privacy and that he would not examine her for virginity reasons. He did say he would talk with the girl alone to see if she did have concerns to talk to him about. It did result in the girl's requesting birth control pills, and she was referred to the adolescent gynecological clinic at the hospital. In this type of situation, the mother and daughter were counseled separately, with the goal being to relieve the anxiety of each one so that a more comfortable and less suspicious relationship could develop between the two.

Police intervention. There are situations in which police come upon a parked automobile in which the occupants are engaged in sexual activity. The girl may have consented. However, such a situation may come to the attention of hospital staff if the girl is underage and her anxiety is sufficient to cause her to be either confused or agitated at the time.

In one situation, a 14-year-old girl got willingly into a car with two men, one of whom was known to her. The 16-year-old youth she had been dating was one of the occupants, and the driver of the car was the 35-year-old uncle. The police happened onto the car, and the girl said she was forced to have sex. The charges were dropped at court the next day when the mother agreed the girl had gone willingly in the car.

Like adult sex-stress victims, the girls in the sex-stress situations seldom press charges unless the parents take the initiative, and then the charge is usually statutory rape rather than forcible rape.

These statutory rape laws are a reflection of society's ambivalence over the issue of sexuality during adolescence. They state that under a certain age – for example, under 16 in some states – by definition a female is incapable of consenting to sex; so that even if she says she consented, the law says she did not, and the male can be taken to court. Further evidence of the ambivalence on this issue is that the dividing age between being legally incapable or capable of consent varies from state to state. Usually the parents, not the victim, wish to pursue a statutory rape charge.

Parental intervention. There are situations in which the parent perceives some danger to the daughter's reputation and assumes responsibility in the matter. For example, in our adolescent sample, this might happen if the girl was missing overnight.

The parents became concerned and either notified the police or waited for the daughter to come home. The men were usually in their 20s and 30s and the girls between ages 12 and 15.

In one situation involving a 13-year-old girl, the foster mother said:

Joan didn't come home when she was supposed to, so we called the police and reported her as a runaway. Then someone said they had seen her, so her father went looking for her and heard where she was. He told the police but they were unable to find her. Then on Sunday Joan came home to change her clothes – she had new clothes on. She said she was going to a banquet with this boy she met. I called the police and they talked with Joan who took them back to the apartment. They found her clothes and the man was seen running out the back door and across the yard.

In this case, the man was apprehended by the police, and at the probable cause hearing, the case was bound over to the grand jury. The case was scheduled for trial, but at the time of the trial, the man defaulted; that is, he did not appear for trial, so a warrant for his arrest was issued.

Fifteen months after the assault, he was arrested and pleaded guilty to one of three counts: The abuse of a minor. Counts two and three were placed on file without change of plea. He was sentenced to five to seven years.

Contracting for Sex

A number of prostitutes who contract for sex find out later that the client does not live up to the contract. He becomes perverse, becomes violent, robs her, or does not pay for services obtained. As a result, prostitutes often feel they are in danger and, as a result, sometimes turn to the police for protection. The police, in turn, bring the woman to the hospital for medical attention. These women often have a number of concerns as the case below illustrates. A 19-year-old woman, whose assailant demanded oral, vaginal, and anal sex, went on to describe his more sadistic acts:

[He] was tying me to the bed and beating me with his belt – it hurt so bad as he flung it straight across my back. I was afraid he was going to kill me. I was never so scared in my whole life. You have to go along with male chauvinism in this society. Men will have sex one way or another. They will pay, steal, or something. But this guy was crazy; he was insane. He needs to be put away. What if he gets a virgin or some young girl next time?

Contrary to public opinion, the prostitutes in our sample who were victims of sex-stress situations did not follow through with pressing charges. They would often identify the man and have him arrested, but then they would fail to show up in court the next day for the arraignment. With only one exception, they did not pursue the case any further.

Contracting with the assailant for money means that his subsequent attack does not fall within the legal definition of rape. And these women are not included in our analysis of the rape trauma syndrome. However, we do consider these women as victims of the sexual confidence game as more broadly defined, and they are deserving of counseling in their own right.

Summary

This chapter presents a typology of sexual victimization developed by analyzing 146 cases admitted to Boston City Hospital with a complaint of rape or sexual assault. The cases are categorized according to the criterion of whether or not the victim consented and they fall into three main groups: 1) rape-sex without consent; 2) accessory-to-sex-inability to consent; and 3) sex-stress situation – sex with initial consent.

This chapter emphasizes how the victim views rape; i.e., as an act initiated by the assailant and as an act that is primarily life-threatening rather than sexual in aim. The methods used by the assailant to gain access to and control of his victim are distinguishing features of the attack. Some assailants use physical strategies and some use linguistic strategies. The cases are further categorized as 1) a blitz rape in which the assailant makes a sudden, surprise attack, or 2) a confidence rape in which the assailant verbally gains the victim's trust and then betrays it.

Chapter 8 – The Rapist's View

A. Nicholas Groth

In order to more fully appreciate what the rape victim is a victim of, it is helpful to understand the dynamics of the offender. What prompts men to rape? What are such offenders like? Do they progress from less serious to more aggressive offenses? What determines their choice of victims? What can a potential victim do, when faced with such an assailant, to deter him? Will the offender return? These are some of the questions commonly asked about rapists, and it is difficult to provide simple and unequivocal answers to them. One of the major obstacles to the development of definitive knowledge about men who commit sexual assaults is access to such offenders.

Rapists and child molesters characteristically do not self-refer to mental health agencies for a variety of reasons. Some fear that disclosure will result in their incarceration in a mental hospital or correctional institution. Others do not appreciate that their behavior is inappropriate or symptomatic. And those who may voluntarily seek out consultation and treatment find few community-based programs and agencies responsive to their needs. Human service providers have not been trained to work with such clients. Even those sexual offenders who are apprehended and convicted will find few rehabilitation programs within the criminal justice system specifically addressing their needs. The result is that sexual aggressors, for the most part, have not come to the attention of behavioral scientists. Without an opportunity to work with and to study a sizable number of such persons, a body of information has been slow to develop regarding this form of sexual psychopathy. Rather than having a sense of who they are, what they do, and what motivates their offenses, we are left instead with stereotypes and myths about men who rape.

Although clearly a sexual offense, society has been slow to recognize rape as disordered sexual behavior. The American Psychiatric Association's *Diagnostic and Statistical Manual of Mental Disorders (DSM-IV)* does not list rape as a sexual deviation, nor will it be found in the World Health Organization's *International Classification of Diseases (ICD-11)*. Rather than being understood to result from psychological determinants within the offender, rape is more often viewed as the outcome of external, situational factors.

Stereotypes of Rapists

There are two common stereotypes of the rapist. At one extreme he is regarded as a perfectly healthy, "red-blooded," sexually aggressive, macho male, whose offense is simply an extreme product of his cultural conditioning elicited by a provocative and seductive but punitive woman. At the other extreme he is thought of as a bizarre, demented, oversexed "fiend," filled with lust and perverted desire, who stalks his prey at night when the moon is full. In the former situation the offender is seen as a totally normal individual who is essentially a victim of circumstance; in the latter as some type of inhuman creature whose predatory assaults are his only source of gratification. Both stereotypes reflect the erroneous but popular belief that rape is motivated primarily by sexual desire – the normal desires of a healthy male or the warped impulses of a sex fiend. This mistaken notion is an insidious assumption, for it follows from such a premise that if the offender is sexually aroused, then it must have been the victim who aroused him because it is towards her that these impulses are directed. From that point on, responsibility and accountability for the offense, to a large extent, become shifted from the offender to the victim, and it is she who becomes the accused by police, family, friends, and even herself. In court it becomes the central aim of the defense attorney to impeach the victim's credibility by showing that by her dress, conduct, conversation, and/or behavior, she invited the assault; and either deliberately or unintentionally, that she aroused the sexual urges of her assailant, and he is the victim of her provocativeness.

Yet, in working with identified rapists, both convicted and not convicted, it becomes apparent that sexual desire is not the dominant motive in rape; nor is sexual frustration, for a variation on the myth that the victim has sexually enticed the offender is the view that the offender is a sex-starved male who must resort to rape to relieve his sexual tensions and frustrations. The majority of rapists we worked with were married and engaged in regular sexual relationships within, and often outside of, their marriages. Nor did many complain that their wives were inattentive or unresponsive to their sexual needs and interests. As one offender put it: "The only good thing about our marriage was the sex; we had good sex together, but that's all we had. Out of bed we couldn't talk; we couldn't communicate; we had nothing going for us. Sometimes right after I had sex with my wife I would go out and rape someone." Those offenders who were not married also were sexually active and had access to a number of sexual outlets in their lives. Masturbation, prostitution, and consenting heterosexual and/or homosexual relationships all offered opportunities for sexual gratification. In reality, no offender had to resort to rape to achieve sexual relations. If sex is not a primary motive, then what is?

Rape: Power, Anger, and Sexualty

Clinical work with offenders and victims reveals that rape is in fact serving primarily nonsexual needs; it is the sexual expression of power and anger. Rape is motivated more by retaliatory and compensatory motives than sexual ones; it is a pseudosexual act, complex and multidetermined, but addressing issues of hostility (anger) and control (power) more than desire (sexuality).[1] The defining issue in rape is the lack of consent on the part of the victim. Sexual relations are achieved through physical force, threat, or intimidation. Rape, therefore, is first and foremost an aggressive act and, in any given instance of rape, multiple psychological meanings may be expressed in regard to both the sexual and the aggressive components of the act.

Typology of Rape

The most basic observation one can make regarding rapists is that not all such offenders are alike. They do not do the very same thing in the very same way or for the very same reason. In some cases, similar acts occur for different reasons; in other cases, different acts serve similar purposes. From our clinical experience both with identified offenders and with victims of reported sexual assault, we find that in all cases of forcible rape, three basic components are always present: anger, power, and sexuality.[2] The hierarchy and interrelationships among these three factors, together with the relative intensity with which each is experienced and the variety of ways in which each is expressed, may vary from one offense to another. Yet there is sufficient clustering so that distinguishable patterns of rape become evident: the anger rape, in which sexuality becomes a hostile act; the power rape, in which sexuality becomes an expression of conquest; and the sadistic rape, in which anger and control become eroticized. In every act of rape, then, both aggression and sexuality are involved; but it is clear, however, that sexuality becomes the means of expressing other, nonsexual needs and feelings which operate in the offender and motivate his assault. Rather than being primarily an expression of sexual desire, rape is, in fact, the use of sexuality to express issues of power and anger. It is a sexual act that is concerned much more with status, aggression, control, and dominance than with sexual pleasure or sexual satisfaction. It is sexual behavior in the service of nonsexual needs and, in this sense, rape is clearly a distortion of human sexuality.

Anger Rape

In some cases of sexual assault it is very apparent that sexuality becomes a means of expressing and discharging feelings of intense anger, rage, contempt, hatred, and frustration; the assault is characterized by excessive brutality. Far more physical force is used in the commission of the offense than would be required simply to overpower and subdue the victim. Instead the assault is one of explosive physical violence to all parts of the victim's body. This type of offender approaches his victim by striking and beating her. He tears her clothes, knocks her to the ground, uses abusive and profane language, rapes her, and frequently makes her perform or submit to additional degrading acts.

The rape experience for this type of offender appears impulsive more than premeditated. He will typically describe being in an angry, frustrated, and depressed frame of mind. Quite often a precipitating stress can be identified that involves a significant woman in the offender's life – his mother, his wife, his girlfriend, or some such person. The conflict he experiences in this relationship reaches a crisis level and then becomes activated by some upsetting altercation or frustrating interaction with this individual. The resulting fury is released and discharged in a sexual assault against a victim who may be, but more frequently is not, the actual person towards whom the offender harbors such feelings. Nor does the precipitating event inevitably involve a woman. It may be that he lost his job, was rejected from the Armed Services, had an automobile accident, got into a fight at a local bar, or some such thing. What appears significant is that this type of rapist does not report feeling sexually aroused at the time of his offense, but instead is feeling troubled and hostile. His controls give way, and he describes a sudden surge of anger or a feeling of rage flooding through him. The aim of this type of offender is to vent this rage on his victim to retaliate for what he perceives as wrongs done him. Sex becomes a weapon, and rape is the means by which he can use this weapon to hurt and degrade his victim. Sex itself is regarded at some level of experience as base and degrading, and this offender typically finds little or no sexual satisfaction in the rape. His subjective reaction to the sexual act is frequently one of revulsion and disgust, and often he experiences difficulty in achieving or sustaining an erection during the assault.[3] His intent is to hurt his victim, and his assault is brutal and violent. His motive is revenge and punishment. In extreme cases, this may result in homicide.

The anger rapist finds it difficult to explain his assault, when he cannot deny it, except to rationalize that he was drunk or on drugs. Often the specific details are lost to his memory in that he becomes "blind with rage" during the assault. Satisfaction and relief result from the discharge of anger rather than from sexual gratification. Pleasure is derived from degrading and humiliating his victim.

His relationships to important women in his life are fraught with conflict, irritation, and irrational jealousy, and he is often physically assaultive toward them. His sexual offenses tend to be episodic and sporadic, triggered by conflicts in his relationships to these actual women in his life.

The anger rapist commits sexual assault as an expression of his hostility and rage towards women. His motive is revenge and his aim is degradation and humiliation.

Case: Derek is a 25-year-old married man and father of four. His mother abandoned the family shortly after his birth. Throughout his life, his father reminded him that his mother was a "whore and never to trust any women; they were no good." During his adolescence Derek became acquainted with his mother and once, while drunk, she exposed herself to him and asked him to fondle her. He fled, terrified. In vain efforts to win his father's recognition and approval, Derek put a premium on physical toughness. In high school he played sports "like a savage" and then entered the Marine Corps. He had an outstanding service record and after discharge got married (against his father's wishes) and attended college. One day he got into a dispute with his female history teacher over the merits of the Vietnam War and felt she was ridiculing and humiliating him in front of the class. He stormed out of the room, very angry, thinking "women are dirty, rotten bastards" and went to a bar for a few drinks. On his way to his car he spotted a 40-year-old woman (whom he described as looking older) in the parking lot. He grabbed her by the throat, hit her in the mouth; ripped off her clothes, and raped her. Prior to this offense, Derek's criminal record consisted of arrests for gambling, loitering, and being drunk.

Power Rape

In this type of sexual assault the offender generally employs only whatever force is necessary to overpower his victim and gain control over her. The evidence of such power and control is that the victim submits to sexual demands on the part of the offender. The offender places his victim in a situation through verbal threat, intimidation with a weapon, and/or physical force where she cannot refuse or resist him, and this provides the offender with a reassuring sense of power, security, strength, mastery, and control. In this fashion, he compensates for underlying feelings of inadequacy, vulnerability, and helplessness.

This type of rapist often shows little skill in negotiating interpersonal relationships and feels inadequate in both sexual and nonsexual areas of his life. Having few other avenues of personal expression, sexuality becomes the core of his self-image and self-esteem. Rape becomes the means by which he reassures himself of his sexual adequacy and identity, of his strength and potency. Usually the aim of the assault is to effect sexual intercourse as evidence of conquest and, to accomplish this, the victim is often kidnapped, tied up, or rendered helpless in some fashion.

Because it becomes a test of his competency, the rape experience for this offender is one of anxiety, excitement, and anticipated pleasure. The assault is premeditated and preceded by an obsessional fantasy in which, although his victim may initially resist him, once overpowered, she will submit gratefully to his embrace since she will be so impressed with his sexual abilities. In reality, this offender may often be handicapped by impotency or premature ejaculation. If not, he still tends to find little sexual satisfaction in the rape. The assault is disappointing for it never lives up to his fantasy.

Often he must convince himself that his victim became attracted to him, really wanted sex but could not admit it, and clearly consented nonverbally to, and enjoyed, the sexual contact. Yet at some level he realizes that he has not found what he is looking for in the offense; he senses that something he cannot clearly define is lacking. He does not feel reassured by either his own performance or his victim's response to the assault and, therefore, he must go out and find another victim – this time the "right one."

The offenses become repetitive and compulsive. The amount of force used in the assault may vary, and there may be an increase in aggression over time as the offender becomes more desperate to achieve that indefinable experience that continues to elude him. Usually there is no conscious intent on the part of this offender to hurt or degrade his victim; his aim is to have complete control over her so that she will have no say in the matter and will be submissive and gratify his sexual demands. Aggression, then, may constitute a show of force or a reaction to resistance on the part of the victim. That is, when the victim resists the advances of her assailant he retaliates by striking or hitting her. Aggression here usually becomes expressed less as an anger motive and more as a means of dominating, controlling, and being in charge of the situation. Rape becomes an assertion of the offender's virility or a reassurance of his competence – a reflection of the inadequacy he experiences in terms of his sense of identity and effectiveness.

The power rape may be precipitated by some perceived challenge from a female or threat from a male which activates the offender's feelings of inadequacy and insecurity. Rape then constitutes the way in which this person asserts his identity, potency, mastery, strength, and dominance; the way in which he denies his feelings of worthlessness, rejection, helplessness, inadequacy, and vulnerability.

Case: Warren was a 20-year-old single male on leave from the military. He picked up an 18-year-old student he met at a bar and drove her to a secluded area. She begged to be let go, but he grabbed her and said, "You don't want to get hurt, baby – you want to get laid. You want it as much as I do." He forced her to submit to intercourse and then offered to buy her dinner. While out on bail he committed an identical offense. As an adolescent, Warren had been involved in a number of sexual incidents involving exhibitionism and sexual play with children. He was seen for treatment at a local mental health center. As a teenager he had no steady girl friends and in the service, he was being supported by a 30-year-old man in exchange for sexual favors. Warren, however, does not regard himself as a homosexual. Apart from his two rape offenses (and two earlier ones for which he was never apprehended), he had been arrested for motor vehicle violations. Although of above-average intelligence, his academic and vocational accomplishments were mediocre. The only activity he has pursued with any degree of diligence has been body-building.

Sadistic Rape

In the sadistic rape, aggression itself is eroticized. The offender derives satisfaction in the sexual abuse of his victim. Sexuality and aggression become intertwined into a single psychological experience: sadism. The assault itself appears ritualistic and usually involves bondage and torture. Sexual areas of the victim's body – her breasts, genitals, and buttocks – become the focus of injury. The rape experience for this type of offender is one of intense and mounting excitement. He finds pleasure in the victim's torment, anguish, distress, and suffering. His assault is deliberate, calculated, and premeditated. The victim is stalked, captured, abused, and in extreme cases, murdered. The nature of the assault may or may not involve the offender's genitals – the victim may be raped with an instrument or foreign object, such as a spoon or bottle. In some cases, sexual penetration may take place after she is dead.

Such assaults are repetitive, but interspersed with other less dramatic offenses, such as consenting sexual relations in the offender's life. For this sadistic offender, anger and control become sexualized in terms of the offender's finding intense gratification in controlling, hurting, degrading, and often times destroying his victim.

Case: Eric was a 30-year-old divorced man charged with first-degree murder. His victim, a 20-year-old woman he picked up at a singles bar, was tied to a tree, whipped, raped, sodomized, and slashed to death. Although found to be sane, Eric claimed he was high on drugs and couldn't remember what had happened. He had a criminal record that included assault and battery, breaking and entering, nonsupport, and motor vehicles violations. At the age of 17 he had tied a 13-year-old neighbor girl to a bed and assaulted her. He beat his children and burned his wife with cigarettes during intercourse. Shortly after his conviction, Eric committed suicide.

Multiple Motives Underlying Sexual Assault

Although different patterns of rape are apparent, they all have a common motivational base: power. In some cases, the offender asserts his power[3] by controlling his victim (the power rape); in other cases, by controlling and hurting his victim (the anger rape); and in still other cases, by controlling, hurting, degrading, and destroying his victim (the sadistic rape). Anger, power, and sexuality are evident in all rapes, but the role each of these components plays and the pattern in which they interface may vary from one offender to another.

Rape is a complex, multidetermined act which, in addition to expressing anger and asserting control, also serves to compensate for feelings of helplessness, to reassure the offender about his sexual adequacy, to assert his identity, to retain status among peers, to defend against sexual anxieties, to achieve sexual gratification, and to discharge frustration. In this sense the act of rape is equivalent to a symptom: It expresses the conflict, defends against anxiety, and partially gratifies or discharges the impulse.[4]

Rape: An Act of Aggression

The proposed conceptualization of the issues of power, anger, and sexuality in rape have several implications. Clinical work with offenders and victims indicates that for both the initial impact of rape is not sexual. Although the act is sexual, what is traumatizing to the victim in the offense is the jeopardy her life is in, her helplessness and loss of control in the situation, and her experience of herself as the object of her assailant's rage. This is important to appreciate because the etiology of the vicitm's trauma is the offender's pathology. To acknowledge a rape assault means to recognize that there is a victim and an offender. Rape is more than an illegal act and more than an extreme of cultural role behavior. From a clinical point of view, it is important that rape be defined as a distortion of sexuality and that the pathology of the offender be recognized.

Rape is an act of aggression. In some offenses, the assault appears to constitute a discharge of anger. In other cases the aggression seems to be reactive to the resistance on the part of the victim; i.e., when the victim resists the advances of her assailant, he retaliates by striking, hitting, or hurting her. Hostility is quickly triggered and released sometimes in a clear, consciously experienced state of anger, or in other cases, what offenders will describe as a state of fear or panic. In still other offenses, the aggression becomes expressed less as an anger motive and more as a means of dominating, controlling, and being in charge of the situation – an expression of mastery and conquest. And in a fourth variation the aggression itself is intrinsically gratifying. It becomes eroticized with respect to the offender finding excitement and pleasure in both controlling his victim and hurting her whether or not sexual contact is achieved. These variations on the theme of aggression are not mutually exclusive and, in any given instance of rape, multiple meanings may be expressed both in regard to the sexual and the aggressive components of the offense.

Those offenders who sexually assault children show similar dynamics. Sex may become a weapon and a means of discharging anger and frustration when it plays a part in the battering of a child (the anger assault). It becomes an expression of power and control when the offender uses threat, intimidation, and force to overcome his victim's resistance and gain sexual access to the child (the power assault). Aggression as an erotic experience is seen in the offender who finds excitement and pleasure in the deliberate and intentional infliction of pain and sexual abuse on the child victim (the sadistic assault). These types of assaults are essentially rapes where the victim is a child. Fortunately, the majority of sexual encounters between adults and children are not marked by violent aggression or brutality. The most common means of achieving sexual contact with a child victim is through enticement (the pressured assault). In this encounter, the adult attempts to enlist the child's cooperation and participation in sexual acts through bribing the child with gifts or treats, rewarding the child by misrepresenting moral standards, and/or exploiting his position as authority as an adult. In the pressured offenses the child is generally highly valued by the offender. He sees children as loving, affectionate, warm, trusting, clean, and attractive. He feels safer and more comfortable with them and in many respects idealizes and identifies with them. There is no intent to harm the child. The risk of such encounters is more psychological than physical: the premature exposure to adult sexuality and the forfeiture of more age-appropriate, developmental sexual experiences; the use of sex to gratify nonsexual needs, such as approval, recognition, acceptance, and the like; the burden of maintaining secrecy and guilt and fear surrounding disclosure; the sense of exploitation and betrayal by trusted persons; etc.

The sexual victimization of children ranges from encounters at one extreme where there is no physical contact between the adult and the child (such as in indecent exposure) to encounters at the other extreme that result in the death of the victim (the lust murder). In order to assess the impact of such victimization, attention needs to be paid to such variables as the type of sexual activity encompassed in the assault, the relationship between offender and victim, the duration of the sexual involvement, the means by which the offender gains access to the child, and the motives underlying the sexual assault.

Recognition of the various determinants in the psychology of the offender may help counselors more fully appreciate the impact of sexual assault on the victim. Dispelling myths and misconceptions about the offender helps to prevent the compounding and perpetuation of the victimization.

Summary

Accounts from both offenders and victims of what occurs during a rape suggest the issues of power, anger, and sexuality are important in the understanding of rapist's behavior. All three issues seem to operate in every rape, but the proportion varies and one issue seems to dominate in each instance.

The proposed conceptualization of the issues of power, anger, and sexuality in rape have several implications. Clinical work with offenders and victims indicate that the initial impact of rape is not sexual for either group. Although the act is sexual, what is traumatizing to the victim is the life-threatening nature of the assault, her helplessness and loss of control in the situation, and her experience of herself as the object of her assailant's rage. This is important because the etiology of the victim's trauma may be interpreted as the offender's pathology. The clinical typology offers one approach to differentiating offenders with regard to identification, disposition, treatment planning, and prognosis.

References

1. Groth AN, Burgess AW. Rape: A pseudosexual act. *Int J Women's Studies*. 1977;1:207-210.
2. Groth AN, Burgess AW and Holmstrom LL. Rape: power, anger, and sexuality. *Am. J. Psychiatry*. 1977;134:1239-43.
3. Groth AN, Burgess AW. Sexual dysfunction during rape. *N Eng J Med*. 1977;297:764-766.
4. Groth AN, Burgess AW. Rape: a sexual deviation. *Am J Orthopsychiatry*. 1977;47:400-406.

This chapter is reprinted with permission from Burgess AW, Holmstrom LL. *Rape: Crisis and Recovery*. West Newton, MA: Awab; 1986.

Chapter 9 – Persistence Pays for Six Children Abused in Day Care

Alex Smith, Esq, and Ann W. Burgess, DNSc

A long complex civil trial in **B, C, P v. County of Orange**, 1752/90, Sup. Ct. Orange Co. NY (6/19/97) ended with monetary awards to six children in three families who were sexually abused in a county-managed day care center. The case came to the attention of authorities in January, 1990, when a mother noticed vaginal blisters on her two-year old daughter. Her pediatrician diagnosed the condition as condyloma, said he believed the girl had been sexually abused, and reported his findings to Child Protective Services. This case is reviewed for its legal issues and the behavioral profile of the children over time.

The Legal Proceedings

The three families alleged that their children were sexually abused in a day care center licensed by defendant County of Orange. The day-care center was located in the City of Middletown, NY. The County, in November 1988, certified defendant Sheila Wilson as the operator of the day care center, and permitted defendant John Heater to act as "substitute provider." The complaints in these actions alleged time spans regarding the abuse of the six infant plaintiffs comprising the period from November 1988 to February 1990.

The plaintiffs consisted of four girls whose ages at the time of the abuse ranged from one-and-a-half to five years. Two of the infant plaintiffs were boys whose ages at the time of the abuse ranged from three to six years. All of the infants were repeatedly fondled and sodomized, and some were forced to engage in oral sex. The children were often held down and muffled so that their screams and crying could not be heard.

Neither Heater nor Wilson appeared in these actions. Both were arrested in February, 1990, and their day care operation was shut down. Heater and Wilson were sentenced to lengthy terms in state prison after they entered guilty pleas in 1990 to an indictment charging sexual abuse of a child in 1988.

Plaintiffs in these actions alleged, *inter alia*, that the County was negligent in ascertaining the qualifications or lack thereof of Heater and Wilson. Plaintiffs emphasized that Heater was previously convicted of a sexual abuse felony for which he served time in state prison, and that the County should have learned of this conviction before permitting Heater to act as substitute provider. Plaintiffs also emphasized that Wilson's exhusband was a convicted child molester and still had visitation privileges with Wilson's children who lived in the day care center. Finally, Plaintiffs emphasized that Wilson herself had been sexually abused as a child.

Initial Trial Finds No Proximate Cause

The plaintiffs' cases were consolidated and tried before a jury in October 1993. In a midtrial decision, the trial court determined that due to the County's certification process and the plaintiffs' justifiable reliance on same, the County owed a special duty to all three families. This finding of special duty meant that the County was not shielded by common law immunity. However, the jury found that the County was negligent, but that its negligence was not a proximate cause of the injuries suffered by the infant plaintiffs.

Special Duty Appeal

Plaintiffs appealed and emphasized this important issue involving New York municipal liability:

> Where a trial court determines that a municipal defendant owes a special duty to certain plaintiffs, arising out of a special relationship with those plaintiffs, what role, if any, should the judgmental error doctrine play in the deliberations of the jury? Should the jury be instructed, as they were here, that even if there is a special duty, the municipality cannot be held liable for injuries caused by discretionary acts or decisions?

The charge directed the jury to ignore any discretionary decision-making or acts of the County and to focus solely upon ministerial actions – defined by the trial judge as violations of the state regulations introduced into evidence. Although the jury found the County negligent, the finding of negligence must have related solely to violations of the regulations, as opposed to any discretionary decisions or actions taken outside the jury's perception of the purview of the regulations. The jury then found that the ministerial negligence did not proximately cause the injuries suffered by the infant plaintiffs.

On the appeal, plaintiffs argued that no one knows if the jury would have found that negligence associated with discretionary acts or decisions proximately caused those injuries. This wasn't known because the trial judge removed all discretionary decisions and actions from the jury's consideration.

In 1993, the Appellate Division, Second Department (New York's intermediate appellate court), agreed with plaintiffs' arguments and reversed. The Second Department held that the existence of the special duty meant that the County would be liable for negligence in ministerial and discretionary decision-making, and that the jury should be so charged. The Second Department denied the County's motion for leave to appeal to the Court of Appeals (New York's highest court), and the County decided not to seek leave from the Court of Appeals itself.

Inconsistent Verdicts at New Trial

The case again came to trial in May 1997, and consumed about four weeks. The judge charged the jury with basic negligence principles and did not get into the special duty or judgmental error doctrines. However, the jury returned a verdict that the County was not negligent as to the P and B families, but was negligent as to the C family; the percentage of fault —as determined by the jury – was 10% allocated to the County, 40% allocated to Heater, and 50% allocated to Wilson.

This resulted in vigorous arguments as to whether the verdicts were inconsistent. The only rational apparent distinction was that the C family was totally dependent upon the County for welfare benefits, while the B and P families were not. But a verdict based upon such a distinction would fly in the face of the 1993 ruling that the County owed all three families a special duty. It thus appeared that the jury impermissibly delved into the immunity issues.

The verdict also created a dilemma for plaintiffs' attorneys: If the verdicts were determined to be inconsistent, the jury would have to redeliberate with regard to all three families – i.e., the C family would lose its verdict. If the verdicts were not inconsistent, the C family would retain its verdict. This created a conflict of interest, and plaintiffs' attorneys arranged for separate counsel for each family.

After two days of deliberation, the trial judge ruled that the verdicts were consistent, and directed plaintiffs' attorneys to proceed with the damage phase on behalf of the C family. The jury returned a verdict of 2.4 million dollars; if reduced to the 10% share, this would equal $240,000 or $80,000 per child (there were three children in the C family).

Postverdict motions were made for a mistrial on behalf of the B and P families due to the inconsistency of the verdicts. A postverdict motion was also made on behalf of the C family that common law joint and several liability principles should apply, which would result in the County being 100% liable for the entire 2.4 million dollar verdict.

Ultimately those motions were withdrawn as all parties settled. Families B and P were also awarded monies for the children. Thus all children received structured annuities payable beginning on their 18th birthdays.

Behavioral Profiles of the Children

There are several unique and instructive behavioral features to this case:

- The defendants confessed and gave details of their abuse of the children that can be compared to the children's experience.

- The length of this case allowed assessment of the children from disclosure in 1990 to trial completion in 1997.

- The victims were of diverse cultures and genders with one African-American child, two Asian-American children, and three Causcasian children.

- The victims were of diverse socioeconomic means with one family on public assistance, one family where both parents worked, and one family who was initially on public assistance but then off when the single mother became employed.

Family B: The girl from family B is the only daughter of a single mother. She was two years old at time of abuse over an eight-month period. While she has consistently had no specific memory of the defendants or their actions, defendant Heater said that this child kicked and screamed and carried on during the abuse. Her behavior profile at age five included sleep problems, nightmares, yelling and shouting during sleep, regression in speech and toilet training, and sexualized behaviors of rubbing and inserting objects into her vagina. Her behavioral profile at age 10 notes her to be clingy and dependent on adults, not socializing well with peers, slightly overweight, many physical symptoms of stomachaches and headaches, accident-prone, and whiny.

Family P: The eldest boy of family P was age five at the time of the abuse, which lasted an eight-month period. Upon interview, he noted that "Sheila would come in and tell me to lay down. She'd massage my back. John would send me to the bedroom, take my pants down and don't want to say it because every time I do I get scared and I'm afraid he will break out of jail and kill me. When John finished with me he'd put Vaseline on the part I don't want to say so Mom and Dad won't know. He said he'd do something to Mom and Dad if I told." Behavioral profile of this five-year-old: nightmares about snakes, bedwetting, masturbating, and back-talking to parents. Behavioral profile at age nine: grades had dropped to average, dreams of snakes continued, he had few friends, was rebellious, a poor eater, weighed 45 pounds, a nail biter, bed wetter, fights with younger brother, and isolates himself from the family. Behavioral profile at age 14: argumentative, can't pay attention for long, complains of loneliness, disobedient at home and school, fears snakes, likes to be alone, sometimes lies, headaches and rashes.

The younger brother in the P family, who was age three at time of abuse says, said in an interview at age six that he did not remember John and Sheila; but then he remembered Sheila letting him make a cake. He states a bad thing happened at the house but did not detail any more. When asked to draw what the baby sitters looked like, he drew John with hair and a mustache and the snake tattoo on his hand. He draws Sheila and a cake. Behavioral profile at age six: hits other children, is fearful, has temper tantrums and nightmares of snakes, enuresis, holds his genitals while talking or standing, difficulty concentrating or sitting still, doesn't feel guilty after misbehaving, impulsive, overeats junk food, is a bed wetter. Profile at age 11: argumentative, fear of snakes, nervous eye twitch, rashes, poor school performance, secretive, shy, moody, and overly concerned with neatness.

Family C: The youngest sister in the C family was age one when the abuse started and had a 10-month exposure to the abusers. When examined, she asked if the doctor would touch her like John and Sheila did. A behavioral profile at disclosure included nightmares, difficulty joining in activities with other children, fear when left alone, sexualized play with her dolls, and fear of bathrooms. She is still afraid of bathrooms, the dark, can't be left alone, can't have anything wet on her, changes her underwear multiple times a day, and is sexually explicit with her dolls.

The middle sister in the C family, was age three during the abuse period. At disclosure confirmed that Sheila held her down and they both licked her and laughed. Behavioral profile included easily cries, upset when mother leaves, nightmares, sad and lethargic; school problems, and sexually preoccupied. On interview she reported intrusive thoughts of the defendants and said to avoid thinking of Sheila and John, she thinks of Santa Claus. Her drawing of the abuse was detailed and sexually explicit. At age 11, she has emotional problems, is in a special program at school, has difficulty concentrating, is moody, has temper tantrums. She is preoccupied with her appearance, but has a kind teacher and is doing well. She has had counseling and has been on antidepressants.

The oldest sister was age five during the abuse and witnessed and experienced an excessive amount of frightening sexual and aggressive behavior by the baby-sitters. A behavioral profile includes: depression, moody, withdrawn, fearful of the baby-sitters getting out of jail, sexual preoccupation, and bedwetting when under stress. She was physically aggressive herself, bullying and being argumentative. She was suicidal and placed on medication. At age 13, she has been classified as emotionally disturbed, is in a special school that is smaller and with less pressure; she has done well. She is diagnosed as learning disabled with an inability to concentrate and to get along with her peers.

Effects of the Trauma

Psychological trauma interrupts children's normal development. The major developmental issues that were delayed by the abuse in this case include: 1) mood stability; 2) the development of strong interpersonal relationships; 3) the development of a positive self-image; and 4) achievement of scholastic success. Although all children received short-term counseling, information is not available as to whether or not trauma therapy was used. The defense cross-examination of the plaintiff's expert on psychological damages to the child focused on a house fire, parental drinking, parental divorce, a mother's boyfriend, and a grandfather's death as causes to the children's symptoms.

Chapter 10 – Gang Rape of a Schoolboy and Duty to Protect

Ann Wolbert Burgess, DNSc, and Robert R. MacDonnell, Esq

The social stigma of male rape is believed to be responsible for the low reporting rates and reluctance of victims seeking treatment. The situation becomes more complicated when the victim is a child and a third-party (such as a school) is the location of the crime. When the rape is on school property, the question is raised as to where the line is drawn for a school's duty to protect its students. Does the school's duty end at the dismissal bell; does it end when the child walks out the school door; or does it extend to the school property? This case is presented to discuss a boy's reaction to multiple rape and the liability issue facing the school.

The Crime

John Doe, born in Georgetown, Guyana, moved with his family to New York when he was eight. He began fourth grade, worked hard at school, adapted to the country and language, passed his courses, and entered the fifth grade.

On September 19, 1991, nine-year-old John, after school had been dismissed, spent some time in the schoolyard playing with a friend before getting his schoolbag and starting to leave. While in the schoolyard, he was approached by three adolescent youths who suddenly grabbed his school bag, saying if he wanted it back, he was to do them a favor. His friend abandoned him and ran. One of the assailants took out a blade, and told him to keep walking or he would not get back his school bag. He was taken across the schoolyard through a hole in the schoolyard fence to an alley adjacent to the school, punched in the chest, and knocked to the ground. He was threatened not to scream or his throat would be slit. He was forced to kneel down and suck each youth's penis. He was ordered to "suck harder" by the youth who held a knife to his throat. He vomited three times. One youth ordered him to lower his pants and attempted to anally penetrate him. Another youth urinated on his back. Before the youths left, John was threatened with death if he told anyone. John said that both a teacher and a girl in the schoolyard saw his abduction from the schoolyard.

John's brother found him in the lower level of the schoolyard. Mrs. Doe, concerned that John was late coming home, had sent the older brother to look for him. Upon returning home, John was able to tell his mother of the assault. Mrs. Doe then telephoned the police who took a statement and transported John to the hospital. Although John cooperated with the police, he did not identify any of the three youths.

There were no arrests.

Victim Reaction

John received crisis counseling by a school counselor twice a week for the remainder of the school year. The counselor's report indicated that he was still frightened about going to school for fear of running into the assailants and that he had recurring nightmares. He was also seen by a social worker at the emergency department and a psychiatrist for a forensic evaluation in November 1991.

The psychiatrist's report noted John's anxiety about returning to school for fear others would find out and tease him. He described the incident as a "secret," and only two other children were believed to have been aware of the assault. John was sensitive to any sudden noise, for example, when hearing a knock on the door, he'd become scared. In his dreams and nightmares he described himself being kidnapped by a stranger or someone grabbing him in a crowd. He would wake up screaming. He also was fearful when seeing 13-year-old youths. He withdrew from shopping and riding the subways. He became fearful of attending the junior high school that he believed the assailants attended.

The family moved several times in the intervening years. His mother described him as a changed boy. He rarely went outside and required a family member to accompany him to and from school. He isolated himself from friends. He became short-tempered, irritable, angry, depressed, and paranoid. He avoided girlfriends for fear they would find out "what happened to him." He would spend his weekends at home, watching cartoons on television. He either avoided watching films with any hint of violence or sexual content or would become angry when such a show was on television. He stopped playing sports with his friends either at school or on weekends.

He slept in the same bedroom as his grandmother. He would awaken in the early hours and stand looking out the window. Over the years, although his grades were passing, he did not regularly attend classes, "hanging out" instead. He had difficulty adjusting to high school and the older students. He worried about getting passing grades. He described sleeping a lot during the day, but not during the night. He had trouble looking people straight in the face; he did not like people looking at him. Safety and the motivations and intentions of people were suspect.

In a 1997 evaluation, he reported being unable to talk about the rape with family or friends. He continued to think about the rape. He said he would like to go to counseling, but found that talking about it "made me feel worse." He was consistent in his description of the rape. He made sketches of the assailants. He drew one wearing a clown mask (with wide grin and teeth), one with a knife, and one who urinated on him.

The civil trial with a jury of five men and one woman began in February 1999. Three witnesses were called for the plaintiff. The school custodian confirmed that there were holes in the fence between the school and the alley. The teacher observed by John to have witnessed his abduction admitted that a girl had reported to her that a boy was being "roughed up". She claimed to have done a visual of the school yard and did not see any problem. She also claimed to have chased 12 to 15 children who were playing. She then got in her car and left. The psychiatrist described the impact on John. At this point, the defense made their third and final offer, and it was accepted.

Discussion

There were two important points for the civil trial. The first was the issue of the school's duty to protect. Research indicated one appellate decision that held a school liable when a girl was assaulted walking down the outside stairs of a school immediately at dismissal.

The second was the issue of treatment and permanency of damages. John had received counseling during the school year. This counseling gave a rational and validation for his emotional reaction to the traumatic event and facilitated his ability to continue in school. This latter was critical in preventing a school phobia.

But how to explain that he had not continued counseling independent of school? John acknowledged his difficulty in talking about the assault, that he'd rather push it out of his mind or deny he had any problems (he was successful with one counselor who felt he did not need further counseling).

In clinical terms, he developed avoidant behaviors because he was terrified not only of being cut during the assault, but of being killed later if he revealed the perpetrators. There was a reality that three assailants knew him. One witness, the girl who tried to stop the youths, was later stabbed to death by another girl supposedly in an unrelated incident. We do not know the full basis of the murder of this girl, but she was the one person who tried to defend him. The second witness, the teacher, refused to admit that she had seen anything.

The remaining witnesses were the perpetrators. The fact that they have not been apprehended makes seeking treatment and the effects of treatment difficult because John continues to feel threatened. John's avoidant position indicates he remains disconnected from his feeling of terror, e.g., he handles the terror by moving away from emotion.

One hopes that as John gains confidence in himself he will be able to avail himself for treatment of the symptoms of his distrust of people, his suspiciousness of others and their motives, and concerns about intimacy which cover his sense of shame over the rapes. Currently, his avoidance behavior comes out in interpersonal relationships. He keeps his distance from people, and he denies himself intimate relationships. He fears closeness for a variety of reasons that would be best addressed in counseling. However, he took an important step in his junior year in high school to make the varsity football team. This was his first attempt in seven years to venture out by competing and joining a group where he could express himself in a masculine way. A second area of strength is his academics. He has maintained fair grades and has hopes of attending college. Treatment for John will be difficult because the perpetrators have not been apprehended and still know him. To date, his accomplishments have been through sheer will power and the support of his family.

Chapter 11 – Liability of the Negligent Landlord

Ann Wolbert Burgess, DNSc, and James Wilkens, Esq

When is a landlord of negligently secured premises liable to a tenant injured by a third party's criminal attack? While landlords have a responsibility to protect tenants from foreseeable harm, the New York law states a tenant may recover damages only if they show that the landlord's negligent conduct was a proximate cause of the injury. At issue in the following case is the landlord's failure to take the required minimal security precautions that allowed an intruder to gain access to the premises through a negligently maintained entrance. The hurdle was to prove the perpetrator was not a tenant or a guest of a tenant.

Facts of the Case

Marisela was 12 years old in April of 1991. She was living with her parents and brother in a New York City Housing Authority (NYCHA) project known as the Adams Houses, located in the Bronx. Born in Puerto Rico, she moved with her parents to the Bronx in 1985. Marisela attended elementary school, was bilingual, received average grades, and was progressing well in school when the rape occurred.

Around 9:30 AM, Marisela, her brother, and some friends did some preaching (Jehovah Witness). Maricela then returned to the lobby of her apartment building. This lobby had two perimeter doors. It had a front lobby door which was supposed to be self closing and locking. However, the lock did not work. There was also a rear lobby door – an exit door. The exit door had no handle on the outside and was designed to self-close and lock. Once it was locked, the rear lobby door was supposed to be inaccessible to anyone, including tenants. In fact, there was not even a handle or latch to permit it to be opened from the outside at all. Unfortunately, the door was broken and would not close properly. NYCHA records reflected the fact that the door and the door lock needed replacement for almost two years prior to the incident.

While Marisela waited for the elevator to bring her to her apartment, she saw a young man enter the building through the defective rear door lobby. He entered the elevator with her and others, but did not select a floor. Everyone except Marisela and this stranger exited the elevator at earlier stops. Marisela exited the elevator at the 18th floor; the man followed her out of the elevator. As Marisela was about to knock on her door, the man grabbed her, covering her mouth. He dragged her to the stairway exit and up the stairs to the 21st floor. He forced her through the door to the roof landing. He threatened to kill her if she did not do as he said. She was hit and forced to remove all of her clothes. The man then raped and sodomized her. Marisela feared she would be thrown off of the roof. The assailant then ran down the stairs and was observed running out that same rear lobby door.

The Civil Suit

On Marisela's behalf, a civil law suit was filed against NYCHA in May 1991. NYCHA was represented by a large mid-Manhattan law firm, Wilson, Elser, Moskowitz, Edleman, and Dicker. In January of 1992, depositions of Marisela and her mother were conducted by Alan Kaminsky, Esq, a partner at Wilson *et al*. Marisela's mother testified through a Spanish interpreter. Kaminsky's questioning centered around the concept of tenants having "propped open" the rear door. If this was true – that the rear door was not defective, but merely propped open by tenants, NYCHA could not be held liable.

In early 1993, NYCHA moved to have the case dismissed via summary judgment on the "propped open" theory. Plaintiff's opposition to the defendant's motion pointed out that the "propped open" language did not come from the plaintiff or her mother, but from NYCHA's attorney himself. Judge Saks agreed with plaintiff and the matter proceeded to trial.

At trial before Judge Barry Salman and six male jurors, the defense, without notifying plaintiff's counsel, produced two witnesses, one of whom said that she saw Marisela and the perpetrator enter the lobby together through the front door. This testimony was contrary to the witness's own written statement, which was not produced until trial. Defense also produced a police detective who testified that it was his opinion that Marisela and the assailant knew each other, but admitted that this was "just a hunch."

The jury came back with a defense verdict finding that the perpetrator did not enter through the rear door.

Plaintiff appealed on the basis that 1) defense did not disclose the two lobby witnesses prior to trial, and 2) the judge allowed a police detective to give his opinion that Marisela and the perpetrator knew each other even though the detective admitted his opinion was based on a hunch and not on fact.

The Appellate Division, 1st Department's decision on December 27, 1995 was to order a new trial. The second trial began August 13, 1996 before Judge Stanley Green, also with a jury of six men.

At the second trial, plaintiff counsel again called three witnesses: the reporting police officer, Marisela, and a rape trauma expert. The expert testified that the blitz style of attack and type of rape were not consistent with a victim and offender knowing each other. Medical findings were consistent with a forced first sexual encounter. The expert also testified as to the rape significantly changing Marisela's life in several critical ways. The family moved, Marisela withdrew from friends, and stopped attending school. She was terrified to venture out alone. It was three years before Maricela returned to classes and entered a computer training program and subsequently took her GED. She continued to have occasional nightmares of a faceless rapist. She had spontaneous thoughts of the rape when reading or hearing about crime. She avoided traveling alone, elevators, and reminders of the rape. She never felt safe. A major problem was partner intimacy. Her boyfriend, with whom she had a daughter, lived across the street, and she saw him on weekends. That the offender had not been apprehended added to her fear.

The defense strategy was the same as at the first trial, but plaintiff counsel was able to show how the lobby witness testimony had changed over time as she met with the NYCHA investigator staff four to five times; that is, her testimony was different than statements given to NYCHA. The second witness was ineffectual, and the police detective was not called. Defense also called a psychiatrist whose testimony was that Marisela was fine because "after the rape, she was able to have sex and had also gotten herself pregnant."

The trial took two weeks and the jury was out for two days. The jury had to answer specific questions. They found that the perpetrator had entered the rear door; that NYCHA was negligent; that the negligence was a proximate cause of the rape; and that the perpetrator was an intruder and not a guest or a tenant of the building.

The jury in a five to one verdict awarded $250,000 for past pain and suffering and $250,000 for future suffering.

However, Judge Green set the verdict aside, stating New York law was such that the plaintiff could not identify the perpetrator and categorically prove he was not a tenant or guest of the building. Thus, as a matter of law, a tenant could not succeed in the suit.

Plaintiff appealed and in April 1998, the Appellate Division upheld the judge's decision. The Superior Court in granting the motion argued that "in a building of over 150 apartments and hundreds of tenants, it was unlikely that the plaintiff or anyone else would know every tenant or every guest. Further, the fact that the assailant did not disguise himself and ran out of the building offers no support to the plaintiff's position. Crimes such as this are often spontaneous and an assailant would likely not want to go to a location where he could be found or identified. Thus, the jury's finding that the assailant was an intruder is based solely on speculation and surmise and cannot be sustained."

Plaintiff requested and was granted an appeal to the Court of Appeals and on November 24, 1998, the Court of Appeals reversed the Appellate decision and reinstated the jury decision. The opinion written by Chief Judge Kaye stated, in part, "the plaintiff – who knew most of the building tenants by sight – and another building and a frequent building visitor all testified that they did not recognize the assailant, who entered and left the building through the broken rear door and made no attempt to conceal his identity, even though there were several people in the lobby and elevator who could have identified him. Finally, when he entered the elevator, he did not push a button to select a floor. Based on this evidence, we cannot say "there is simply no valid line of reasoning and permissible inferences which could possibly lead rational men to the conclusion" that the assailant, who entered and left the building through a negligently maintained door, was an intruder (Cohen v. Hallmark Cards, 45 NY2d 493, 499)."

What was the effect of this long court process on the young victim? At the end of the first trial, the first question of whether the perpetrator entered the rear door was answered no by the jury. Marisela at this time was 15. She was distraught over the verdict because she interpreted that the jury thought she not telling the truth. At the second trial, when she was 18, during jury deliberations, she told her attorney that if the jury answered yes to whether or not the perpetrator entered through the rear door, would indicate to her that they believed her. That, she said, would be her measure of vindication.

Chapter 12 – Rape Trauma Syndrome

Ann W. Burgess and Lynda Lytle Holmstrom

Sometimes I think the feelings are more intense now than they were at first. I was on the trolley and two guys came and sat down across from me. They looked like the two that raped me. I could almost feel like I was being grabbed again. I just have to keep thinking intellectually that it isn't going to happen. I know intellectually it won't, but my gut reaction is so intense...I feel people are following me. I still look at every car that goes by even though I know the guys are locked up...Sometimes it gets so intense; seems worse than it ever was. Rape victim, age 21, three months following the rape

The above quote captures some of the distressing and repetitive symptoms that a victim continues to experience long after the rape. The symptoms this victim describes are mentally and physically reliving the rape, fear of seeing the assailant again, and fear of another attack.

One of the conclusions we reached as a result of our study of 146 rape and sexual assault victims was that victims suffer a significant degree of physical and emotional trauma during the rape, immediately following the assault, and over a considerable time period afterwards. Victims consistently described certain symptoms over and over. We define the cluster of symptoms that most of the victims experienced as the rape trauma syndrome (in contrast to two other syndromes described from the study of accessory-to-sex and sex-stress). The rape trauma syndrome has two phases: the immediate or acute phase, in which the victim's lifestyle is completely disrupted by the rape crisis, and the long-term process, in which the victim must reorganize this disrupted lifestyle. The syndrome includes physical, emotional, and behavioral stress reactions that result from the person being faced with a life-threatening event. This chapter discusses the two-phase reaction as well as the counseling implications of the syndrome.

The Acute Phase Disorganization

Immediate Impact Reaction

A prevailing myth about rape victims is that they are hysterical and tearful following a rape. We did not find this to be necessarily true in our victim sample. To the contrary, victims described and indicated to us an extremely wide range of emotions in the immediate hours following the rape. The physical and emotional impact of the incident may be so intense that the victim feels shock and disbelief. As one victim said, "I remember doing some strange things after he left such as biting my arm...to prove I could feel...that I was real."

We saw many of the victims at the hospital within the first few hours after the rape, and two main styles of emotion were shown by the victims: expressed and controlled. In the expressed style, the victim demonstrated such feelings as anger, fear, and anxiety. The victims expressed these feelings by being restless during the interview, becoming tense when certain questions were asked, crying or sobbing when describing specific acts of the assailant, and smiling in an anxious manner when certain issues were stated. In the controlled style, the feelings of the victim were masked or hidden, and a calm, composed, or subdued affect could be noted by the counselor.

Physical Reactions

Rape is forced sexual violence against a person. Therefore, it is not surprising that victims describe a wide gamut of physical reactions. Many victims described a general feeling of soreness all over their bodies. Others would specify the body area that had been the focus of the assailant's force, such as throat, chest, arms, or legs. On telephone follow-up one victim stated: "I am so sore under my ribs. I can't sleep on my one side. The pain just stays there; it doesn't go away. I guess he really hurt me although the X-ray didn't show anything. It hurts when I breathe and I can't wear any clothes that fasten. It hurts to swallow and bothers me to eat. I think he loosened my teeth because they hurt."

Sleep Pattern Disturbances

Rape victims have considerable difficulty with disorganized sleep patterns in the acute phase, complaining that they cannot fall asleep or, if they do, they wake up during the night and cannot fall back asleep. Victims who have been attacked while sleeping in their own beds may awake each evening at that time again and find they cannot fall back asleep. It is not uncommon for victims to scream out in their sleep.

Eating Pattern Disturbances

A marked decrease in appetite following the rape is generally noticed by the victims. They may complain of stomach pains or describe loss of appetite, such as the food not tasting right. Frequently, victims feel nauseated just thinking of the assault. It is important to determine whether the symptom of nausea is related to the emotional reaction following the rape or is a reaction to antipregnancy medication.

Symptoms Specific To Focus of Attack

Victims will also report physical symptoms specific to the area of the body that has been the focus of the attack. Victims forced to have oral sex may describe irritation to the mouth and throat. Victims forced to have vaginal sex may complain of vaginal discharge, itching, a burning sensation on urination, and generalized pain. Those forced to have anal sex may report rectal pain and bleeding in the days immediately following the rape.

Emotional Reactions

Prevailing stereotypes of rape are that the main reactions of women are to feel ashamed and guilty after being raped. We did not find these to be the primary reactions in the majority of victims we saw. To the contrary, the primary feeling expressed was that of fear – fear of physical injury, mutilation, and death. It is this main feeling of fear that explains why victims develop the range of symptoms we call the rape trauma syndrome. Their symptoms are an acute stress reaction to the threat of being killed. Most victims feel they had a close encounter with death and are lucky to be alive. One victim said, "I am thankful it was not worse. It could have been worse. I am just thankful I am here today and that I have my life."

Victims express other feelings in conjunction with the feeling of fear of dying. These feelings range from humiliation, degradation, guilt, shame, and embarrassment to self-blame, anger, and revenge. Because of the wide range of feelings experienced during the immediate phase, victims are prone to experience mood swings. One victim who was employed as a librarian said: "Sometimes I am nervous inside. A book falls at work and I jump. On Monday and Tuesday I was really jumpy. Now I sort of have some energy. I want to calm myself down and I try…I can feel the tension building up…and I can get quite irritated and snap at people at work."

Many victims can realize their feelings are out of proportion to the situation they are in. They will report feeling angry with someone and later realize the anger was unfounded in that situation. Women become quite upset over their behavior which, in turn, produces more distress for them. One 21-year-old woman said, "I am on the verge of tears all the time. It is just awful! I am trying to be so independent; trying to live my own life, and I am falling on my face with each step I take."

In a serious parenting situation, a 27-year-old woman went to a mental health clinic five days after the rape saying, "I am coming to pieces. I took a strap and beat my four-year-old son today for a minor thing he did. He didn't cry that much, but I cried for two hours. I have never done such a thing before."

Victims also report feeling irritated with people during the first few weeks when the symptoms are acute. Seeing a car similar to the one in which the woman was abducted, or seeing a man who looks like the assailant will evoke a strong emotional reaction. Victims become cautious with all people. One hospital employee said, "At work, one of the doctors grabbed me in a joking way and I gasped. I could hardly stand it. Three days ago I would have laughed back, but it was all I could do to keep from screaming." Another victim said five days after the rape, "I came around the corner of a store and this guy bumped into me. I burst out crying. I expect [the rapist] to be everywhere. I don't know if I cried because I was relieved it wasn't him or what."

Thoughts

The victim continually tries to block the thoughts of the assault from her mind. She will say she is trying to blot it from her mind, to push it from her mind, but the thought of the assault continually haunts her. Five days following the rape one victim said: "I have trouble keeping the whole thing from coming into my mind. There are just so many thoughts running through. Once at work the thought came into my mind and it hit me and I lost my breath, the feeling was so intense."

Another victim said one week following the rape: "I try not to think about it, but the thoughts keep coming into my mind. I was at a friend's house and saw a big long knife like the one he used on me and it freaked me out...I see beer and get the same reaction...I can be doing something and it just comes into my mind. I tried to sleep with the lights, on but that didn't help. I haven't even been able to sleep."

There is a strong desire for the victim to try and think of how she could undo what has happened. She reports going over in her mind how she might have escaped from the assailant, how she might have handled the situation differently. However, she usually ends up saying that she would have been beaten or killed if she did not do what the assailant demanded.

Victims vary as to the amount of time they remain in the acute phase. The immediate symptoms may last a few days to a few weeks. And more often than not, the acute symptoms overlap the symptoms of the long-term process.

The Long-Term Process: Reorganization

A 20-year-old rape victim said, five months following the rape: "I still seem upset and edgy all the time. I just don't feel like being with people. I just couldn't stand to be near guys, so I went to Europe for a trip. I felt better after the trip; it forced me out to meet people. I went by myself and made myself not be afraid. I came back and hearing of murders in the city made me think back again. Still have dreams about it. Past couple of weeks have been thinking about it; even saw a guy that looked just like the rapist."

The rape represents a disruption in the lifestyle of the victim, not only during the immediate days and weeks following the incident, but well beyond that to many weeks and months. Various factors seem to influence how the victim copes with the rape crisis, such as the victim's personality type, the people available to her who respond to her distress in a serious and concerned manner, and the way in which she is treated by the people with whom she comes into contact after the rape.

In four lifestyle areas – physical, psychological, social, and sexual – we found that the victim had to cope with the following symptoms during the long term reorganization process.

Physical Lifestyle

Immediately following rape, victims report many physical symptoms related to musculoskeletal pain, genitourinary difficulties, gastrointestinal upset, and general malaise, as well as eating and sleeping pattern disruption. The health area that victims have most difficulty with over a long-time period is gynecological and menstrual. Victims report chronic vaginal problems and changes in menstrual cycle functioning.

117

Psychological Lifestyle

Dreams and nightmares are a major symptom with the rape victim and occur during both the acute phase and long-term process. One victim reported that her husband said she was screaming out in her sleep. He went to touch her to calm her down, and she screamed even more.

Victims report two types of nightmares following the rape. One type is a situation in which the victim dreams of being in similar circimstances and is attempting to try and get out of the situation, but fails. These dreams are similar to the actual rape itself. As one victim described her dream, "The man came back again and was trying to force me in the hallway, and I was screaming and trying to get away. I was fighting as hard as I could...and then I woke up." Another similar dream theme was reported by one of our referral cases. The victim was seen for the initial interview in the intensive care unit of a suburban hospital. She had taken an overdose of assorted medicines upon hearing from the police that the assailant was out on bail. She was rushed to the emergency department of the nearest hospital when her condition deteriorated to the point of her becoming unconscious. The counselor talked with her the next day, while she was still in the hospital. During the interview, the victim reported the following dream:

"The guy was here in the hospital, and I kept telling the staff he was here. But no one listened; they made me believe they didn't hear me. It was like no one believed me. The guy kept coming toward me...and I couldn't get away. Then I woke up."

In talking with the victim about her own interpretation of the dream, she said she was very upset over the fact that the assailant was out of jail, and she could not understand his being released. She said, "Here I am in the intensive care unit, and I have to have someone with me if I even want a cigarette. I am a prisoner sitting in here, and he is free out there."

The second type of dream occurs as time progresses. The dream material changes and often the victim will report mastery in the dream. However, the dream content still is of violence, and this is disturbing to the victim. Often they will see themselves committing acts of violence, such as killing and stabbing people. Therefore, the power gained in this second type of dream may represent mastery, but the victim still has to deal with this violent image of herself.

In other dreams, the relationship to murder is also seen. In the case of four young women, three of whom were raped, one of the raped women reported this dream two months after the rape: "The three of us were out on a date with three nice guys. We came back to the apartment after the date. Someone said, "Is June home?" One of the men went in to open June's bedroom door to see if she was home. He shut it quickly and came out and said to call the police. We all went to see what had happened. June was lying on the floor dead. She was killed with a knife, and there was blood and everything all over. She had sheets around her and it was so horrible." This dream included feelings the victim had about the roommate escaping the entire incident as well as the victim's feelings about the rape and what she felt had happened.

Phobias

A common psychological defense that is seen in rape victims is the development of fears and phobias specific to the circumstances of the rape. Victims will develop phobic reactions to a wide variety of circumstances. One such circumstance is being in crowds. As a victim stated, "I haven't been socializing. I haven't had any urge. This has really affected me. I haven't been out in a crowd since this happened."

Other victims are fearful of being alone after the rape. One victim said about entering her apartment, "I am still looking behind doors. I always leave the door open when I enter. It is all I can do to get into the apartment and turn the light on. I just can't relax. I always think someone is there." This victim was grabbed and raped six times after she entered her apartment by the assailant, who was inside waiting for her. He also removed all the light bulbs from their sockets and was wearing rubber gloves and a mask.

The woman may develop specific fears related to characteristics noted in the assailant, such as the odor of gasoline that one assailant had on his hands or alcohol which the woman could smell on the man. One victim who worked as a saleswoman said, "The other night, a male customer came in and had some of the same features – a moustache – as the guy who raped me. I could not go over and wait on him." Some victims describe a very suspicious, paranoid feeling. One 25-year-old victim said that when she got on the bus she felt as though the bus driver and everyone on the bus knew she had been raped. She had extreme difficulty sitting on the bus for the duration of her ride. A 35-year-old woman said: "I get out of work and I am very nervous and afraid. I am not like I was. I leave work, and I can't wait to get home. I think of it all the time. It is a real fear. I worry that something will happen to me; maybe I will get it again on the street. People know people, you know. My thoughts really scare me. Maybe someone wants to hurt me because of this."

The occurrence of a second upsetting situation following a rape can easily produce additional fearful feelings. One 19-year-old victim said: "While at work, my typewriter and purse were stolen. It isn't that unusual for such a thing to happen. But I just panicked. I would look behind me when I got off the trolley. I took my name off my mail box. I did everything I could to make myself anonymous. I got so paranoid from this incident. Really shook me for days."

Some victims feel a global fear of everyone. Such feelings can be intense, even months following the rape. One 22-year-old victim said two months following the rape: "I keep jumping when I walk anywhere. People really frighten me. So many things scare me. I never used to be frightened; didn't fear things. Now I can't stand it. I moved to a fourth-floor apartment and when it is locked I wish it had bars on the windows. That would make me feel safe. One night I went to bed and my roommate was out. I started hearing sounds. I was certain someone was there. My heart was beating so fast, and I was trembling. Then my roommate came in and suddenly everything was OK. I thought I'd die till she came in."

Social Lifestyle

The rape very often upsets the victim's normal social routine. In some cases, not just one, but many aspects of the victim's life were changed.

Many victims are able to resume only a minimal level of functioning, even after the acute phase ends. These women go to work or school, but are unable to be involved in more than business type activities. Other victims respond to the rape by staying home, by only venturing out of the house accompanied by a friend, or by being absent from or stopping work or school.

A common response was to turn for support to family members not normally seen on a daily basis. Often this meant a trip home to some other city and a brief stay with parents in their home. In most of these cases, the victim told her parents what happened. Occasionally the parents were contacted for support, although the victim did not explain why she was suddenly interested in talking to them or being with them. One 24-year-old teacher visited her parents and sister in another state during a school vacation. She said: "I did not tell my parents. Mother would be very upset and would worry about me every second that I might be raped again...She is also very Victorian about such matters. ...My father might have a heart attack if he knew. But I did tell my sister. She was very understanding... She said she almost was raped a couple of weeks ago...But it was good to be home – a good change of pace."

There is often a strong need to get away. One victim said: "I felt so caged in. I couldn't open a window for fear something would happen again, and I felt like screaming at times. I had to get a change of scenery."

Moving was another response that changed victims' lifestyles. Many victims changed residence specifically because of the rape.

In one of our referral cases, four young women had to make decisions about moving. Three of the four roommates were sleeping in their apartment when three men broke in and robbed and raped them. In talking with one of the victims three months after the rape, she said: "I could never let my roommates know how I felt about their moving out. They just couldn't stand it any longer. They had only been in the apartment one and a half weeks before the rape, and afterwards the place just got to them. Sue moved in with friends and plans to move into the dormitory as soon as she can. Nan took another job for the summer and moved out of state. My roommate who wasn't here that night just comes and goes as she feels like and that makes me mad. I couldn't tell them I resented their moving out because if I said that, they probably would have stayed. But the fact is they moved out and I have to depend on myself. I am all alone, but I plan to move in two weeks in with another girl. The apartment is on the fourth floor."

Another victim described how she was looking for an apartment: "I figured out that the guy must have come in through the bathroom window – he jimmied the lock...This time in looking for an apartment I said no first floors, no easy accessible fire escapes, no windows that are ground level. I have to get one where no one can get me."

Another change victims make in their lifestyle is to change their telephone number. Many victims request an unlisted number. The victim may do this as a precautionary measure or after receiving threatening calls. Victims fear that the assailant may gain access to them through the telephone. They are also hypersensitive to obscene telephone calls which may or may not be from the assailant.

Sexual Lifestyle

Many women report a fear of sex after the rape. The normal sexual style of the victim becomes disrupted following a rape. The rape is especially upsetting if the victim has never had any sexual experience before the rape in that she has no other experience to compare it to and no way to know whether sex will always be so unpleasant. For victims who had been sexually active, the fear increases when the boyfriend or husband confronts the woman with resuming their sexual pattern.

Some women are explicit about their lack of sexual desire after the rape. One victim said: "I don't feel like having anything to do with men. I'd rather just avoid them. I had my boyfriend stay here with me for protection. He slept on the floor. He knew how I felt, and he was good about it. He didn't like it, but he didn't hassle me." Other reactions can be noted with men in general. One victim commented as follows six months later: "For the first month, it was no go. I couldn't let [my boyfriend] get near me. I wouldn't let him know it bothered me, but every now and then I would get this awful feeling. I still get it…just a couple of weeks ago I was with my family and an old family friend of my father gave me a hug, and I got cold and stiff. I said to myself, "If Dad wasn't here you would probably do something to me." That was a terrible feeling to have this paranoid feeling toward an old friend, but it is still how I feel about men, I guess."

There are also women who are not currently involved sexually with a man when the rape occurs. One victim stated on hospital interview that she was glad she was not involved with a man at that point because she would be fearful of how she would handle the sexual part of the relationship. But two months following the rape, this victim said: "At first I thought it was good that I wasn't close to any man at that point in my life. But now I have a big question in my mind as to how I will be in a close relationship with a man. I know it has affected me in a sexual way, but I have no idea to what degree."

Implications Counseling Rape Trauma Syndrome

We found that counseling based on the following assumptions was effective in working with rape victims manifesting the rape trauma syndrome.

Short-Term Issue-Oriented Model

Victim counseling is an issue-oriented crisis treatment model. The focus of the initial interview and follow-up is on the rape incident, and the goal is to help the victim return to her previous lifestyle as quickly as possible. The rape represents a crisis which, in turn, disrupts the victim's lifestyle in four areas: physical, psychological, social, and sexual.

Crisis Requests of the Victim

The victim is considered normal, that is, an individual who was managing adequately in her lifestyle prior to the crisis situation. In this context, the victim is viewed as a customer of emergency services who has specific requests; one who seeks particular services from the professional.

Crisis Intervention

The rape is viewed as a crisis situation, and previous problems that are not associated with the rape are not considered priority issues for discussion in the counseling. This would include such issues as interpsychic or interpersonal issues, family problems, academic problems, and drinking and drug use problems. Victim counseling is not considered psychotherapy. When other issues of concern are identified by the victim that indicate another treatment model, referrals are generally offered to the victim if so requested.

Counselor-Initiated Model

The counselor takes the active role in initiating the follow-up contact. This approach is different from the traditional methods where the patient is expected to be the initiator. The counselor goes to see the victim and also makes the first telephone contact as opposed to having the victim make an office appointment for follow-up.

Compounded Reaction to Rape

In our victim sample, we also saw people who described a past or current difficulty with a psychiatric condition, a physical condition, or behavior patterns that created difficulty for them living in this society. These victims were frequently known to other therapists, physicians, or agencies. It became quite clear in working with these victims that they needed more than crisis counseling. We did provide support for these victims, especially if they pressed charges against the assailant, but we then assumed a secondary position in the belief that the professional or agency already having a relationship with the victim should provide the main support. It was noted that this group developed additional symptoms, such as increased physical problems, depression, increased drinking or drug use, suicidal behavior, and psychotic behavior.

It appears that under the stress of rape, the victim will regress according to her vulnerability. Such vulnerable positions are portrayed with a history of previous psychiatric symptoms, a poor access to a social supportive network, or with simultaneous problems, such as family, financial, or academic, as well as recurring problems such as alcoholism. A careful study of such background data helps to predict the victim's vulnerability and allows the counselor to deal with it or be prepared to refer the victim for psychotherapy, or to enlist the aid of a previous therapist with the victim's permission.

Silent Reaction to Rape

It seems to be a fairly well-accepted statement made by police and law officials that there are many victims of rape who do not report the assault. Such information should alert counselors to a syndrome that we call the silent reaction to rape. This syndrome occurs in the victim who has not reported the rape to anyone, who has not dealt with feelings and reactions to the incident, and who, because of this silence, has further burdened herself psychologically.

We became aware of such a syndrome as a result of listening to life history data reported by the victims we saw. A number of our victims stated they had been raped or sexually molested as children or adolescents, as well as when adult women. Some of the victims never told anyone and kept the burden within themselves. The current rape reactivated their emotional reaction to the prior experience. The victim would talk as vividly about the previous assault as the present one, thus indicating that the incident had never been adequately settled or integrated as part of a victim experience. Rather, victims had carried the unresolved issue.

Counselors who suspect the patient has a history of being raped should be sure to include in this evaluation interview questions relevant to the possibility of the victim's having been subjected to rape, attempted rape, or other molestation. The most effective treatment when a silent reaction to rape has been diagnosed is to refer the client for victim therapy.

Summary

Rape trauma syndrome is the acute or immediate phase of disorganization and the long-term process of reorganization that occurs as a result of attempted or actual forcible rape. The acute phase includes 1) the immediate impact reaction (either expressed or controlled emotions); 2) physical reactions; and 3) emotional reaction to a life-threatening situation. The long-term process includes changes in lifestyle, specifically physical, psychological, social, and sexual.

There are two variations to the rape trauma syndrome. In the compounded reaction to rape, the victim experiences not only these symptoms, but also a reactivation of symptoms of a previously existing condition such as a psychiatric illness. In the silent reaction to rape, various symptoms occur,but without the victim ever mentioning that a rape had occurred.

Specific therapeutic techniques for each of these reactions are described in this chapter. Crisis counseling is effective with victims developing the typical rape trauma syndrome. Additional professional help is needed for victims with compounded reactions. And the silent rape reaction means that counselors must be alert to certain clues that indicate the possibility of rape even when the person never initiates mention of an attack.

Reprinted with permission from Burgess AW, Holmstrom LL. *Rape: Crisis and Recovery*. West Newton, MA: Awab; 1986.

Chapter 13 – 1992 K-Mart Abduction

Ann W. Burgess and Paul A. Minor

Failure to provide security in a store's parking lot proved costly for K-Mart. Paul Minor of Biloxi, attorney for the family, told a Jackson, MS federal jury that this was not only a horrible crime, but that K-Mart did not protect its customers, and that management had been warned that going without security for an extended time period was like playing Russian Roulette. The psychological impact of crime causes a rippling effect to the family of a victim. This case is reviewed for its jury verdict based on inadequate security and the psychological trauma experienced by one family.

Case Background

Shortly before 8:30 PM. in late October 1992, a 31-year-old mother and her 12-year-old daughter had finished shopping at K-Mart and were loading bundles into their 1990 Chevy Blazer. Suddenly, the mother was faced with a man wearing a ski mask. He told her to be quiet, to get into the car, threatened to kill her if she screamed, and held a knife to her side. She saw a second man, without mask, walk up behind her daughter. The mother was ordered to enter the car via the driver's side and to climb over to the passenger's side; her daughter was ordered into the back seat and was held at knife point by the man wearing the ski mask. The mother was asked for her wallet, which contained a small amount of money and then they were driven to an ATM machine where the assailants obtained about $350. The mother attempted to open the car door on several occasions in order to escape, but she and her daughter were threatened with their lives if she tried again.

The mother asked that they be returned to the shopping mall, but the driver proceeded down several back roads ending up at a construction site. She was ordered out of the car and raped at gun point by each assailant. While in the car, the assailants asked many questions, such as where they lived and the school the daughter attended.

Subsequently, as the mother and daughter were released, the assailants threatened to return either to their home or school and kill them if they reported the incident.

The mother and daughter ran to a nearby house for help and to call the police. The house had a "Beware of Dog" sign, and the man who answered the door held a shotgun. He explained that she was the third person to be come to his door after being dropped off in that location. The woman immediately called 911; she was advised to have her husband drive her to the hospital for a sexual assault examination.

The two Jackson teenagers, both 16, pleaded guilty to charges of armed robbery, rape, and two counts of kidnapping each. They were sentenced to 125 years each in the state penitentiary.

Expert testimony covered the areas of negligent security, classification of juvenile rapists, and psychological trauma. Testimony was provided that the security service was fired in July, that the store went 82 days without any type of security service, that management had been advised to hire temporary security guards, and a new service was due to begin two days after the woman and her daughter were abducted. A list of prior recent robberies in the parking lot were introduced.

The juvenile offenders, classified as power-reassurance rapists, were described as easily deterred, given their age, lack of criminal history, and compliance with parental authority. The juveniles were high school students with average grades who were stealing the car and money to give as a wedding present to one of the juvenile's mother. The mother's fiancé had dropped the youths off at K-Mart 90 minutes before the abduction where they had been observed by a loss prevention guard while on a dinner break. They had also attempted to approach a male customer during this time period. After committing the crimes, one youth returned home to request permission from his mother to stay overnight at the other youth's house. The mother said he could after he cleaned the kitchen. Testimony stated the youths would have been deterred by surveillance cameras, the presence of a uniformed guard in a parking lot, and/or written notices about roaming security.

The mother was diagnosed as suffering from chronic posttraumatic stress disorder. She found it extremely stressful to have to return to the crime scene with the police as well as look at mug shots and police line-ups. She was concerned that her daughter's memory became blocked about the event, felt guilty that her daughter was with her, and that her family was traumatized by what had happened; also, the fact that a police officer was assaulted by the assailants trying to escape. She had to deal with her husband's guilt that he had gone hunting that day rather than driving them to the store.

She felt numb for weeks as though she "had died;" she had severe stomach pains. She developed depression, loss of appetite and was unable to sleep. She had nightmares, became fearful, especially of contracting AIDS. She had increasing difficulty concentrating. She had mood swings and flashbacks of the rape. She also had fears of the assailants or their family and friends retaliating.

Her husband needed to drive her shopping; she panicked when boxed in an area. She had nightmares of the assailants family and friends inflicting harm. She became phobic to parking lots and garages and clothing such as ski masks and black and gray clothing. Her relationship with her husband was seriously affected.

The daughter described the two scariest parts of the evening: (1) when the driver took her mother out of the car and (2) holding her at knife point. The daughter did not know what they would do to her mother or to herself. The masked assailant kept the knife on her leg. When the first assailant came back, she thought he had killed her mother until the man said that her mother was behind the bushes. The men talked, with the first assailant saying, "I got her, I got her good." She then heard his ask if he "had the coke and the pipe." The second man then left the car and went into the field with her mother; the first assailant walked around the back of the car and stood guard until the second assailant returned with her mother.

The daughter not only experienced direct psychological trauma from being held hostage at knife point, being abducted, and witnessing the ATM robbery, but she suffered vicarious traumatization from the separation of her mother in which she used her own imagination of what might be happening, e.g., she and her mother being killed. Having these vivid images and fear in this heightened state triggered her autonomic nervous system response. With such a heightened arousal state, the thoughts became as powerful as the actual event. In fact, the traumatic state was so severe that she developed traumagenic amnesia of the crime for weeks. The terror of the experience was overwhelming and not cognitively integrated in her mind. She blocked her emotion and split off the affect associated with the crimes. It was not until she was in a safe environment and was sitting in class three weeks later that the psychological shock wore off. When the traumatic memories broke through, she became overwhelmed with tears and had to leave school. She described how she recited children's poems and tongue twisters over and over as a method of coping both during the ordeal and for months later.

Her parents decided that she should transfer to a private school. She had great difficulty with this decision as she missed her friends. She had significant trouble concentrating in class and being able to complete assignments. Her grades dropped; she was unable to leave home alone, her parents became overprotective.

She continued to use avoidant defenses to block out the memories. Talking to attorneys required a week to recuperate from the distressing feelings. She would become nauseated and vomit. She had nightmares and difficulty sleeping. In one dream she and her mother are waiting in the car in a store parking lot to meet her father. They see a man with a knife; Dad takes off and the man slits her throat; she feels warmth on her neck and then gets cold. She believes most of her dreams to come true, and she is fearful this experience could happen again.

One of the assailant's girlfriends said, "It was a gang initiation." Also, this girl wrote a school paper on how the family ruined her relationship with her boyfriend by "sending the boys to prison."

The father had been hunting the day of the abduction and had come home and fallen asleep. He was awakened by a telephone call from his wife, hysterical, and stating she had been raped, did not know where she was, and was telephoning from a house where she went for help. He got directions to the house and took his son to his parents. He was so upset that his father drove with him to the house; they then drove his wife and daughter to the hospital. His wife continued to be distraught and his daughter was upset but was "trying not to show it."

The next week was very difficult as the assailants remained at large, and he was fearful they would return. He began driving around to see if he could find their car; he returned to K-Mart to try to retrace what had happened. He was relieved when the assailants were caught about a week later. The car was returned full of rice and with a damaged bumper. The father said the hardest part of the ordeal was thinking of what happened to his wife and daughter. The thoughts continue to intrude on his mind constantly. He thought of it while working on his tractor. He had thoughts of what he would like to do to the assailants. He would become so upset thinking about what happened that it would interrupt his work, and he had to pull over and stop working. One time he cut his chin on a grinder because he was not concentrating on what he was doing.

He felt guilty that he had gone hunting that day instead of driving his wife and daughter to the store. He was unable to resume hunting for months after the event; his wife had to help him get back to hunting.

He experienced many symptoms: feeling irritable and moody; not enjoying activities he once did, for example, going out with his wife and listening to music. The entire month of October was a reminder. He was very angry over what happened; he cried. He worried whenever his wife and daughter left he house. He admitted to being very strict with his daughter. He found it easier to sleep in a chair than a bed. He bought his wife a gun to protect herself.

To explain the cause of the posttrauma symptoms in this family, testimony was given on the current research on the neurobiology of trauma. Testimony covered how trauma impacts on the limbic system in the brain, in particular, the key regulatory processes that control attachment, emotion, sleep, appetite, sex, aggression, and memory. The limbic system, sometimes called the brain's "alarm center," protects the individual in the face of danger. It is the beginning place where all sensory information enters the human system and is encoded. When trauma impacts, the neurohormonal system releases epinephrine, which helps during dangerous states in learning. However, when the individual is trapped and cannot remove herself, either through fleeing or fighting, there is a particular type of learning, termed trauma learning, that occurs that does not allow a reduction of stress through adaptive means of the fight/flight response. The individual becomes immobilized and as the level of autonomic arousal increases, there is a move into a numbing state through the release of opiates in the brain. This numbing state accounts for disconnection of the processing and encoding information. In a sense, when the trauma is over, the alarm system remains somewhat stuck between the accelerated fight/flight response and the numbing state. This produces the alteration in an adaptive capacity that becomes fixed in its patterning and is difficult to change or extinguish. In essence, there is no resting of the alarm system; it remains damaged. It is not altered by new experiences in the environment.

Outcome

On May 19, 1997, the mother was awarded $1.7 million, the daughter was awarded $1.2 million, and the husband $500,000 following the week long trial before US District Judge Henry T. Wingate.

Chapter 14 – What A Difference a Jury Makes

Ann W. Burgess, Barry A. Cohen, and Christopher P. Jayson

The outcomes of civil suits depend on many issues. A recent case in Florida shows that different juries presented with the same case can result in vastly different verdicts. When a premises liability case was tried on the issues of liability and damages, the jury failed to award damages for pain and suffering, mental anguish, or loss of enjoyment of life. A second jury in the same case, presented with only evidence of the impact on the victim, reached a vastly different result and rendered a significant verdict for the plaintiff.

Case Facts

A 35-year-old mother of twin sons was transferred to the Florida area. She looked at Lofton Apartments. She asked about crimes in the area and was told there were only car break-ins. She then moved into the first floor apartment with her sons.

The break-in and rape happened within a week of her move. A friend had been visiting her the day after a big east coast storm. Her friend left around 9 PM or 10 PM; her sons were in bed. She fell asleep in her bed with the lights and television on and her window open. Suddenly she was awakened by a man yanking the covers off. She screamed; he told her to be quiet or he would kill her. The intruder was wearing short sleeved blue hospital scrubs. He, at one point, yelled, "Surprise." He carried a videotape camera and apparently recorded the assault. She described him as "scary calm." Before exiting, he robbed her wallet and a photo album from the living room.

Ms. Doe then made sure her children were safe, locked the door, and called the police. She called the nanny to watch the children, and she went to the hospital with the police. After the hospital, she called the office to cancel a sales meeting and was out of work about two weeks. She also called the company health hot line for a referral for a therapist.

The traumatic assault had a serious impact on Ms. Doe's life. Her description of the attack revealed her helplessness, humiliation, and fright. She moved shortly after the attack to another apartment in Lofton Place; she then moved to a house in October 1993.

In the weeks and months that followed, she had dreams and nightmares. She had difficulty sleeping; she was tormented by many thoughts of the rape; it was on her mind constantly. She had crying spells. She talked with counselors from Rape Crisis Center and found it helpful.

She described how her whole life changed. She felt insecure about whom she could trust. She developed a "superawareness" and spent a great deal of energy checking and double checking for her personal safety. Her main coping mechanism was to think that the outcome could have been a lot worse, e.g., torture or her sons witnessing the rape. She had nightmares where she woke up in a cold sweat. She would wake up at night and eat whatever was in the refrigerator. She gained 20 pounds after the rape. The assailant was not been apprehended, and she worried that he would return. She was anxious seeing anyone in hospital scrubs or who reminded her of the assailant.

The First Trial

The case went to trial in November 1998, in federal court. The plaintiff's case focused on misrepresentations made when Ms. Doe rented her apartment. The complex employees admitted that they were trained not to advise prospective tenants about crime in the complex. In fact, even though Ms. Doe specifically asked about prior crime in the complex when she leased her apartment, she was not told that there had been a sexual assault in the complex two months earlier.

After hearing testimony of two security experts, the plaintiff's psychiatrist, and an expert in rape trauma, the jury found that the apartment complex and its managers misrepresented existence of prior crime in the complex. However, based on defense arguments focused on the plaintiff's open window at the time of the assault, the verdict was mixed. In an apparent compromise verdict, the jury found that the defendants made misrepresentations, but apportioned 70% of the fault for the incident to the plaintiff and only 30% to the apartment complex. In addition, the jury awarded plaintiff all of her medical expenses, but awarded no damages for pain and suffering, mental anguish, loss of enjoyment of life, or other non-economic damages.

The Second Trial

Because it was undisputed at trial that the plaintiff suffered from posttraumatic stress disorder from the incident, and because it was undisputed that the plaintiff experienced pain and suffering, mental anguish, and loss of enjoyment of life as a result of the assault, the trial court granted a new trial solely on the issue of the plaintiff's damages. Plaintiff's counsel conducted focus groups to determine the best means to impress the jury the significant impact that the assault had upon the plaintiff.

A second trial was held in June 1999, before a new jury. This time, the only testimony and evidence presented was the impact the assault had on the plaintiff. Without hearing the controverted evidence and testimony on the defendants' liability, the jury awarded the plaintiff $1,568,450 in damages.

Chapter 15 – Physician Sexual Misconduct

Ann W. Burgess and Robert K. Prentky

There are a wide range of professionals who exploit their position of authority to sexualize and occasionally assault those in subordinate positions to them. In addition to recent clergy cases, there are many other instances of healthcare and psychiatric professionals who sexualize their clients. Cases involving sexual misconduct by healthcare professionals in an authority position who use sex to take advantage of another with less power have been neglected in the clinical and professional literature. These situations include sexual misconduct – that is, situations in which a person is used primarily for one's own gratification, profit, or selfish utilization. This case presentation illustrates how difficult it was for female patients to come forward and report the doctor and for the prosecutor to be successful in a conviction.

Background

It took a jury less than an hour to acquit a 35-year-old physician of sexually assaulting a 15-year-old patient at a medical center where she was recovering from knee surgery. As that patient at age 24 reported: "I was 15, and it was as if I didn't know what I was talking about, and he's a doctor, he knows what he's talking about, and let's give him another chance. I had the feeling the courts were protecting the doctor at trial. They kept telling me I probably was delirious from the medication. I kept telling them the nurse said I was clearheaded and able to answer questions. It seemed like I was put on trial and not him."

A year later, this same physician was charged with sexually assaulting four patients and of raping a 78-year old patient. The prosecutor believed it would not be an easy case because the victim-witnesses had "credibility" problems. One patient returned to this physician twice after the first abuse; one patient had a prior victimization history; a third patient was deaf, had an incest history with two family members, multiple marriages, and a substance abuse and psychiatric history; and the oldest patient had a long medical history of strokes, Parkinson's disease, diabetes, arthritis, ulcers, etc.

The prosecutor decided to have expert testimony on two questions: Why would women not immediately come forward with charges, and why would a patient return to a doctor who had sexually abused her?

Trial Testimony

At trial, Victim A testified that she was 23-years-old when she first saw Dr. M. for stomach pain. After performing an examination, Dr. M asked her to step into an adjoining office where he then asked Victim A whether she could cook, whether she "pleased" her boyfriend, and how often she had sex with her boyfriend. Dr. M then instructed her to refrain from sex and to schedule another appointment. Five days later Victim A returned to Dr. M and he once again asked her questions regarding her sex life. Two weeks later, Victim A returned for a third visit. At this time, Dr. M asked her whether she knew how to "please a man" and asked whether she would "please him." The doctor then approached her and began rubbing his pelvic area against her, all the while continuing to ask her to please him. Victim A sat down, frightened. Dr. M then took Victim A's arm and placed her hand on his zipper. Victim A pulled her hand away and said, "No." A nurse then opened the door and told the doctor there were several patients waiting. The doctor instructed Victim A to return. She scheduled an appointment, but did not return. One week later, she told her boyfriend of the doctor's actions. The boyfriend testified as a "fresh complaint" witness.

Victim B testified to a gynecological examination the doctor performed. While she was lying on the examining table with her legs raised stirrups, the doctor asked her whether she gave her boy friend "head," whether she enjoyed sex, what kind of sex she enjoyed, whether she enjoyed "sixty-nine," and whether she had orgasms when she had sex. Without gloves, the doctor then began an examination by inserting a speculum into Victim B's vagina. After removing the speculum, the doctor then began an examination by inserting two fingers into Victim B's vagina; the defendant was still gloveless. Placing the other hand on the victim's stomach, the doctor began to move his fingers slowly in and out of Victim B's vagina for a period of three to four minutes. After removing his fingers from Victim B's vagina, the doctor examined her breasts by placing himself between her legs and reaching up to her breasts. The doctor rubbed his pelvic area against the victim's pelvic area throughout the breast examination, which lasted three or four minutes. The doctor then attempted to stick his fingers (still gloveless) into Victim B's rectum, but stopped when she screamed. Two weeks later, Victim B returned to the doctor for an examination that took place without incident. This was the only examination where a nurse was present. One month later, she returned for another visit. On that date, the doctor placed a gloveless finger in Victim B's vagina, he again rubbed his pelvic area against her during a breast examination, and again tried to place his finger in her rectum. This was the last visit with the doctor. At the same time, Victim B told her boyfriend of her experiences with the defendant, and he testified as to Victim B's complaint.

Victim C testified that she was 78-years-old when she visited the doctor's office. Dr. M told Victim C that she looked pretty and he stuck his tongue in her mouth. Dr. M then picked Victim C up, placed her on the examining table and pulled her pants and underwear down saying he wanted to look at a rash on her back. The doctor then inserted his penis into Victim C's rectum. She cried out in pain. The doctor then put his penis into her vagina and "satisfied himself." Victim C testified that her pants were bloodied when she returned home and that she told her husband. The husband testified as a fresh complaint witness and also testified that he saw the bloodied pants.

Victim D, a 38-year-old partially deaf woman, being treated by the doctor for stomach pain, testified about an examination during which the doctor put his gloveless fingers into her vagina for "at least two minutes." When he removed his fingers he rubbed her clitoris "three or four times." The doctor then began to pinch her nipples, but he stopped when she said it was painful. The doctor then asked if she engaged in oral sex, what positions she had sex in, how often she had sex, whether she enjoyed giving "head," and if she would do it to him. Victim D responded, "No way." At a subsequent visit, the doctor asked her a series of questions about her sex life. Suddenly, as she was partially disrobed on the examining table, the doctor pulled her from the table and onto his lap, as he sat on a chair. He then put his hand between the victim's legs and began rubbing her pelvic area. Victim D got up and left. Victim D's boyfriend testified as a fresh complaint witness.

Outcome

Two experts testified. First, a gynecologist testified as to normal procedure during gynecological examination and second, a psychiatric nurse clinical specialist in rape and sexual assault for rape trauma syndrome.

The physician testified and attempted to refute the allegations; however, he was convicted on all charged counts of sexual assault and rape. He was sentenced to prison for seven to 10 years.

On appeal, the defendant raised a number of issues: the joinder of six indictments; duplicative convictions; denial of continuances; expert testimony on delayed reporting in the context of a trust relationship; and ineffective assistance of counsel. The judgments were affirmed. (See Commonwealth v. Mamay, 533 NE 2d 945 (Mass. 1990).

Crime Classification

From a classification of the doctor's sexual misconduct, this case illustrates the opportunistic nature of the crimes as they occurred when a nurse was not present indicating the highly impulsive nature to the behavior. The doctor had high social competence given his length of employment as a physician, his private practice, and his marriage.

Although the physician was not interviewed by any prosecution experts, his behavior, as described by the victims, appears to be consistent with a Type 6 High Social Competence Rapist classification using the MTC:R3 System.[1,2] Profile characteristics are as follows –

- Aggression instrumental
- No evidence of gratuitous violence
- Minimal antisocial impulse level in adulthood
- High interpersonal and social competence
- High sexualization
- Behavior driven by rape fantasy
- Interest in victim as sexual object
- History of other paraphilias may be present, but no history of sadism
- Offense planning and premeditation are evident

The deviant behavior was repetitive. Following the trial, newspaper accounts reported that a state police report compiled for the trial indicated that the doctor had been accused of sexual misconduct in another three additional states over a 10-year period, but no formal charges had been brought against him. Among the most suspicious were charges of sexual harassment brought by prisoners at a state prison for women. The question was raised, if the allegations were "unsubstantiated," why was he asked to resign.

Discussion

The abuse details from these women are difficult to process and is one reason why both the victim herself and those listening want to deny that a doctor could so behave so dangerously. Indeed, one of the reasons the women returned is due to their own disbelief in the doctor's sexual intent.

This denial explained, in part, the delayed reporting by the victims. When Victim A was asked why she waited four months before telling a fellow worker about the assault, she testified, "I thought it was in my head that he was doing something wrong." The remaining three victims came forward to the district attorney's office after there was media coverage of the physician's arrest. There were many more victims who came forward with four testifying at trial. However, there were many victims who remained loyal to the physician and said they did not believe he committed the acts.

References

1. Knight R, Prentky R. *Handbook of Sexual Assault*. Thousand Oaks, CA: Sage; 1990.
2. Prentky RA, Burgess AW. *Forensic Management of Sexual Offenders*. New York, NY: Kluwer Academic/Plenum; 2000

Chapter 16 – "No Screaming. I Don't Leave Witnesses"

Ann W. Burgess and Peter S. Everett

These words were coldly whispered to a 31-year-old woman who had just been raped and repeatedly stabbed by a stranger who had pried open the patio sliding glass doors to her first floor apartment while she sat at her dinette table.

On August 27, 1993, Jane Roe had returned home around 9:30 PM after working her second job. She spoke briefly to her roommate who then left on a date, said goodnight to her roommate's daughter and mother who retired for the evening in a front bedroom, and settled down with a cup of coffee to write a letter to a childhood friend. At about 11 PM she heard the blinds next to the sliding glass door rattle and looked up to see a man holding a small gold-colored gun in one hand and a metallic object with a small blade on the end in the other. He had entered the locked unit under cover of darkness, since the building's exterior floodlights were burned out. Her first thought was that her girlfriend and boyfriend were playing a sick joke; her next thought was this could not be happening.

The perpetrator forced Ms. Roe into her bedroom at gunpoint, ordered her to remove her pants and raped her. When finished, he stood up, turned his back, and pulled up his pants. Hearing a bump on the wall, he jumped and asked if there was anyone else in the apartment. When he learned there was, he went to their bedroom door, opened it a little, closed it, went to the kitchen and came back with a long knife. Declaring he would leave no witnesses, he stabbed her at least 10 times, presumably leaving her for dead. Bleeding, she managed to get herself to a neighbor's apartment who then called the police. She said she knew she was dying as the blood was pouring out; she found it harder and harder to breath; and she felt herself "slipping." The police immediately called for the paramedic, and she was rushed to the hospital and taken for emergency surgery.

This case illustrates (1) life-saving emergency treatment; (2) successful litigation in a state hostile to landlord liability cases; and (3) documentation of damages to the victim.

Emergency Treatment

Two factors contributed to Ms. Roe surviving the attempted murder attack. First, she was able to seek help. When her first attempt to call 911 failed, she managed to get to a neighbor who was able to call.
Second, the quick response by law enforcement, paramedics, emergency medical staff, and hospital personnel provided the life-saving action and treatment.

Investigative Forensics

Forensic specialists documented blood trails and forced entry. Inside the apartment there was a blood trail from the victim's bedroom to the kitchen and from the kitchen to the front door. There was a secondary blood trail (several drops of dripped blood leaving the main blood trail at the hall way and going to the sliding glass doors). This secondary blood trail continued on to the patio going in a direction behind the building. An examination of the outside of the sliding glass door revealed there were many little pry marks on the door and matching marks on the door frame indicating the door had been pried open. The pry tool used did not have a wide tip and only left a pointed type of impression.

Latent fingerprints were found on one of the blinds. Blood was found on the victim's mattress cover. The kitchen drawer was processed for prints. There was a large pool of blood on the kitchen floor and on the kitchen table. The telephone was off the hook, and it appeared that the blood was there from the victim when she was using the telephone to call 911.

Emergency Intervention

Ms. Roe suffered extraordinary penetrating knife wounds as a result of the crime. She remembered hearing one paramedic crying and saying, "I've lost her," in the ambulance; she heard another medic praying. She required resuscitation and received blood transfusions at the hospital. She recalled a nurse indicating, "She's still alive;" a nurse later told her they worked so hard to save her because she was fighting so hard to live.

Ms. Roe was given a sexual assault exam under anesthesia, using a PERK kit prior to her surgery for repair of the multiple lacerations. She was given tests for sexually transmitted diseases.

The surgeon's initial operative report identified ten distinct stab wounds, ranging up to 15 cm. One wound was a quarter inch from her heart, and there was communication of the right breast wound and the central chest wound, suggesting the knife wound did pass through the sternum. She had a wound to her groin as well as defense wounds to her arm, hand, and chest area. She underwent major surgery on her left arm and hand in an attempt to repair nerves badly damaged by her multiple stab wounds.

Ms. Roe's physician expressed concern over her physical security in the hospital and ordered that her room be closed at all times, required visitors be cleared, and ordered that she be situated near a nursing station. Nursing notes documented Ms. Doe's fear that the perpetrator would return. She was hospitalized for eight days.

Following her discharge from the hospital, Ms. Roe was unable to use her hand. Her surgeon noted that she had no sensation in her left thumb and index finger and had lost flexion of the radial fingers of her left arm. That signified potential damage to the medial nerves of her left arm. She underwent exploratory surgery, which revealed that the stabbing had completely lacerated the medial nerve necessitating a nerve graft using the sural nerve from the outside of her left foot and lower ankle area.

Liability Issues

The Virginia state courts are noted to be reluctant to hold third parties accountable for negligent security issues. Clear and convincing evidence is needed to win summary judgments. This case won on two counts: the nonsecure sliding glass doors and the burned out floodlights.

Sliding glass doors

The sliding glass door to Ms. Roe's ground- floor unit was only equipped with a simple lock and no device (i.e., a charley bar) to prevent it from being lifted off its tracks and the lock bypassed. The management company failed to equip the sliding glass doors with a secondary lock, even though 1) it had such devices on-site, if tenants knew to ask for them, and 2) 14 months earlier a tenant in a neighboring complex managed by the same management company had been the victim of a rape, strangulation, and attempted murder by a criminal who entered through a sliding glass door in a ground floor unit.

The City of Williamsburg had enacted an ordinance (section 5-189 of the Buildings and Building Regulations) effectively requiring a secondary locking device. The Code requires that the chief of police inspect all sliding doors that provide access either directly or indirectly to any multifamily dwelling unit in the city which contains five or more units. The inspection was to have been made upon the first vacancy of any covered apartment after May 8, 1980, and the landlord was required to arrange for the inspection. The code section states: If such inspection reveals a sliding door which can, with application of vertical force not exceeding 400 pounds from its exterior side, be removed from its track, or have its locks disengaged by movement of the door within the space of clearance provided for installation and operation, the chief of police shall so notify the landlord in writing, and the landlord shall, at its own expense, within 30 days of such notification, take such steps as are reasonably necessary in order to limit the vertical movement of the door within its frame.

The Chief of Police for the City of Williamsburg confirmed that no inspections required by section 5-189 had been requested for the apartment complex where Ms. Roe lived. The trial court overruled the Defendants' demurrer to a negligence per se count based on the Ordinance.

Burned out floodlights

Two months before the attack, Miss Roe's roommate notified management that the exterior lights illuminating the rear of her building were broken. The management company sent a maintenance worker to the apartment. Ms. Roe personally took him to the back of the building and pointed out one of the broken light fixtures. The maintenance man indicated he would return to fix the light. The lights remained burned out until shortly after the attack, when the management company fixed certain lights and requested a police security survey, coincidentally arranged to take place after the lights were repaired. The trial court overruled the Defendants' demurrer to an oral contract count based upon the promise to repair the floodlight.

Damages

The rape and near death experience has had lasting psychosocial effects on Ms. Roe. She had no immediate family (her parents and two brothers were dead), but an aunt who lived in the area was able to provide support and a temporary residence.

Ms. Roe was evaluated four months after the crime in December 1993 and diagnosed to be suffering from rape trauma syndrome. She was in constant pain from her surgeries; was unable to return to her apartment; dropped out of graduate school; and could not go back to work. She feared living alone; became depressed; had sleep problems; and she lost 15 pounds. She had to confront the fear of AIDS and pregnancy. She had memories of blood flowing from her stab wounds and flashbacks to a feeling she was dying.

Ms. Roe was evaluated one year later in February 1995. She had received counseling and in the interim was placed on antidepressant medication. Only a few of her prior symptoms had been partially relieved. She continued having sleep problems, feeling emotionally drained, tired and worn out, and was plagued with an inability to concentrate. She was working part-time and continued to live with a friend. Her social life was "on hold" as she had broken up with her boyfriend after the assault.

Ms. Roe was again evaluated five years later in March 1998. In the time period, she had moved several times and had various roommates to share expenses. She had trouble controlling her diabetes, her appetite fluctuated depending on her stress level, and she needed sleeping pills. She had considerable anxiety when dating, could not handle stress, had decreased energy, and her difficulty concentrating was causing her to make many mistakes at work. Because of the errors, she was referred to the Employee Assistance Program. Although working, she was underemployed in a clerical position. She lost her motivation for school; the attack derailed her career trajectory. She had several courses of counseling for posttraumatic stress disorder.

Over the five years, Ms. Roe regained much of the use of her hand, and she experienced significant regeneration of the radial nerve. Her surgeon concluded that she had made "a remarkable recovery considering the severe nature of her injuries," but did sustain a 50% permanent partial impairment of her left arm. She has very significant residual scarring, a constant reminder of the rape and attempted murder, and it is the scarring that prompts people to ask "what happened."

Law enforcement conducted an extensive investigation, and an artist's sketch was run in the local newspaper. Photos of 19 suspects were shown to Ms. Roe with no positive identification. One suspect, arrested for a rape in another apartment complex about three weeks later, had a similar pattern of turning his back to his victim when redressing, but Ms. Roe was unable to identify him as her attacker. The criminal case remains open.

A civil suit began in the fall of 1993; the case settled in February 1999. Everett's co-counsel in this case was Eileen Wagner, Esq.

Chapter 17 – Abuse Instead of Respiratory Therapy

Ann Wolbert Burgess, Troy A. Brookover, Owen P. Eagan, and Michaela J. Rosenberger

Hospitalized patients with respiratory problems require careful observation and skilled nursing attention due to the life-threatening nature of their distress. Two separate cases are reported that recently settled involving respiratory therapists as sexual predators.

Abuse Case Involving Child Patient

A case happening in the Southwest involved a three-year-old boy, who was hospitalized after three days of respiratory distress, including fever, cough, and difficulty breathing. He was diagnosed with pneumonia, and orders were written for him to have respiratory therapy every six hours. The boy was in a semiprivate room with another child; both mothers were sleeping-in with their children.

Close to midnight a respiratory therapist came in to the room stating he would give the boy a second breathing treatment. The boy's mother saw the therapist put medicine into the container of the mask and place it on her son's face. The boy was on his side facing the wall with his back to the therapist. The therapist then laid down on the bed facing the boy; the machine vibrator was on. Then the therapist got off the bed, turned the boy on his side facing him and started pulling his pants down. The boy began to moan. The mother said she saw the therapist standing with penis exposed, thrusting his hips towards, on, and about the boy's face and mouth. His mother was shocked and when she asked what he was doing, the therapist covered himself with his clipboard and exited the room. The mother tried to follow him, but found the door blocked from the outside. When she was able to open it, she noted the therapist adjusting his pants. She called for a nurse, stated her son had just been molested and said she wanted to leave with him immediately. Both her husband and a police officer were called.

149

In the following months, the boy had many posttrauma symptoms. He had difficulty sleeping, would wake up crying around midnight, and come into his parents bed. He lost his appetite, lost weight, was easily upset and frightened if his mother left, became angry easily, and would throw things. He withdrew from playing outside with other children and was argumentative with his siblings. His mother said the abuse was never talked about and that she hoped he would never remember.

Abuse Case Involving Vulnerable Adult Patient

A case on the East Coast, a 55-year-old married mother was diagnosed with amyotrophic lateral sclerosis (also called Lou Gehrig's disease). Within six months she was confined to bed and by 10 months she was admitted to a hospital for chronic ventilator management, ongoing medical management, and chronic care. She was unable to move or talk and communicated by blinking her eyes once for yes and twice for no. The use of a communication board allowed her to spell out words using the eye-blinking method.

The woman's sister would visit in the afternoons, and her husband would visit after dinner in evening. The day after she was transferred from an intensive care unit monitored with cameras to the intermediate unit not monitored by cameras, the sister told the husband that his wife seemed upset, as she was tearful during the visit. The husband was unable to learn anything during his visit because his 10-year-old son was with him, but was also aware something seemed wrong. The next evening his wife cried as she was able to spell out, with the communication board, that a short, fat bearded man came to treat her. He pulled the window curtains shut and the patient privacy curtain around her bed. He lifted up her hospital gown, touched her breasts, twisted her nipples, spread her legs apart, and inserted two fingers into her vagina. She knew it was not medical equipment or a catheter. She was unable to scream, cry out for help, or fight him off due to her paralyzed condition. This happened two days in a row. Her husband made an immediate complaint to the nursing staff.

In the days and weeks following, the patient became suspicious of staff and very attentive to her environment. When hearing a noise, her eyes would search the room; she became hyperalert. In addition to her medical condition, anxiety, fear, depression, and sleeplessness became dominant clinical features.

Lessons from the Cases

These two cases were similar in several respects: the victims were vulnerable and unable to protect or defend themselves, the predators selected victims they thought could not communicate, the complaint was made through a family member, and the victims expressed their emotional distress through behavior and symptoms. Also, the hospital staff's response was the same; they defended themselves by saying it was hearsay, nothing had happened, that the patient misinterpreted the treatment, and that the stories by the family members were inconsistent.

Information about the Offenders

In the child molestation case, the respiratory therapist had been fired before this employment for fondling the genitals of a male patient, a second complaint made against the therapist at that hospital. The hospital had dismissed the first complaint as not being true with the understanding if a second complaint were made, they would fire him, which is what happened. On his job application form, he wrote reason for leaving "pending," and no one asked about it during the interview at the children's hospital.

In the adult victim case, the respiratory therapist consistently denied anything had happened. He had no prior criminal record. However, he pled *nolo contendere* in the criminal case and at the department of public health services for the state licensing issue. He received several restrictions on his license, including that he not work with patients.

Subsequent Civil Suits

Different liability issues were involved in the civil suits. In the child case, the hospital did not do a background or criminal history check, and they did not do reference checks. Either or both would have provided sufficient information for them not to hire him. He had prior convictions for sexual molestation and improper conduct with children. He was on probation for said convictions at the time of this incident, and the employers did nothing to develop his criminal background history or to prevent a convicted pedophile from working in a children's hospital.

In the adult case, plaintiff's attorney argued that the defendants were negligent in failing to provide for their patient's safety. The hospital had the duty to communicate with her meaningfully (more than to say hello and how are you) on a daily basis. The staff could have been trained by the speech-language pathologist in the use of her letter board. The hospital staff also had a duty to closely observe her 24-hours-a-day or, in the alternative, not to move her from the unit monitored with cameras.

As to the settlements reached, the East Coast case was sealed and resolved to the parties' mutual satisfaction. In the Southwestern case, the respiratory therapist was not a hospital employee, and the plaintiffs settled with the hospital prior to filing the litigation against the offender, his employer, and the parent company. The total settlement in the case was $600,000.

A critical question is how does an organization's response to a sexual abuse complaint influence legal and offender issues? In these two cases, the immediate position of the hospital was to deny and move to a he said/she said position. One thing for sure is that denial reinforces the predator's behavior. That the child molester could constantly get by with assaults on patients just heightened his propensity to offend and under conditions that appear high risk for being caught. The point is he feels he can get away, and the fact is his denial of his own predatory behavior is reinforced by the denial tactics of the hospital in defending themselves against litigation. Eluding detection and defense tactics bolsters confidence in his behavior.

Need for Communication with Impaired Patients

Hospitals who care for patients with impaired verbal skills must be able to work out a communication system. In the adult abuse case, the staff failed to understand or observe her distress or just ignored it. The nursing notes were never found for the two days she was abused. But because her family knew her mood and how to communicate with her, they immediately realized her distress and sought help.

This case speaks to the duty to care for a patient and the clinical monitoring of adjunct staff. A patient who cannot communicate requires staff to take the time to learn how to communicate with that person and to set up a system of communication that is shared with the staff. She had a communication board, but rather than it being at her bedside, it was noted to be in her closet.

Organizations should move beyond an automatic denial of abuse and work to determine the credibility of reporters of abuse who are vulnerable by age or impaired with neurological disorders or other handicaps. Education as to the presentations of abuse and the dynamics of the offenders would be helpful to this goal.

Chapter 18 – Neurobiology of Rape Trauma

Carol R. Hartman and Ann W. Burgess

What has been done in the basic sciences on the topic of violence and psychological trauma? What are the etiological factors to symptoms encountered in the trauma response? This chapter reviews some of the basic research, indicating that sexual violence creates changes in the nervous system that have lasting consequences to victims. These consequences become a challenge to our clinical efforts and to the development of intervention services.

Basic Research

From the beginning of our work with victims who had been raped and/or sexually assaulted, we have believed that a certain type of learning occurred during the assault. This learning had to be understood on a sensory, perceptual, cognitive, and interpersonal level. We have pursued our thoughts about the presentation and level of symptoms. This has led to an assumption that this special type of learning is a manifestation of dysregulation of primary processes related to fundamental operations in the management of information, that is, information generated internally as well as in the environment. This assumption that something structurally and functionally changed because of the trauma and that this change was basic to the array of symptoms that we witnessed is now more clearly documented in basic research regarding brain, behavior, and posttraumatic stress disorder (PTSD).

The brain may be understood to be an array of neurons organized into circuits. Different circuits process different kinds of information, and they do so in different ways. Researchers are giving much more attention to the question of just how and where experience-dependent circuit changes take place, because that is how and where memory is stored.

As background for the presentation of neuroscience findings related to response patterns to rape trauma, it is important to organize the symptoms into two broad categories: positive symptoms and negative symptoms. Positive symptoms refer to those manifestations of hyperarousal. This arousal can be of a consistent tonic nature, e.g., someone is consistently tense, or it can be phasic with episodic periods of being startled, frightened, or terrorized by external and internal cues.

This is in contrast to the group of symptoms that are classified as negative symptoms. These symptoms range from a sense of numbness, apathy, and depression to various states of dissociation. The assumption is that this presentation of positive and negative symptoms occurs after traumatic events and represents compensatory patterns of organization of a damaged alarm system. This disregulatory process is responsible for the biphasic characteristics of one outcome of the trauma response which is PTSD. The mounting scientific evidence indicates that the disruption of the alarm system is central to the basic processes and operations for coding, sorting, sequencing, and developing information systems, be they visual, auditory, kinesthetic, olfactory, motor, or gustatory.[1,2,3]

To begin to understand why there is disruption in arousal and numbing processes, we have to remember that the natural response set of the human being is to protect and promote survival. All incoming information is processed on the most fundamental level of awareness of threat. The major neuro-arrangement for the intake of stimulation, its categorization, and its organization of action begins in the systems that relate to the flight/fight/freezing aspect of the alarm system. These primary points for directing and regulating response are located in the pons and limbic system and the cerebral cortex. Research on the impact of trauma on neurological systems and ultimately on higher cortical functioning will elaborate on this major premise.

Pitman[4] evaluates research on the arousal and alarm system and its relationship to PTSD by organizing the key symptoms as follows. First are the tonic symptoms: These are the symptoms a patient manifests most all of the time, especially when evoked by salient environmental stimuli that reminds the person of the traumatic event. Next are phasic symptoms: These are frequently intermittently experienced symptoms. They are the dramatic symptoms of flashbacks, reliving experiences, nightmares, and intrusive, recollective thoughts of the traumatic events. The third are a mix of tonic and phasic symptoms which are not necessarily tied directly to salient cues in the environment, but are presented when there is mild or sometimes no stimuli. These symptoms are hypervigilence, insomnia, and exaggerated startle response as well as generalized physiological reactivity (phasic). There are also the avoidant symptoms, such as a diminished interest, numbing, estrangement, and avoidance of reminders.

Giller[5] arranges the symptoms in terms of their specificity to the traumatic event itself: Intrusive symptoms, such as flashbacks, are those symptoms most closely allied with the event itself. The next are avoidant symptoms, including the numbing, detachment, and restricted affect. These symptoms are most often a direct response to the psychic representation of the traumatic events, i.e., a memory. Last are the least specific symptoms in that they can be associated with situations and stimuli that have minimal connection with the actual event. These are the irritability, hypervigilence, increased startle reaction, and difficulty concentrating.

Krystal[6] explains these constellation of symptoms by a variety of models derived from animal and human research, thus laying down the foundation for the biology of trauma. First is the Noradrenergic-Alarm Model or LC Model (Locus Coerulus). Research basic to this model suggests that the LC activation impacts on the limbic system during stress. This activation is aimed at not only alerting and preparing of the organism, but through elaborate feedback systems, modulates the surge of noradrenergic hormones. In trauma, research suggests that this basic regulation of the LC process is altered resulting in a flooding of noradrenergic and adrenergic hormones that lead to overlearning and stimulation of key areas of the limbic system as well as the activation of the opioid, diazapine systems that lead now to the numbing, amnesias, and dissociative experiences.

A second model, supported by animal and clinical research, is the Fear-Enhanced Startle Model.[6] This model suggests that during a traumatic experience there is a sensitization of pathways that involve the startle response during a fear provoking situation. Subsequently there is an enhancement of the fear response without direct association to the traumatic stimuli. Neuroscience theories considered in this model are those that focus on the suspected phenomena of "kindling." The area of sensitization assumed is the amygdala in the limbic system. This nonassociative fear enhancement is felt to be central to the long-lasting fear response found in many survivors of trauma.

A third model is the Traumatic Alterations in Neural Activity and Memory.[6] This model attempts to explain three major characteristics of memory disturbance associated with trauma. One is the long-lasting effects, if not lifelong disturbances of memory. Second is the impairment and fragmentation of memory experienced as intrusive thoughts, nightmares, and flashbacks. All of these characterized as if the event, upon recall, is being relieved. And third is the hyperarousal and defensive posture (lack of trust) found in unrelated stressful situations. The assumptions here, gathered from research on the Aplysia snail, is that microstructural changes appear to play a role in the long-lasting traumatic enhancement of alarm, avoidance, and memory. Transient avoidance learning operates through a spectrum of intracellular processes that increase or decrease the activity of simple sensorimotor systems. The activation of this system is via the brain stem and limbic system. Severe or repeated exposure to aversive stimuli produces long-lasting enhanced reactivity in the snail. This activation impacts on the long- and short-term memory of the snail. Evidence for molecular change was obtained when products were injected that blocked gene transmission material (RNA) and gene translation material (DNA). When these products were given (during traumatic exposure), long-term avoidant learning disappeared. When they were not given, long-term avoidant learning occurred. Further, if the gene products had appeared, the blocking agents did not work after the trauma; thus, there was a chronic state of avoidance. There was a proliferation of certain receptor sites and a reduction in others under conditions of trauma and trauma with injections.

A fourth model explaining the manifestations of PTSD is that of Inescapable Shock (IS). van der Kolk[3] has summarized the findings from primate studies and human subjects. The research on monkeys, dogs, and humans under different stressful situations in which escape was limited or prevented provides evidence for massive multisystem brain activation. This activation results in the depletion of noradrenergic, dopaninergic, and serotonergic neurons, in the alterations in receptor function systems as well as benzodiazepine and endogenous opiate systems.

These animal studies, combined with the poignant studies on maternal deprivation and its impact on affective regulations, social behavior, and vulnerability to stress have led to a fifth model on the biology of trauma. This model combines the IS, maternal deprivation findings, and the concepts of hormonal dysregulation. This combined model suggests that the PTSD symptoms may arise purely from activation-induced disturbances in homeostatic neuronal systems and not as goal-directed, learned responses. Rather, stress-induced dysregulation may produce learned behavioral syndromes that adaptively dampen arousal through mechanisms, such as cognitive patterns that decrease level of arousal or phobic avoidance.

Implications of Models for Human Response to Trauma

The implication of these models and the latter in particular, for clinical practice, resides in a movement away from mentalistic explanations regarding the symptoms of victims. We suggest that social, behavioral patterns are more profitably understood as adaptive responses to biologically driven phenomena than as psychologically derived conclusions. For example, the woman who remains in a battering situation may be more directly assisted in moving to protect herself when the overwhelming numbing state is addressed as an adaptive response to the disorganizing experience of a noradrenergic flooding. Her self appraisal is altered, if not impaired by biological alterations that impact on differentiation and discrimination of internal and external cues. Rather, repetitive nonfunctional behaviors dominate. To interpret her behavior in terms of psychological motivations, that is, feeling deserving or to blame, is better understood as psychological reasons given by the woman to explain her confusion in taking more functional actions. That is, she blames her response selection on personal will and motivations, rather than on a biological response to overwhelming threat.

Pitman[4] reviews the major positions put forth in the animal models with existing studies of traumatized human populations and cautions in extrapolating from animal models to human models. Nevertheless, human clinical studies deriving many of their hypotheses from animal models do suggest a strong argument for the biological underpinnings for much of the behavior we witness in people who have been traumatized.

The pattern of response to trauma, abstracted from the models and research data, can be summarized as follows. Basically, three key circuits are activated when a person is confronted with a traumatic stressor. First, the preparatory circuit mobilizes the body for an emergency and is influenced by the locus coeruleus and Raphe nucleus that secrete two known catecholamines that are associated with different states of stress. There is the noradrenergic hormone associated with arousal and serotonin, which has a major function in modulating the noradrenergic system initiated by the locus coeruleus. This is the seat for arousal and when in a disregulated state, is a source of unresolved stress and positive symptoms.

Second, the stress response circuit is known for increasing the secretion of the corticotropin releasing factor (CRF) and in some cases cortisol. This is one of the main hormones mobilizing the body to fight/flight (handling the emergency). This hormone is regulated by key structures in the limbic system. The pituitary gland responsible for CRF interacts with the hypothalmus (limbic structure). This circuitry is innervated by the adrenergic system. In PTSD, there is an increase in norepinephrine and a decrease in cortisol. The ratio of norepinephrine/cortisol is a biological benchmark for PTSD. This circuit interacts with the third circuit and accounts not only for fight and avoidance responses but accounts for negative symptoms, such as detachment, dissociation, and apathy.

Third, the blunting circuit is regulated by hormones secreted from the opioid-benzodiazepine system. This response blunts the feeling of pain. This circuit includes the locus coeruleus, hypothalamus, and amygdal, which registers strong emotion.

Stress and/or trauma have been shown to alter all three key circuits. These circuits interconnect via feedback loops that aim at achieving homeostasis. Rather than these adaptive systems being depleted, they accommodate the imbalance to preserve a protective response as well as homeostasis. These accommodations err in priming the alarm system to react with less provocation and less capacity to discriminate error.

Disorder behaviors are assumed to arise out of stress/trauma overwhelming these adaptive systems, throwing them into states of dysregulation via processes of hyposecretion and/or hypersecretion. Dysregulation occurs in the primary center for the regulation of major life-engaging functions, e.g., sleep, memory, attachment, sexual behavior, aggression, and self-defense (limbic system). Stress/trauma is seen to have a significant effect on personal and interpersonal behavior patterns. This includes actions and thinking.

After Circuit 1 has been activated and a person has moved into Circuit 2, the release of CRF can lead to an increase in plasma cortisol, which leads to an increased tryptophan hydroxylase (which is a neuro activator, activating seratonin circuits) which, because of sustained stress/trauma results in decreased serotonin, which results in a decrease in its modulating effects. The result is an unchecked excretion of norandrenalin from the locus coeruleus. This is just one example of dysregulation. There can be dysregulation in the HPA axis or between the opioid system and the noradrenergic system.

All three circuits influence memory. Experience is remembered at a basic level that some refer to as taxonomic or primarily categorical memory. The key aspect of this memory is that it is sensorimotor and not related to time and space. Therefore, it is immediate, as if it is happening.

The primary memory system is basic to higher order memory structures. When there is dysregulation of sensory input, alterations in primary memory influence the elaboration of secondary memory. When there is inference with basic categorization (discrimination, sorting, etc.), there is disruption in the processing and storing of information on a secondary level. For example, the interpretation cues that clarify the intentions and motivations of others can be disturbed because basic patterns of

158

response are limited by a restricted repertoire of response, which is also biased to produce avoidant responses.

Trauma and its Impact on Cognition

The pursuit of the biological underpinnings of trauma suggests that trauma response may be understood as an adaptive consequence of change in the alarm system of living organisms. The call to arousal and preparation for fight/flight and the analgesic inducement to manage and control physical pain and injury and maintain psychic integrity are basic operations in the survival of the species. When there is an accumulation of stress due to factors that restrict the resetting of the various innervated hormonal systems, adjustments occur that influence the basic structures and operations of the brain. Alterations in the behavior of victims can be seen in victim assumptions regarding cause and effect; in attention, cue selection, and interpretation; in the presentation of self; in attributional patterns; in memory and sequencing of intra and interpersonal experiences; in levels of consciousness; in self-appraisal capacities; in the modulation of emotion; in repetitive behaviors; in disturbed sleep patterns; and in the integration and expression of moral judgment. While psychological explanations have been useful to some extent in the treatment of victims, the maintenance of severe symptoms over time suggests a need for a broader frame of reference for understanding and treatment.

For years, there has been an emphasis on higher order cognitive function, direction, behavior, and motivation. MacLean[7] stated that it came to him as a wondrous insight, that thought emanates from the "animal brains" in man. In his famous discussion of the "triune brain," he posits that the initial response to introceptive and proprioceptive stimuli is addressed first in the primitive brain areas and elaborated in the more advanced area of the brain, such as the cortex and the frontal lobe.

Recognition that symptom formation may reflect learning has been basic to the behaviorist position. Pitman,[4] adopting a behavioral perspective, suggests that the symptoms of PTSD might be explained by two types of learning, classical conditioning and operant conditioning or instrumental learning. He suggests that there is nonassociative learning and associative learning, thus explaining the generalization of fear/anxiety responses.

Foa and Kozak[8] challenge this traditional two-factor learning paradigm and suggest that symptoms of PTSD are best explained by fear structures in memory that take into account information about the feared stimulus situation; information about verbal, physiological and other behavioral responses; and interpretive information about the meaning of the stimulus and response elements of the structure.

Edelman's model of memory and learning[9] suggests more complex alterations in basic perceptual categorization processes, which are highly dependent on basic survival. In turn, these alterations at the primary level of consciousness influence higher-order consciousness.

While this does not rule out the appraisal schema proposed by Foa and Kozak,[8] it suggests that at a primary level of consciousness, categorical discriminations and categories are reorganized. This reorganization influences the higher-order consciousness, in particular, conceptualizations of the present state of events. Thus, the response on the primary consciousness level shapes and influences reorganization of the higher-order consciousness. This hypothesis then makes some of the judgment errors in victims who are subject to revictimization as understandable as victims who manifest exaggerated fear to innocuous situations.

The important point is that the fear schema arises out of a primary consciousness that consists of basic memory processes that for all intents and purposes are out of awareness and are only suggested in the higher-order consciousness. The survival, adaptive orientation of the primary consciousness is such that trauma alters saliency and discriminatory mappings. This leaves to clinical efforts the task to search out and identify these alterations and devise interventions that reestablish more flexibility at the level of primary consciousness as well as at the level of higher consciousness. The model of learning assumed by Pitman appears simplistic as to what is known regarding brain functioning and the fear schema suggested by Foa and Kozak can gain strength by the theoretical proposition of Edelman.

Dissociation, Trauma, and Memory

In trauma, there is biological evidence that the alarm systems functioning is severely altered. Of particular importance is the alterations in arousal and analgesic systems. The result is discontinuity in the basic operations of selecting and cateorizing new and ongoing experiential stimuli and developing new memory constructs.

The influence of dissociation and hyperarousal on memory and learning at this basic level alters thinking (solving problems) and is at the heart of understanding the impact of trauma on cognition.

160

Altered states of consciousness was pivotal in Pierre Janet's conceptualization of causes of repetitive behaviors, be they reenactments of a basic upsetting experience or fragmented stereotypes. He believed that altered states of consciousness brought about these patterns because of severe trauma which had, with its contextual basis, been dissociated from conscious awareness. He believed that trauma overwhelmed and impaired the capacity of the individual to feel, think, and act in a unified, purposeful way. The key lay in how memory is stored, retrieved, and integrated in the face of "vehement emotional" experiences.[10]

Freud[11] struggled with the concept of fixation and the concept of repetition compulsion throughout his intellectual career. While Freud viewed psychological trauma rooted in infantile sexuality, Janet noted how a variety of traumatic experiences result in the disruption of personality and behavior and are marked by disturbances in memory.[12] Van der Kolk and van der Holt[12] concluded their presentation of Janet's work on trauma and psychological adaptation by noting that after more than a 100 years, nothing much remains to be learned about how memories operate, are stored, and interact with emotions and behavior in order to diminish their hold over current experience.

Clinical Implications

These current neurobiological findings have direct implications for clinical practice. First, the long-term symptom sequelae of rape and sexual abuse victims has to be understood not only from a psychosocial-political perspective, but from a biological basis. Trauma learning is realized in alterations in primary and secondary memory processes. The search for appropriate biological interventions that can reestablish dysregulation is an optimum outcome. However, the associative damage done via the prolongation of symptoms and the interpersonal violations require a variety of approaches from self-help support groups to focused psychotherapeutic approaches.

References
1. Aysto S. Neuropsychological aspects of simultaneous and successive cognitive process. In: Williams JM, Long CJ, eds. *Cognitive Approaches to Neuropsychology.* New York, NY: Plenum;1987:229-272.
2. Horowitz M. Intrusive and repetitive thoughts after experimental stress. *Arch Gen Psychiatry.* 1976;32:1457-1463.
3.van der Kolk BA. *Psychological Trauma.* Washington, DC: American Psychiatric Press; 1987.
4. Pitman R. Biological findings in PTS: implications for DSM-IV Classification. Unpublished position paper. NH Veterans Administration Medical Center/Dept. of

Psychiatry, Harvard Medical School Research Services, 151. Veterans Administration Medical Center, 718 Smyth Road, Manchester, NH 03104; 1989.

5. Giller E, ed. *Biological Assessment and Treatment of Posttraumatic Stress Disorder*. Washington, DC: American Psychiatric Press; 1990.

6. Krystal J. Animal models for posttraumatic stress disorder. In: Giller E, ed. *Biological Assessment of Posttraumatic Stress*. Washington, DC: American Psychiatric Press; 1990:1-26.

7. McLean P. *The Triune Brain in Evolution*. New York, NY: Plenum; 1990.

8. Foa EB, Kozak MJ. Emotional processing of fear: exposure to corrective information. *Psychol Bull*. 1986;99:20-35.

9. Edelman G. *The Remembered Present: A Biological Theory of Consciousness*. New York, NY: Basic Books; 1989.

10. van der Hart O, Horst R. The dissociation theory of Pierre Janet. *J Trauma Stress*. 1989;2:399-411.

11. Freud S. Beyond the pleasure principle. In: Strachey J, trans & ed. New York, NY: Liveright; 1961.

12. van der Kolk BA, van der Hart O. Pierre Janet and the breakdown of adaptation in psychological trauma. *Am J Psychiatry*. 1989;146:1530-1540.

Chapter 19 – Delayed Reporting of the Rape Victim

Ann Wolbert Burgess, William P. Fehder, and Carol R. Hartman

Great efforts are made to encourage women to immediately report a rape. However, societal expectations concerning the reporting of rape are in conflict. One is that if a woman is raped she should be too upset and ashamed to report it, and therefore this crime goes largely unreported. The other is that if a woman is raped she should be so upset that she will report it. Both expectations exist simultaneously; it is the latter one, however, that is written into law. This legal principle was researched and reported by Brownmiller to have been carried since the 13th century, when according to Henry of Bratton (Bracton), who lived and wrote in the 13th century and is considered an authority for the ancient Saxon times, the procedure a raped virgin was to follow went like this:

She must go at once and while the deed is newly done, with the hue and cry, to the neighboring townships and show the injury done to her to men of good repute, the blood and her clothing stained with blood and her torn garments.[1]

The rule then continues that if the accused man protests his innocence, the raped virgin must then have her body examined by four law-abiding women sworn to tell the truth as to whether she was defiled or is still a virgin.[1]

In more modern language, this is called "making a fresh complaint." The assumption is that if she really has been raped, she will make it known to others immediately. In modern procedure there is often the same interest in the state of the hymen, although the examination of the raped victim today is by a hospital staff.

While suspicions about women, their motives, and their truthfulness are realities that the victim faces when immediately reporting her experience to the officer or nurse, we were interested in what happens to the case when the report is delayed. Because this issue is often the centerpiece of a defense strategy, the authors reviewed cases representing a range of rape circumstances and identified three major reasons for the delayed reporting: (a) impaired cognitive processing; (b) altered states of consciousness; and (c) cognitive dissonance.

Impaired Cognitive Processing

Women may be raped who have impaired cognitive processing, that is, they are mentally retarded, suffer delusional or hallucinatory experiences, or can be aphasic. Such conditions place them in a particularly vulnerable position to being abused and to being believed. Their reasoning is challenged; their capacity for expression can be compromised; and their ability to express themselves can be unique to them and not understood by others and thereby challenged on accuracy and consistency.

Rape During an EEG

A 38-year-old woman with a childhood history of physical and sexual abuse by her father and other family members and a long psychiatric history of bipolar depression, substance abuse, and psychotic episodes where she describes seeing Satan and her mother's house burning down, reported to state hospital staff one morning that the EEG technician had sexually assaulted her the previous evening during an EEG. About a week later, a 35-year-old psychiatric patient diagnosed as a borderline personality, conduct disordered, drug abuser, and with a seizure history, who was told by her psychiatrist that he had ordered an EEG for her, refused the procedure. When he inquired as to her reluctance she detailed her assault by this technician the previous year. Subsequently, the staff psychiatrist questioned the only other female state hospital patient for whom he had ordered an EEG and who was still hospitalized. Although she was deemed too psychotic to effectively testify, she said the EEG technician was "a dreadful man who had given her a sexual enema."

Four other women were located by the attorney general's office who had EEGs performed by this technician within the three-year statute of limitation. A fourth patient, a 34-year-old, divorced, mentally retarded mother of one, with a diagnosis of chronic schizophrenia and epilepsy, described being given a large green pill before the technician attached the electrodes. She felt groggy about 20 minutes into the test. She said he unzipped his pants and told her to suck his penis for about a 30-minute time period. At the end of the test, the technician told her not to tell anybody because he was married and had two small children. She did not tell anyone until she was interviewed by the investigator for the attorney general's office. She believed the technician had a romantic interest in her. A fifth patient, 35 years of age and with a psychiatric diagnosis of depression, dementia, compulsive sexual behavior, and occasional hallucinations, described an EEG given by the technician as taking about two hours. She described being sexually fondled, orally sodomized with the technician then saying she should not tell anyone because he could lose his job and that he would see her after she got out of the hospital. She told no one because she was embarrassed and thought what happened was "dirty." A sixth patient, a 29-year-old woman with a psychiatric history of depression, self-destructive behaviors, posttraumatic stress disorder, and borderline personality, described being given a pill by the technician before having the EEG and then described how the technician placed electrodes in her groin area, tried to find her pulse in her crotch area, and fondled her nipples. A seventh patient, aged 27 and with psychiatric diagnoses of substance abuse, suicidal ideation, and multiple personality disorder, described feeling groggy from medications given prior to the EEG. He forced oral sodomy on her. Afterwards, he said he would like to take her out and asked for her telephone number; she provided it. After he left, she said she became upset, confused, scared, and felt there was nobody she could talk to. She asked for some medication to help her sleep. She said the incident worked on her mind for the next few days and when discharged, she got drunk. Sometime later she told her psychiatrist about the incident.

Case discussion: Several elements have coalesced into delayed reporting of sexual abuse by these victims. Each appears to have been given a pill by the EEG technician. Many medications are known to produce partial or complete amnesic states. Some examples of these medications are benzodiazepines, barbiturates, ketamine, and scopolamine. Psychiatric patients sometimes develop ineffective mechanisms for dealing with drives and desires which can result in hallucinated images and delusional thoughts that are ineffective in producing satisfaction of drives and desires (Levick S, personal communication). Although these patients are able to perceive real situations they may confuse reality with unreal thoughts and be reluctant to reveal sexual abuse by an authority figure for fear that they are mistaken in perception.

Expert testimony was required around the issue of delayed report and evidence of resistance. Psychiatric patients experience reality as do nonpsychiatric patients. It is their ability to communicate their condition and have it validated that is difficult. A silent response is typical of victimization, especially when by an authority person. There is great fear of retaliation or of not being believed.

The seven patients were chronically victimized women who were used to being disqualified. When women reporting rape have a psychiatric history, there are two ways they may be disqualified: a) if they have incorporated abuse into a delusion system, and b) if staff believes the patient is assuming a chronic victim role.

The defendant was convicted of the rape felony in a trial before a judge.

Rape While Paralyzed and Aphasic

In the following case, Vivian, at age 18, was discovered at home by her mother comatose from a bullet to the head. The shooting left her paralyzed and unable to speak. She spent four months of acute care hospitalization before being transferred for rehabilitative care. During this time, Vivian's mother states her daughter recovered to where she was able to walk down the hall with two restorative aides who simulated her walking. She was able to hold a small glass in her left hand and a fork, but still unable to move or speak by herself. She could move her eyelids and index finger on command. For 14 years, Vivian was cared for at a rehabilitative nursing center. During the 14th year, her mother noted her care deteriorating, that her glasses were always missing, and that she was not receiving oral hygiene care. The mother complained to the nursing supervisor that the male aides who always seemed to be attending her looked unprofessional by their long hair, jewelry, and loud, boisterous behavior.

One evening, when Vivian was 33, her mother received a telephone call from the nursing administrator who told her that Vivian was pregnant. In addition, the administrator said that whoever did it was probably already fired or quit, and there was no use to look for him; that Vivian did not try to fight because they had stripped her and found no bruises; that Vivian was so dehydrated they could hardly get enough urine to do a pregnancy test; and that Vivian's morning vomiting had not been connected to the pregnancy. Although Vivian was evaluated to be in the sixth month of her pregnancy, the administrator said she hoped the mother would choose an abortion as the way out of the situation, so it would not embarrass the nursing home, the mother, or Vivian.

A forensic review of nursing notes over a one-year period indicated withdrawn behavior, flat affect, sleep disturbance, night terrors, and depression. It was also noted that Vivian showed "fear in her eyes" when men approached her. A male activities director noted Vivian was shy and withdrawn when he visited and did not seem comfortable or secure around him and that she diverted eye contact. An investigation revealed that multiple men had sexually abused Vivian and DNA testing was sought to identify the father of the baby.

Diminished Awareness

There are situations in which a woman has diminished awareness of a rape due to an altered state of consciousness. This state can be due to having taken prescribed medications, being in a drugged state, injury or trauma to the head, or being asleep.

166

Rape During Sleep

Pam, a 39-year-old female, is sexually assaulted while sleeping by a staff person at a group home for the mentally ill. Pam had a substance abuse problem and at the time was serving a four-month sentence at the home through a house-arrest program. Pam reported the rape the next morning to another resident; four days later she reported it to staff. When questioned, Pam at first was equivocal. Ten days after she reported to staff, she escaped from the treatment program. She had several subsequent convictions for alcohol related crimes.

At the criminal trial, the defense attorney argued that all three charges of sexual assault (oral, digital, and vaginal penetration) were consensual. The first jury convicted for the first charge of oral sexual contact, agreeing that the victim was asleep during the early hours when the defendant entered her room. They acquitted on the second two charges stating there was no evidence that she resisted. On the second trial, expert testimony was given on the issues of delayed reporting, equivocal reporting, and the emotional disturbances typically experienced by rape victims.

The trial ended in a hung jury.

Case discussion: Sleep is an altered state of consciousness that has not been well researched in the area of trauma and its impact on what is remembered in terms of abuse. There is some research on sleep onset and its association with retrograde and antegrade amnesia. Wyatt, Bootzen, Anthony, and Bazant report on an experimental study in the June 1994 issue of *Sleep*. They studied memory recall in people asleep for 30 seconds and 10 minutes and found if people were asleep for 10 minutes and then they were awakened, they showed severe deficits in free recall presented to them just before they fell asleep. Those people who had not fallen asleep or slept only a matter of seconds did not show any problems in free recall. Although there was this difference in people who slept 10 minutes, those people had impaired deficits of explicit memory; however, for both those sleeping 10 minutes and 30 seconds, there was no difference in the implicit memory. The experiment was to examine the relationship between stages of sleep and memory was tested by auditory means.[2]

Rapid-eye-movement (REM) sleep has two distinct characteristics which could explain Pam's behavior in response to being raped during sleep. The threshold for arousal by environmental stimuli is increased during REM sleep making it the deepest stage of sleep by that criterion. Secondly, the active pattern of brain waves during REM sleep is coupled with a profound loss of muscle tone throughout the body. The skeletal muscles of the eyes, the middle-ear ossicles and the muscles of respiration are the only ones to escape generalized paralysis.[3] Thus she might not have awakened promptly and also might not have been able to resist the sexual assault.

Hypoxia During Rape

During a rape, victims may be physically injured and choked. The loss of oxygen to the brain, also known as hypoxia, can produce diminished memory and result in delayed reporting. This injury occurred in the following case of Gladys.

Gladys, age 19, was three months pregnant. Entering the elevator, she held the door for James, an acquaintance of her brother's, but an unknown man also entered and grabbed her from behind and began choking her neck in an arm hold. She struggled and lost consciousness. When she awoke she was on the roof landing. The unknown male was on top of her and James was pointing a gun at her. She remembers screaming, but not hearing herself. The unknown male told James not to shoot, that he was not finished. Gladys then passed out a second time. When she awoke the men were gone. Her clothes had been ripped off except for one pant leg. Her clothes were strewn about the area. She dressed feeling very dizzy, sore, and in shock. She walked down about 15 flights of stairs to her mother's apartment, who called the housing police and ambulance. Gladys was hospitalized for four to five days. Medical reports indicated she had trauma to the head with intracranial damage, a hematoma to her forehead, and a cerebral concussion with postconcussion syndrome. This syndrome was characterized by diminished and irregular reflexes, ataxia, equilibrium disturbance, severe pressure headaches, anxiety, nausea, confusion, depression, dizziness, apprehension, nervousness, and general debility. She had flashbacks to the rape and the gun pointed at her. She worried about damage to her unborn baby. She had rectal bleeding from an anal muscousal tear and needed further medical treatment for a sexually transmitted disease.

Gladys remembers the elevator and fighting on roof but doe not remember important information in-between these points. When conscious she is clear on what happens. She does not have repression or dissociation perhaps because she was knocked unconscious. Even though she was rendered unconscious for most of the assault, she understood the level of danger and terror. She can not retrieve information related to the fight and struggle for her life and of being overpowered. Although she had no memory of rape, DNA testing implicated James as one of her rapist.

Case discussion: Gladys suffered transient cerebral ischemia from being choked during her assault, which resulted is a temporary reduction in the blood supply to regions of her brain concerned with memory function. Transient cerebral ischemia can trigger transient global amnesia (TGA), which is characterized by sudden-onset anterograde amnesia, retrograde amnesia for recent events, and disorientation in time without loss of personal identity. The victim has insight into the memory disorder. She may also be suffering from posttraumatic amnesia associated with her concussion.

Head Injury During Gang Rape

In the following case, Lynn was delayed in reporting because she initially remembered something happening in a graveyard but not the full details of the rape. One year later, a series of environmental cues converged to increase her distress. Therapy revealed the following.

Lynn, a 19-year-old college coed, came into therapy because of "persistent thoughts about men chasing her in a graveyard, inability to concentrate, and declining self-confidence."[4] Lynn described sitting by a brook on a spring afternoon after a college class in a cemetery. She saw a brown car with three men driving and remembers hearing them yell, "Stay here, honey and we'll come back." She exited the area and next remembers being grabbed, falling backwards, and a man holding her arms. She then returned to campus, took a shower, and went to dinner at the college dining hall. She did not eat, but sat with friends and her boy friend. She was shaking and unable to respond when friends asked what was wrong. Later with her boyfriend she told him of the men in the graveyard chasing her. She asked him to stay the night.

Three months after the event, Lynn began to have repetitive nightmares about men chasing her; she started to feel less confident about herself. She had mood swings and crying spells; she lost weight. She began a sexual relationship with her boyfriend and went on birth control. She began experiencing severe headaches; she had difficulty concentrating; she lost interest in previously enjoyed activities.

One year later, the news media covered a highly publicized rape trial; she dropped a course in order to "think more." She began running again and had a flashback of someone grabbing her shoulder and turning her around. She was disturbed after the run and her boyfriend asked her what was wrong. She didn't know. The next day she met her boyfriend's parents and she felt very uncomfortable when she thought the father was looking at her legs. She traveled home for a semester break. She became upset on the airplane and was not able to read. At home, in the bathtub, she had a flashback of the graveyard. She had planned to visit New York with friends as a birthday present, but was unable to leave the house. She had the first cognitive thought that she might have been raped at the graveyard.

She returned to college but was irritable and cranky; the smallest thing upset her. She was unable to resume sex with her boyfriend. She began to worry that she could run into the men from the graveyard, that they might live in the town. She called her mother and the decision was for her to return home and begin therapy. She agreed to a course of time-limited trauma therapy that would be paced for her ability to tolerate distressing affects. The goal of therapy was to focus her attention to that "day in the graveyard." She had a 10-week leave from school.

Lynn had a full memory several days after the second session. She felt chilled during the memory. She also had a couple of bad days after the session. But the nightmares and a heavy feeling subsided.

On a return visit to the college, Lynn talked with the woman in charge of security at the college. Lynn felt other students should know there had been a rape; the security official did not agree. Lynn felt frustrated not to be able to pursue a legal route.

Case discussion: We do not understand the amount of amnesia with rape. Neurobiologically, intimidation hinders memory recall. Threat to life floods the noradrenergic system and triggers the opioid system, which causes amnesia or a poor encoding of information so that it is fragmented. Lynn remembers part of the rape information. Her sensory encoding is always present, but it is not linked to perceptual/cognitive system. In trauma therapy, the therapist tries to pull the material together so there is no fragmentation of memory. The person can be desensitized to the overwhelming reaction to the information. Experimental evidence exists showing that normal subjects exposed to traumatic stimuli have significant decrease in memory.[5]

Rape During Anesthesia

In the following case, Margaret, a 21-year-old single Catholic business woman, in consulting an orthodontist about braces, was told she first needed five teeth extracted. She made arrangements for the dental surgery. She remembers reading a magazine before her scheduled appointment, walking into a room with a dentist chair, and sitting in the chair. She then remembers lying on a couch in the recovery room, the dental assistant with his mouth on her breast, trying to insert his fingers into her vagina. Margaret grabbed at his hands and told him to stop. He said, "Let me do it," and his fingers went in. She saw the man's genitals were exposed. She then remembers the man lying on her and her trying to push him off. The dental assistant left and when he returned, said he needed to take another x-ray. He assisted her to the x-ray room, took the x-ray, and again put his hands on her breasts.

Margaret needed physical assistance to leave the dental office. She went home and took a nap. When she awoke she told her mother and father what had happened; the incident was reported to the police who arrested the dental assistant. The dentist denied such a crime could have been committed, saying, "Women often have sexual fantasies from the anesthesia."

Two weeks after this experience, Margaret's menstrual period was late; a pregnancy test was positive. She made the decision to have an abortion. DNA tests implicated the dental assistant. He pled guilty and was sentenced to jail.

Case discussion: Intravenous (IV) sedation is frequently used during oral surgery and IV midazolam is an established and effective method for producing the desirable effect of amnesia. The duration of amnesia produced by this technique is uncertain.[6] Other techniques used in oral surgery, such as general anesthesia, also produce amnesia for events during surgery. However, patients have been shown to have implicit memory of events during anesthesia.[7] Whether this patient received IV sedation or general anesthesia, it is certainly possible that she could have awakened at an unpredictable time resulting in the recollection of her assault. Her posttrauma symptoms could be magnified by any implicit memory of untoward events during her anesthesia.

Margaret's sleep and dreams are focal points for her posttrauma symptoms. The dreams show the attempt to process the fear and anxiety during sleep. Essentially, her disturbed sleep and dreams parallel the fact that she was put to sleep, and so she dreams about it rather than showing symptoms in everyday life. That is, she recalls the trauma in the form under which it happened.

Cognitive Dissonance

Cognitive dissonance is where the rape occurs in the context of a socially appropriate situation, but the relationship of victim to offender is one of subservience. Within this context, the perception of what is occurring is managed and controlled by the offender. The woman is confused because she senses something is wrong. These rape situations do not involve impaired cognitive processing or an altered state of consciousness; these situations relate to the context of the victimization and ones in which the woman is confused or unaware of the rules and procedures accompanying the context. Most often, these situations involve authority exploitation in which a doctor or therapist trades on his power to con the patient. The following is an example.

The Cream Treatment

A 50-year-old-woman went to her family doctor of over two years for symptoms related to her rheumatoid arthritis. The physician insisted on a breast and pelvic exam that extended to his rubbing a cream on her vulva and clitoris for over 30 minutes. The woman protested and told him she was embarrassed by what he was doing. He told her to stop acting like a child because she had an irritation and needed the treatment. The woman had an orgasm, and the physician immediately stopped and left the room. This woman later made a complaint to the police and when the physician's arrest was published in the local newspaper, 23 other women came forward with similar complaints about the cream treatment extending over an eight-year period. Some had been in his office for over an hour and were charged $165 for the treatment. These women were between the ages of 19 and 63. Their delayed reporting was due to denial, disbelief, and embarrassment.

The thrust of the physician's defense to the allegations was that the performance of a pelvic exam was indicated in all cases; that he performed a proper exam; that if he touched the patient in their clitoral area at all, such touching was fleeting and incidental; and that if he did massage ointment into their vulva area, such massage was indicated and not improper.

A report was written to answer questions raised by the disciplinary board in the areas of resistance, nonreporting, nondisclosure to family, returning to the physician, repeat exam, patient response, and physician profile.

Resistance: Why wouldn't a patient jump off the table, scream, or assault the physician, and otherwise push him off of her in these kind of cases? During a medical procedure of any type, for several reasons, patients rarely protest, interrupt, stop, or abruptly leave the presence of the physician without permission. First, persons in the presence of a medical authority figure generally assume a subordinate role and do what they are instructed. This behavior is based on a belief that the authority figure is trustworthy and operating on some standard procedure or practice. Second, persons being examined for a medical condition are often anxious and nervous about that condition and reluctant to interrupt behavior that is believed to be in their best interest for a diagnosis. Third, a gynecological examination renders a woman physically compromised. Patients are lying on their back, their legs are bent at the knee, and their feet are in stirrups. They are usually draped and cannot see what is going on. Additionally, there is usually concern and worry that something will be found that is serious and/or life-threatening, e.g., a tumor, cancer, or infection. Because women are in a vulnerable physical position, if the patient goes to move, the physician could control her by pushing his hands and fingers further into her body. The pelvic area contains very tender and sensitive tissue; this says nothing of the embarrassment and confusion felt by the patient. Generally, the patient can not believe she is being violated; rather, she believes the physician is "doing things for her own good."

Statements that the physician makes, such as "Don't move," or "I must continue," disrupts the patient's own reasonable thoughts as sensory information is being processed. Essentially, the person is trying to determine what is happening from a sense of touch and feel and cannot see the procedure. If there is any kind of natural sensory erotic response that comes from the procedure, as in this case, the patient is confused as to what is going on and is embarrassed. The woman questions: Is this being done to me on purpose, or am I having same kind of abnormal response to a treatment procedure because of where it is located?

In this case, none of the women exhibited overt behavior, such as jumping off the table, screaming, or assaulting the physician. Rather, although patients usually silently questioned aspects of the treatment, they either verbally protested or used a coping mechanism to get them through the procedure. Overt behavior was not taken because either the women trusted that he was conducting an ethical treatment or felt powerless to interrupt him. The women coped in various ways, such as protesting the start of the treatment, confronting the physician, or dissociating by reading a book.

Nonreporting: Why would a patient decline to report the incident to authorities? Reasons why a patient would decline to report the incident to authorities include their own confusion as to what happened puts them in the position of not knowing if the experience is reportable. Second, when they think about what they are going to report, their own appraisal of the information leaves them doubtful as to what people will make of it. For example, one woman called an attorney and was told not to report because authorities would probably take the physician's word over hers. Third, they may think they had an aberrant reaction to a legitimate physical exam, so they would be embarrassed saying something. Fourth, people often push distressing experiences out of their mind, yet remain sensitive to them.

As an example, one woman who thought the procedure was wrong first worried that she was the only one with this experience. She thought if she reported, either the procedure would be explained medically, or she would be told that she was exaggerating what had happened and that the reporting would be additionally humiliating. To check out her perceptions, she went to another gynecologist and found his examination was shorter with no manual stimulation and no intrusive questions about sex. When she had a yeast infection she was given a prescription with instructions to apply it herself. Thus she realized it was not her imagination, and she was not overreacting; the examination and procedure were not usual medical practice.

Nondisclosure to family: Why might a patient decline to report the incident to family members? Many of the reasons for not reporting to authorities apply to not reporting to family members. Also, the women are not sure of how to describe the situation and they are embarrassed. The only information the women have to process is that the examination was unnecessary, it was prolonged and, to same, had an erotic component. The women tended to cope with the experience by denying or dissociating the information. One woman confided in a nurse-friend, who told her the procedure was wrong.

Returning to the physician: Why a patient might return to the doctor for further medical care? Patients might return to the physician for several reasons. First, the gynecological care was only one part of their medical care from the physician. Many of the women had known him as being a popular physician; they believed he was trustworthy and that he would not lie to them, e.g., that he really saw a rash or irritation. This doctor was a family practitioner who treated the whole family. Thus, it was not just the woman who could reject him as a family doctor; rather, there were other family members to consider.

Repeat exam: Why a patient would allow him to perform another pelvic exam at a later date? There are several reasons why a patient would allow this physician to perform another pelvic examination. First, a pelvic examination often requires a follow-up for the condition of concern. The examination can be legitimized as a follow-up. Second, women need to have routine pelvic examinations. They have had gynecological examinations before and nothing happened. They may deny that it will happen again. Also, the nurse may be present during subsequent pelvic examinations or they may request her presence. Third, this experience was put in the context of a specific treatment. A pelvic examination does not necessarily mean a treatment procedure to the patient.

In one case, the doctor controlled the patient whose care required a pelvic examination every six months for prescribing contraception. He gave her free birth control pills so she returned. He insisted on the cream treatment due to an irritation. He gave her a prolonged treatment, but when it came time for the next birth control medication, she thinks that she judged him too quickly, so she returns. The second time the cream treatment is uncomfortable and he refused to stop. The third time he hurt her; she was in pain and embarrassed and decided she was not going to return. ("I wanted to get the hell out of there.")

Patient response: How do patients react? There are many reactions from patients to an unethical examination and procedure. First, is the betrayal of the trust between a physician and patient. Second, there is rage, humiliation, stigmatization, shame, and assault to one's self esteem. There is same self-questioning, e.g., "Why me?" or "What did I do?" Third, some women process the experience and determine that this is a bad physician and do not return. They do not report because the nature of the experience is not sufficiently graphic or definitive in their mind to stand up to investigative scrutiny. They are told it will be their word against the doctor.

In many cases, this doctor asked intrusive, sexually focused questions. The questioning was not done in a professional manner to elicit sexual functioning and assessment, if that was his intent. He asked during the examination or made some offhanded comments as she was leaving, rather than writing down her answers to his questions, while she was dressed and sitting in his office.

Several women became quite angry and upset at the procedure. One woman was unable to get the experience out of her mind. She sought validation of her suspicions and was able to put aside her distress and embarrassment and reported it.

Offender Profile: The profile of this physician, analyzed from the statements made by the women-witnesses, is of a doctor who gives the appearance of being a nice man who can be trusted and who is concerned about his patient. He works with his patients and cares medically for all members in a family. There is a family referral network by word of mouth, e.g., mothers refer their daughters to him.

Following the gynecological examination, he targets certain women to begin a cream treatment for a vaginal irritation that was not part of the patient's complaint. He proceeds to gain further control over these women when they protest the procedure by infantalizing them and telling them to be a good girl or not to be a sissy or a wimp. He then proceeds in his strategies of control to do an exploration of their sexual activity and behavior with partners. Next, he begins to manipulate control

175

over their sexual behavior external to the sessions through recommendations of when to have sex. He, in essence, becomes the director of their sexual activities. This then progresses in aggression, as noted in the women who report painful friction on the external genitalia, and his efforts to dominate and control. Another subtle aspect of his control is noted as he introduces the women to another procedure located downstairs from the medical office, e.g., massage. The boundaries are violated further by his seductive suggestion of activities in a hot tub.

Case discussion: Divided attention experiments, such as those performed by Larry Jacoby, demonstrate the acquisition and subsequent use of unconscious or implicit memory.[8, 9, 10] In this paradigm the patient has explicit memory of the expected events that occurred during the gynecological examination and treatment, but the unexpected and untoward events were not well attended and retained in implicit memory. These memories may remain implicit and exert their effect on conscious memory. Thus it may only be through a discussion with another patient with similar experiences that the true meaning of the implicit memory may come to the fore.

The profile of this type of interaction between a physician and a patient indicates a long standing pattern of misuses of professional activities for sexually dominant purposes that violate ethical and legal standards of practice in the physician-patient relationship.

Discussion

What characterized the delayed reporters?

- Psychotic women incorporated the rape into their delusional system, e.g., the offender had a romantic interest in them.
- Being aphasic and paralyzed did not prevent rape trauma symptoms of fear of men from being observed.
- DNA spoke for the women who could not remember the rape as they were unconscious.
- Memory presentation was fragmented, e.g., gaps in memory. Women felt confused. They knew something happened, but did not have full memory; they were disturbed by the fragmentation, but had no hesitation in reporting after one victim came forward.

How does delayed reporting interface with current research on memory, information processing, and the neurobiology of trauma? Memory is basic to reporting. The rape victim usually must be able to voice her experience. This requirement can be challenged in delayed reporting. To understand memory disruption, we outline how trauma impacts on the strategic areas of the brain that are central to memory. These areas of the brain involve the brain stem and the limbic system. Important to memory and emotion are the structures of the hippocampus and the amygdala.

Three major systems of the general response system operate to prepare us to respond to incoming information and information generated within ourselves and decide whether to respond in a self-defensive manner. The first circuit allows us to take in information, focus attention, and come to a general state of arousal and attention. The second circuit allows us to discern danger and to call upon our resources for immediate fight or flight. Combined in this behavioral alerting system is a second level of behavioral reaction that follows if the danger persists. Various forms of sugar are generated and passed on to the brain to sustain its work. In addition, a level of hormones is released in the brain that allow for longer-acting reactions to the dangerous situation. These hormones can remain active for hours if not days.

In a prolonged state of stress and danger, a third system is activated to reduce or inhibit the strong reaction which, if left unchecked, can exhaust and deplete the organism. This third circuit is a numbing circuit and releases natural opiates that numb the system and reduces sensitivity to pain.

The importance of these processes to memory and the recall or lack of memory of traumatic events is linked to the fact that the major systems for the structure and process of memory and emotional response as well as other vital functions, such as sleep, attachment, and emotional regulation, and learning, are located in the limbic system. Already mentioned is the hippocampus, which is a central structure to memory, both implicit and explicit memory, sometimes called the double mindedness of human memory,[11] and the connection with the amgydala, which is the center for emotional reactivity. In turn, through patterns of neuro-networking, the hippocampus communicates with the hypothalamus and pituitary connection to turn off the hormones released within the brain to sustain the organism in the face of life-threatening danger. The hippocampus sends the message that danger has abated or in the face of trauma, it does not send the message and after the trauma event is over, the hippocampus looses its effectiveness to accurately transmit and store information. The question in delayed reporting relates to the storing and retrieval of information.

William James, using introspective techniques to derive a multistore model of memory, divided memory into two storage compartments. Primary memory is the area where new experiences are temporarily stored and remain in the consciousness until they are either forgotten or pass into secondary memory. Information in secondary memory has to be retrieved to be used. According to James' schema, secondary memory is a large repository in which all of our acquired knowledge is permanently stored.[12]

Hebb advanced knowledge of memory by proposing that new information is initially a temporary trace within neurons which is consolidated into a permanent memory trace in the form of a cell assembly of interconnected neurons by an active process.[13] The amount of time it takes for consolidation to occur is controversial. Some physiologists believe that consolidation of memory occurs in seconds others, including Hebb, suggest that the process takes between 15 minutes and one hour. Once the permanent memory trace is formed, the information is in passive storage in that cell activity is no longer needed to retain the information. Hebb's view that structural changes in the pattern of synaptic connectivity are the mechanism of the storage of memory is still favored. The Hebbian mechanism of memory is capable of storing an adequate amount of information in the estimated 10 to the 13 power synapses contained in the brain as long as the basal metabolic rate of the brain is maintained to meet the energy requirements. Cases involving diminished awareness may fall into this physiologic explanation.

Memory systems are altered by gene representations that bias the cellular replacement in favor of cells that over function in avoidance responses. This avoidant or denial response can be noted in the cognitive dissonance case.

Memory research shows that memory is double minded. To quote Louis Tinnin, the double-mindedness of human memory is where the individual comprehends each experience from two fundamentally different points of view at the same time and stores the memories separately.[11] When he or she tries to remember past events only those memories that were verbally encoded ("explicit") can be retrieved. Nonverbal or "implicit" memory functions in parallel and is unavailable to conscious recall. Thus, we suggest that memory is reconstructed. Details can shift, but the event itself is consistent. With trauma, there is dissociation and a disconnection between thoughts, feelings, and behaviors. The information is encoded, but not consolidated. The person is not aware of external stimuli that occurred during stimuli. They do not make the connection between emotional arousal and state of distress to environmental cues. It is nonassociative or implicit memory. When people are in an altered state, e.g., medication/sedation, brain injury, or sleep, it is expected there will be memory impairment. To quote van der Kolk, the memories are in the body.[14] The person feels anxious and distressed; memory is not consolidated enough for free recall. The memory comes back fragmented as if it is happening; information has registered, but it is not recalled in a knowing way. Research suggests the implicit memory cells involved in cognitive processing is damaged or destroyed and that interrupts behavior and affect.

References

1 Brownmiller S. *Against Our Will: Men, Women, and Rape.* New York, NY: Simon Schuster; 1975;16-21.

2 Wyatt JK, Bootzin RR, Anthony J, Bazants S. Sleep onset is associated with retrograde and anterograde amnesia. *Sleep.* 1994;7:502-511.

3. Kelly DD. Sleep and dreaming. In: Kandel ER, Schwartz JH, Jessell TM, eds. *Principles of Neural Science.* 3rd ed. Norwalk, CT: Appleton Lange; 1991.

4. Burgess AW, Hartman CR. Rape trauma and posttraumatic stress disorder. In: McBride A, Austin J, eds. *Psychiatric Nursing: Integrating the Behavioral and Biological Sciences.* Philadelphia, PA: WB Saunders; 1995

5. Kramer TH, Buckhout R, Fox P, Widman E. Effects of stress on recall. *Appl Cognitive Psychol.* 1991:5:483-488.

6. Ho ET, Parbrook DM, Still DM, Parbrook EO. Memory function after IV midazolam or inhalation of isoforane for sedation during dental surgery. *Br J Anesth.* 1990;64:337-340.

7. Ghoneim MM, Block R. Learning and consciousness during general anesthesia. *Anesthes.* 1992;76:279-305.

8. Jacoby LL, Lindsay SD, Toth JP. Unconscious influences revealed: attention, awareness, and control. *Am Psychol.* 1992;47:802-809.

9. Ste-Marie DM, JacobyLL. (1993). Spontaneous versus directed recognition: the relativity of automaticity. *J Exp Psychol: Learn Memory Cogn.* 1993;19:777-788.

10. Allen SW, Jacoby LL. Reinstating study context produces unconscious influences of memory. *Memory Cogn.* 1990;18:270-278.

11. Tinnin L. The double-mindedness of human memory. International Society of Traumatic Stress Studies StressPoints. 1994;3.

12. James W. Association. In: Anderson JA, Rosenfeld E, eds. *Neurocomputing Foundations of Research.* Cambridge, M: MIT Press; 1988:4-14.

13. Hebb DO. The first stage of perception: Growth of the assembly. In: Anderson JA, Rosenfeld E, eds. *Neurocomputing Foundations of Research.* Cambridge, M: MIT Press; 1988:45-56.

14 van der Kolk BA. *Psychological Trauma.* Washington, DC: American Psychiatric Press; 1987.

Reprinted with permission from the *Journal of Psychosocial Nursing*, Slack, Inc. Burgess AW, Fehder WP, Hartman CR. Delayed Reporting of the Rape Victim. *J Psychosoc Nurs.* 1995;33(9):21-29.

Chapter 20 – Mental Retardation Compounds Rape Trauma

Ann Wolbert Burgess, DNSc, Theodore Babbitt, Esq, and Louis Ballezzi, Esq.

People with mental retardation experience sexual abuse in the same settings as most other victims – at home, school, and work. Unlike most other victims, however, their statements of abuse may be easier to try to discredit, and the psychological distress associated with experiences of rape and sexual assault may be harder to document due to their limited communication skills. Also, unlike most victims, except the elderly and persons with an acute mental illness, they are likely to reside in an institution.

This report cites two separate cases of civil litigation involving mentally retarded persons. In both cases, the women tested as functioning at about the same mental levels; one was living at home and one was institutionalized. In both cases, officials at the agency where the assailants were employed denied the rape accusations until convincing evidence was provided for a criminal conviction.

Case 1: Jane Doe

Jane Doe is a 24-year-old African-American woman who has a verbal IQ of 55, a performance IQ of 58, and a full-scale IQ of 54, which places her in the moderately mentally retarded range. Her mental age is equal to that of a five- to seven-year-old child. Testing further indicated her relative strength in her visual attention to detail of known objects as seen on picture completion tests. Particular weakness was seen in her general fund of information, her ability to deal with basic abstract concepts, and common sense judgment based on visual cues.

Jane Doe lived at home with her parents. An older brother lived out of state. Jane was in special education classes until she graduated at age 21. Since that time she has worked in a sheltered workshop folding boxes. Her mother has carefully monitored her life, and she socializes primarily with family.

181

In April 1995, Jane Doe accompanied her mother to Good Samaritan Hospital in West Palm Beach to visit her uncle. A security guard, hired by a major outside security company, saw Jane talking to herself and recognized that she was retarded. He went to the nurse caring for the uncle and asked permission for the mother to go into the treatment area to visit the uncle; thereby, leaving the daughter in the emergency room unattended. He struck up a conversation with Jane Doe, asking her if she was thirsty and if she would like some orange juice. He went to the mother and asked her permission to get her daughter some orange juice. He told Jane Doe that her mother had given permission to go with him to get orange juice and took her to the basement where he sexually assaulted her.

Jane Doe returned to the emergency room in an obviously disheveled condition and refused to tell her mother what had happened until they were on their way home taking the uncle back to his house. Her mother immediately stopped a police officer, they returned to the hospital, and the guard was confronted by the police. At first he denied that anything had happened until his semen was found on the floor at the site of the assault, and then admitted what he claimed was consensual sex. He subsequently pled guilty to the crime of sexual assault of a person with diminished intelligence and was sentenced to eight years probation with the first two years spent under house arrest.

Failure to Properly Screen Employees

The guard had been hired four months before by a company who accepted contracts at a price much lower that those at competing security companies. They pay their guards very little and their screening was abominable. The evidence showed that this guard had been arrested three times for violent assaults in Texas. On his very first day making application for the job, he told the receptionist that he had been in trouble in Texas, and she thought he appeared to be on drugs. This was never followed up on by anyone. On the same day, on being told that he was going to work for one company instead of another, for no apparent reason, he had a near violent fit. The head of personnel advised the manager not to hire him, but he was hired anyway. Within a few days, when he came in to be fitted for his uniform, he appeared with a woman who looked obviously beaten. When the office manager was told that office personnel suspected that the guard had done the beating, his only response was "she probably deserved it."

The screening that was done was supposed to include a complete criminal check. The guard's criminal background was not found because even though a social security verification showed that he used a different name while in Texas, that name was never used in trying to obtain his criminal record. Had it been properly checked out, the guard company would have found that of the three violent assaults, there were still two warrants outstanding for his arrest in Texas because he had fled the jurisdiction to avoid prosecution.

During his four-month employment, he, at one time, reported seeing a spaceship and hid under a desk all night because he was afraid of it. On another occasion, he made an indecent statement that he missed work because he had oral sex on the beach with his girlfriend and contracted strep throat. Just three days before the sexual assault on Jane Doe, he was seen in the parking lot of the hospital, while in uniform, having a sexual encounter with a woman whom he described as his wife's 17-year-old niece. This case involved a claim that this guard should never have been hired and should have been fired long before the event.

Posttrauma Symptoms of Retarded Victim

Jane Doe suffered classic post trauma symptoms of recurrent nightmares where she would see her assailant at the foot of her bed, difficulty sleeping, crying spells, headaches, intrusive thoughts, and fear of the offender and of men in general. Her mother noted changes in her appearance, that she needed to be reminded to dress neatly, and had more memory problems, e.g., when asked to bring a tissue brings soap. She developed a quick temper and was easily frustrated, e.g., she would be doing her puzzle book and suddenly tear pages out of it. While doing dishes at night, she would talk the entire time in language not understood by anyone. She also would sit on the couch tying and untying her shoelaces for long lengths of time. She would spend more time alone in her room and would continually ask her mother why the man did what he did to her. She began counseling within a month of the assault with a psychologist expert in both areas of mental retardation and rape trauma. One question Jane raised with her therapist was her concern that her assailant would be able to simply remove the electronic bracelet he was wearing and go right back to the hospital and rape someone else. She worried a long time with that question before asking. When she was reassured that he would be unable to remove the bracelet without authorities becoming aware of his actions, she was visible more relaxed.

Case 2: June Doe

June Doe is a 37-year-old woman of Italian ethnicity, who has an IQ in the mid-50s which places her in the moderate mentally retarded range. Her mental age is of a six-year-old; testing indicates her reading and comprehension to be about first grade.

Although June has lived at various institutions for the mentally retarded, she came home most weekends and holidays. She has an older sister who described her behavior prior to the known time of the abuse as being able to do projects, took classes, enjoyed dances, participated in the special Olympics, and would return willingly to residential care. She participated in swimming, ball throwing, and the 40-meter dash; she was fondly called Miss Congeniality.

In the early 1980s, June Doe first made reference to sexual abuse when she was home for a weekend and watching her mother make bread dough. At one point, she spontaneously said that the dough looked like a specific staff member's bottom and genitals. Several months later, the sister, who was pregnant, said June commented to her that she was going to have a baby, too; that this staff person was her boyfriend, called her his queen bee, cared for her, and bought her ice cream.

These statements prompted the sister to meet with the institution's administrator to report this information. However, he dismissed it as fantasy; said that it was not true; that June was a funny bunny with a creative imagination; that she was at the age when such thoughts are in her mind or that she wanted to be pregnant like her sister. The sister then went to talk to June's teacher who also dismissed the allegation as a phase the students go through; that none of it was thinkable that it would have happened; that it was her imagination; and that she was lovable and making it up.

The sister then moved away for several years. Upon her return, the sister said that June started talking about the staff member again, stating he was her boyfriend, bought her ice cream, and still did those things to her. June said that he would take off her belt and pull her pants down and push her against the wall. June would demonstrate sexual positions by placing her hands on the wall, bending her elbows, flexing, and saying that the man would be behind her. She also reenact the sexual position on the floor by lying face down or bending over like a dog. June said he would tell her to "get in the position" and "be like a dog." June also told her sister that she did not want to go back to the home because "you get babies there". June also said that the man took her to various rooms and would play with the lights, e.g., turning them off. According to June, other students had things put in their mouth, and "you have to cooperate and be quiet and keep it a secret."

The parents scheduled a meeting with officials who acted dismayed at accusations made about the staff member, saying that such things do not happen at their institution and that there is close supervision of residents. The parents were told not to listen to their daughter and were admonished in that they were hurting the employee's reputation, and name and that they would have to live with the guilt of saying such things. The parents were also told to pray to God so that these comments and actions would end.

Discrediting of Retarded Victim

June's descriptions of the sexual abuse did not end, but rather the accusations continued to be consistent and became more graphic. Another meeting was scheduled at the institution. Again the parents were told that the employee was a good person and not to listen or pay attention to June. The institution made a long list of damaging speculations: that June was fantasizing, that she had dreams of men, that she probably wanted something like this to happen, and that she had seen the parents in sexual positions or watched a television show. They said such an accusation was absurd, that it was a shame to accuse the institution of such a thing, and that there had never been such complaints. Officials discredited, belittled, and demeaned June; they turned the question back to the parents and asked why would the employee have picked June as she was a blabbermouth and not even pretty.

The mother felt embarrassed and ashamed after her meetings with officials believing they were the experts on mental retardation; they continued to provoke guilt and further doubt in the parents over their daughter. The mother followed their advice and told June to stop talking about the employee. June became more upset; she would cry, scream, and hyperventilate; she repeatedly said it was true. One employee witnessed a confrontation in the early 1980s where another employee pulled June aside to ask if "she was going to tell that story again." After June said no, the employee told June he "did not want to hear her talk like that again."

June's outcries and outbursts to protest the abuse were attempts to reengage herself with her parents and have them believe her. This did not occur until 1993 when officials came to the family home to say June had been sexually abused by the employee who had confessed to sexually abusing 15 female residents. The mother said she was too heart broken to absorb everything told her.

Results of Prolonged Abuse

June's symptoms were consistent with a severe posttrauma response. The sexual abuse also had a compounding effect on June's prior vulnerable central nervous system organization. This condition was further compromised by the neurobiological changes associated with the prolonged sexually abuse. The trauma also affected her relationships with members of her family. She had to deal with the fact that she was not believed and that the abuse was not stopped after her first report in 1980. In addition, June was denied treatment for the posttraumatic stress disorder she developed from the sexual abuse.

Effects on Retarded Victim's Parents: When June's parents discovered that their daughter was telling the truth and was damaged by their disbelief, the mother became profoundly depressed and withdrew from family gatherings and working at the family store as she could no longer face extended family members or customers who would ask about June. A serious breach of confidence existed in the primary relationship between June and her parents. The protective loving bond was ruptured, and June became isolated. The suffering of their daughter caused a significant psychological burden that seriously affected the parents marital relationship as well as personal life.

Ease of Discrediting Retarded Victim: The offender noted the ease in discrediting a mentally retarded person. In his confession, he cited places, times, and positions used in abusing June. He explained that he used his knowledge of mental retardation for the selection of victims and to confuse his victims in order to discredit their statements. He also manipulated professionals into minimizing or denying the misconduct or in viewing the behavior as seduction rather than forced and repeated abuse. With June, he traded on her inability to accurately recall detail so it would look like her story was untrue.

Chapter 21 – The Dorothy System and Nursing Home Rape

Ann Wolbert Burgess, DNSc, and David T. Marks, Esq

On April 14, 1998, Texas Health Enterprises, Texas' largest nursing home operator, agreed to pay $4.65 million to the estate of a partially paralyzed woman who was repeatedly sexually abused by a male nurse's aide while bathing or changing her. This agreement was reached days after the company was found grossly negligent and ordered to pay the woman's estate $2.75 million for pain and suffering and mental anguish. Texas Health Enterprises, based in Denton, TX, operates 109 facilities in Texas, including one in Midland, TX, where the woman was a patient. The nursing home's parent company, HEA Management Group, Inc., also was named in the suit, Fough v. Texas Health Enterprises, Inc., No. 95-40847-362 (Denton County, TX District Court).

Dorothy Cooper was only 62 when in January 1991, she suffered a stroke that subsequently resulted in her admission to a nursing home. She also suffered with diabetes, hypertension, and glaucoma. Dorothy, although incontinent, requiring total assistance with dressing and transferring, and confined to a wheelchair, in the first two years at the nursing home was reported to be social and interactive with the nursing staff, able to feed herself, and alert and clear in speech. However, by June, 1993, Dorothy had had hospital admissions for acute bronchitis, chest pain, cystitis, and dehydration, and a diagnosis of presenile dementia was made.

Mistaken Criminal History Searches and Training Abuses

In 1991, Johnny Gordon, a 33-year-old, six-foot, 200-pound man with a criminal history and an outstanding health warrant for gonorrhea, applied to be a nurse's aide at the Texas Health Enterprises facility in Odessa, Texas. Under state law, the facility was required to request a criminal history, which it did, mistakenly classifying him as a female. Searched in state records as a female, the name came up clear of any criminal history. He was hired. Three weeks later he was fired by the assistant director of nurses for slapping a frail and helpless 87-year-old female patient repeatedly.

After some period of time in Kansas, Gordon returned to Texas and in October 1992 applied at another Texas Health Enterprise Facility, Terrace West, in Midland, TX. The required criminal check was done, but the facility submitted a handwritten form to authorities with what looked to be the name of Johnny Cordon. Searched as such in state records, the name came up clear of any record. Again, he was hired by the company. Instead of enrolling him in the required 80-hour nurse's aide training course, he was placed immediately in patient contact, despite a state law requiring that any nurse's aide not receiving certification within 120 days must be removed from patient contact.

Finally, in late May 1993, Terrace West was cited for a training deficiency and directed to enroll uncertified nurse aides, including Gordon, in a registered nurse aide training and competency evaluation program. As a consequence, Gordon was required to attend the course at yet another sister facility, Terrace Gardens, in Midland (Terrace West had been disqualified and prohibited by the State from giving the course due to its record of bad care practices). Under the law, the training facility was required to do a criminal history check. They failed to do so. The administrator testified that they routinely did not do the required check. During the course, a substitute trainer was needed, and the chosen substitute was none other than the assistant director of nurses who had previously fired him for patient abuse. She recognized Gordon and reported him to the administrator of the training facility as well as her own supervisor. Nothing was done.

Despite the fact that as of June 15, 1993, Gordon was recognized and known by the company to be a patient abuser, he was assigned for the next month to provide care to helpless female residents, including the provision of showers and perennial care. Company policy required a female to be present during all female patient showers. However, policy was ignored, and Gordon often gave showers without a female present.

Discovery of Sexual Abuse

In July 1993, evidence from medical records indicated that Gordon had been sporadically sexually abusing Dorothy Cooper. On July 20th, while in the shower stall, Gordon brutally raped her twice with a shower head, then returned her to her bed. There he relieved himself sexually spilling his fluids across her body.

It was this substance (reported as a creamy light, green tinted substance on top of and in between Dorothy's vaginal area that appeared to look and smell like semen) that alerted nurse's aides who reported to the nursing supervisor. But this observation was ignored. Testimony indicated the nursing supervisors left for lunch and to shop for wallpaper. The two aides then reported their findings to a charge nurse who went to Dorothy's room, did a visual check, decided it was a vaginal infection, and called the physician who ordered Monostat suppositories. The aides, still concerned, demanded that the director of nursing call the police. Dorothy was taken to a hospital emergency room where a sexual assault examination revealed bruising to her left thigh and vaginal area that was tender to touch with a brown mucous discharge. She resisted an internal pelvic examination.

Johnny Gordon was arrested, pled guilty to the charges, and was sentenced to five years in prison. Tragically, Gordon's sexual abuse was not confined to the date of July 20, 1993. In May 1993, nursing notes indicated dramatic changes in Dorothy's behavior. She was withdrawing from staff, locking her legs in the bed rails, screaming at night as if having a nightmare, and refusing personal care. Significantly, there was no evidence of this behavior at any time prior to the period of May to July 20, 1993. Additionally, trichomonas was noted in a lab report in May 1993.

Dorothy Cooper lived only one year following the discovery of her sexual assaults. In September 1993, she was transferred, without a discharge care plan for sexual assault, to another nursing home where her sister was a resident. Her posttrauma symptoms of anxiety and agitation went ignored. She complained of lower back pain and leg pain, would cry out and moan, state she was cold, had difficulty eating and sleeping, and had chronic vaginal infections.

The Trial

Trial evidence established that the defendant was negligent in hiring Gordon by 1) failing to check job references, 2) ignoring a two-year gap in his employment history, 3) failing to verify Gordon's nurse's aide certification status with the state of Texas and the state of Kansas, and 4) failing to submit the criminal history checks required under law. It was undisputed that Gordon had previously served time in the penitentiary for felony crimes, which made him ineligible for employment in a nursing home.

Expert testimony on the nature and duration of mental anguish was given. A clinical specialist in psychiatric nursing, testifying for plaintiff, testified that the traumatic nature of the abuse was a permanent injury due, in part, to the posttrauma symptoms and the daily reminders of the assaults that were prompted by bathing and personal care. A defense psychiatrist testified that he thought it was a short-term, upsetting situation, but did not believe that it persisted over a long period of time because her memory was impaired by then due to the vascular dementia; that perhaps it bothered her for two to three weeks.

Jurors found that Denton-based Texas Health Enterprises and its parent company, Health Enterprises Management, Inc., were negligent and that Texas Health Enterprises showed gross negligence.

The Settlement

The settlement agreement requires Texas Health Enterprises to institute a system that will allow them to identify employees fired for abusing or neglecting patients from sister facilities and to make a good faith effort to identify persons already in the system who fall into that classification. All new hires will be checked against the list. Although not required by the settlement, it was strongly suggested that the cross-check system be named, "The Dorothy System," after Ms. Cooper. Dorothy's husband had died just after she entered the nursing home, and she had no children. The heirs to her estate are nieces and nephews. They joined together in an agreement contributing a significant portion of the award to the National Citizens' Coalition for Nursing Home Reform based in Washington, DC.

Chapter 22 – School Harassment Case

B. Joyce Dale, Esq, and Ann W. Burgess, DNSc

There are a number of cases being brought charging a hostile sexual environment in a school setting. One recent case in the Eastern District of Pennsylvania illustrates the difficulty a jury had in applying the law.

In denying the William Penn School District's (WPSD) motion to dismiss, the district court ruled that Title VII (e.g., hostile environment employment situation), was the appropriate analogue for determining the elements that a Plaintiff must prove in order to prevail in a Title IX hostile environment sexual harassment claim. At trial, however, the court instructed the jury that they must find that the school district knew of the sexual harassment and intentionally failed to take proper remedial measures because of the plaintiff's sex. However, it is well established that in a Title VII claim, liability for hostile environment sexual harassment is found when an employer knew, or should have known, of the sexually hostile environment and failed to take prompt and adequate remedial action. To require the Plaintiff to prove intentional discrimination because of her sex, essentially suggests that a Title IX standard gives school districts absolute immunity against Title IX hostile environment sexual harassment claims.

Facts of the Case

Plaintiff Kellie, a special education student in the William Penn School District, alleged that she was repeatedly subjected to sexual harassment by male students over the course of three academic years. The sexual harassment took the form of offensive language and innuendo, sexual propositions, and threats of physical harm. Kellie testified that in eighth grade in Penn Wood West Junior High School, rowdiness, name calling and cursing, and offensive references to student's mothers as whores, were common occurrences in her special education classroom. Kellie further testified that she and other students in eighth grade reported this conduct to a school guidance counselor. Toward the end of the eighth grade, Kellie testified that "sex things came up," including crude sexual invitations, such as "Let me take you home and have sex with you" and "Jerk me off." Kellie further stated that when the boys would say these things to her, she would curse at them, and then she would be suspended from school. She also testified that other students in the class heard these taunts, and she assumed the teacher heard them, too. Kellie and the one other girl in her class reported to a teacher that the boys were calling them names and asked for his help.

Kellie's father testified that toward the end of eighth grade he learned of the above-described sexual misconduct from a neighbor to whom Kellie had disclosed. As a result, when he signed and returned her educational plan for the ninth grade, he notified the school district of his concern about the school's plan to place Kellie in a classroom of all boys for ninth grade.

Nevertheless, in ninth grade, Kellie was placed in a classroom with all boys, including the boys who had sexually harassed her the previous year. In this all-male environment, the harassment of Kellie escalated. This harassment was frequently sexual in nature. It included sexual propositions and language, such as "Want me to take you home and fuck you"; "Jerk me off"; "Come on, Kellie, you know you fucking want my dick;" and "Give me head." Kellie testified that these crude and offensive comments were directed to her every day during ninth grade and affected her ability to concentrate in school. Because of a vision problem, Kellie should have been seated in the front of the classroom in order to gain the maximum benefit from her learning environment. However, she testified that she would often sit in the back of the room to escape the sexual harassment of the boys. Although the school district claimed they had no notice of this sexually hostile learning environment, the school disciplinary records of two boys confirms that school officials directly observed at least some of this offensive conduct.

In late September 1995, Kellie was suspended from school for saying to another student, "Get away from me, you nasty ass." Kellie came home from school crying and upset and complained to her father that she was tired of being suspended when she responded angrily to the sexual taunts of the boys. Her father went to the school and complained to the principal that Kellie was being sexually harassed by the boys in her classroom. The father testified that when he asked if the principal intended to reprimand the boys, he was told no. The principal then took Kellie's father to see the school guidance teacher where he again reported that his daughter was being harassed in school. They replied they would look into it, but the father testified he heard nothing further from them. In October 1995, the father wrote a letter to the school district, again complaining that his daughter was being sexually harassed by the boys in her class and pleading for help from school officials. Later that month, the father had to go to the school because Kellie has been suspended again. On that occasion, the father and a friend met with the guidance counselor and principal and again told them that Kellie was continuing to be sexually harassed by the boys in her class. The father testified that the response of these school officials was dismissive – "Well, they're boys." At the end of October, Kellie met the with school psychologist to whom she reported the continuing sexual harassment and who made note of such in his report. The father also testified that after that meeting he attended another meeting with additional school officials, where he again complained of Kellie's sexual harassment at school. The school officials who attended this meeting signed a Comprehensive Evaluation Report, dated December 7, 1995, wherein they acknowledged that Kellie had reported the sexual harassment. During a routine visit in November 1995 from her itinerant vision teacher, an employee of the Delaware County Intermediate Unit, Kellie disclosed that she was being sexually harassed by the boys in her class. When the vision teacher reported this to an official in the WPSD, the school guidance counselor said he was aware of the problem and was working on it.

However, the school took no corrective action other than to suggest Kellie transfer to another school across town or to a vocational school, an alternative Kellie and her father believed was too dangerous. The father testified that Kellie continued to complain to him about the sexual harassment at school during ninth grade and, at one point, even considered allowing Kellie to leave school when she reached age 16 so that she could escape the sexual harassment. When the father informed the guidance counselor of this plan, the guidance counselor wrote to the father and expressed concern that Kellie was seriously depressed and suffering from extremely low self-esteem due to the problems she was having at school. The school, although obviously aware of the sexually harassing environment, as well as the emotional toll on Kellie, took no adequate action to remove Kellie or the offending boys from the increasingly dangerous situation.

By May 1996, the climate in Kellie's classroom had deteriorated to such an extent that, on May 21, 1996, while a substitute teacher was in charge of the classroom and the class was watching a movie in a darkened room, one of the boys in the classroom exposed his penis to Kellie and a second boy grabbed her breast. Kellie and a male classmate ran from the classroom and went to the school guidance counselor's office. Before they could tell him what had happened, he told them to get out of his office. Following this assault, Kellie's father refused to allow her to attend school for the remainder of the school year.

Kellie has just recently completed tenth grade at the high school in WPSD. In tenth grade she continued to be sexually harassed, although not as frequently or severely. This sexual harassment was also reported to school officials. During the 1996-1997 school year, WPSD contracted with a counselor through Life Guidance Services, who conducted group counseling sessions in Kellie's classroom, with Kellie in attendance, without permission from her father. Over the weeks, the sexual comments and innuendo grew so out of control that even the counselor was offended. Kellie finally walked out of the classroom when the boys began to ask crude questions of the counselor, such as had "he ever jerked off or had sex with prostitutes."

As a consequence of the indifference of WPSD to the plight of Kellie, she suffered serious emotional distress. She was diagnosed as suffering chronic posttraumatic stress disorder, having symptoms of depression, feeling socially isolated and inferior to her peer group, and having suicidal thoughts. She also suffered loss of educational opportunity. Tellingly, when Kellie was evaluated for classroom placement in March 1987, her overall IQ was reported to be 99, well within average range. However, when she was evaluated during the 1995-1996 school year, the year when the sexual harassment seriously escalated and she was sexually assaulted, her IQ was reported to be 77, described in the report as low-average to borderline level of intelligence.

Charge to the Jury

The Plaintiff's case was brought for action under a law known as Title IX. That statute provides that: No person in the United States shall, on the basis of sex, be excluded from participation in, be denied the benefits of, or be subjected to discrimination under any education program or activity receiving Federal financial assistance.

Sexual harassment of students can be a form of discrimination prohibited by Title IX.

The Plaintiff claims that she was subjected to a sexually hostile educational environment in the William Penn School District. In order to establish this claim under Title IX, the District court judge in his charge to the jury said the plaintiff must prove each and every one of the following six elements by a preponderance of the evidence –

1) She was a member of a protected group
2) She was subject to unwelcome sexual harassment
3) The harassment was because of sex

4) The harassment was sufficiently severe or pervasive so as to alter the conditions of her education and create an abusive educational environment
5) A reasonable student in the plaintiff's position would find harassment sufficiently severe and pervasive so as to create an abusive educational environment
6) The School District knew of the harassment and intentionally failed to take proper remedial measures because of the plaintiff's sex

Jury Verdict

Before the jury rendered its decision, the eight-member panel asked US District Judge Harvey Bartle III if its verdict could be accompanied by a statement. Bartle told the jury its legal obligation was to render a verdict first, after which jury members were welcome to make an informal statement.

The jury had earlier asked for an explanation of Bartle's instruction on how to prove a violation of Title IX. Bartle said the girl needed to show the district "knew of the harassment and intentionally failed to take prompt and adequate remedial action because of her sex." That instruction proved to be the linchpin in the school district's victory.

The day after the verdict was delivered, a jury member contacted the Plaintiff's attorney and said they had been stuck on the sixth element, that they did not understand the instruction for the sixth element, and that all but one juror were willing to find the school district liable. However, one juror refused to find the school district liable because he felt the plaintiff did not prove the school district intentionally discriminated because of sex.

In an appeal, Plaintiff's attorneys will be urging the court to adopt Title VII for institutional liability, that is, that an institution is liable for a sexually hostile school environment if the school knew, or should have known, of the sexually hostile environment and failed to take prompt and adequate remedial action.

Chapter 23 – Memory Presentation of Childhood Sexual Assault

Ann W. Burgess, Carol R. Hartman, and Timothy Baker

A first-grade teacher at an American-sponsored European school for military dependants wrote the following end-of-the-year summary on one of his seven-year-old students:

Jim is a bright, inquisitive, and highly verbal boy who can display an insightful interest in subjects at times. This interest is very erratic. When Jim loses track of what is occurring around him, he can become intensely focused upon some physical activity. These activities sometimes consist of pulling a foot up under himself and rocking or taking some small objects (a crayon, eraser, piece of string, a rock, etc.) and manipulating it.

When Jim becomes involved in one of these activities, he becomes completely unaware of his surroundings and is unable to take in oral directions, particularly for a switch of the class activity. Failure to take in directions initially often results in his being out of step or hurriedly trying to catch up with classmates.

An area of major concern during the year has been Jim's marked indifference to his own misbehavior. Several serious incidents resulted in sustained denial that continued in the face of overwhelming evidence of Jim's playground misbehaviors were attributed to the actions of others, but he was unable to see his own fault or modify his behaviors.

While I see a great deal of potential in Jim, I am very concerned that his failure to maintain focus puts him at risk of underachieving academically and that his physical actions and lack of remorse for misbehaviors will be detrimental for his personal growth and social skills formation. It is my hope that in his new school/community Jim will be able to get some assistance in overcoming these barriers to his progress.

What would account for Jim's presentation of unfocused attention and misbehavior? With the current news media attention on "repressed memories" and "false memory syndrome," few therapists would suspect or dare to suggest to parents any connection between Jim's current symptoms and a past traumatic event. But that is precisely what is proposed in this article; that indeed, some of Jim's school behaviors derive from a three-month traumatic episode that occurred five years before and that he, at age seven, has repressed that verbal memory. Such rationale lies in the current research on traumatic memory research and very early childhood abuse. Jim is part of a prospective study of children's memory processes and presentation following documented extrafamilial childhood abuse.

Method

While many studies of traumatic memories have been retrospective,[1] we have the opportunity to follow the natural presentation over time of childhood traumatic memories in a sample of children. Periodically, the parents of the children are interviewed.

The objective for this clinical project was to classify the children's recollections of what happened to them. Using a conceptual framework based on neurobiology of trauma and information processing,[2,3] memory research and encoding of declarative or procedural memory,[4] and psychodynamic theory that suggests past experiences can be presented through words, images, and physical symptoms as well as behaviors of reenactment and repetition,[5] a four-dimensional model was devised to classify children's memory processes as somatic, behavioral, verbal, and visual. This model summarizes how memory presentations were made by children at three different points in time and allows for establishing if there were alterations, elaboration, or dropping out of these means of presenting memories about abuse experience.

A decision was made as to the presence or absence for each of the four levels of memory by three independent raters. Agreement between two or three of the raters provided the rating. The sensory and behavioral memories were classified through parent verbal report for disclosure interview and verbal and symptom checklist for second and third interview. The verbal and visual memories were classified from child information at the time of each interview.

Day Care Sample

Information on 34 physically, psychologically, and sexually abused children from three separate groups was documented over three separate time periods. The abuse was validated through court martial proceedings in one case and civil settlements in all three cases. One of the authors (AWB) evaluated 24 of the 34 children for the civil suits.

The families were of similar socioeconomic background. Eighty-two percent of the children were Caucasian and 12% were Black. Sixty percent of the children were female and 40% were male.

Group A includes 10 children. At the time of initial disclosure interview in 1983, seven children were two and under and three were under five. The average age was 2.6. The Center provided a range of services, including day care and drop-off care. Multiple children made accusations of ritualistic abuse against a male teacher who was also a high priest of a satanic sect and his wife. Children reported group sexual activities with other children and with a doll; playing "games" in bed; and being brought to a house with a black room where sexual activities of an occult nature ensued. Fondling and penetrating sexual acts were reported by the children as well as threats to themselves or their parents if they told.[6]

Group B includes eleven children. At the time of the initial disclosure interview in 1984, the average age of the children was 2.7 years. Five children were under the age of two; five more children were between 2.7 years and 4.5 years old, and one child was six years old. The youngest child was three months old. Children had been in the Center from three months to two and half years before abuse disclosure.

The children were cared for at a free-standing facility that hired a variety of people to care for the children. The program was extended as a drop-off center for school age children in the afternoon. Three perpetrators (two women and one man) were named and several locations cited for where the abuse occurred: (1) at the Center, the nursery, the utility room, the bathroom and play yard; and (2) outside of the Center, a van that took them to a school and a house. Four children reported that masks and black robes were worn by the perpetrators. Objects such as pencils and fingers were used to penetrate vaginas and rectums. Children were threatened with harm to themselves and their parents if they told; they witnessed and heard the abuse of other children.

Group C includes 13 children. At the time of the initial disclosure interview in 1989, five children were two and under, six were between 2 1/2 and 4 1/2, and one was seven years old. The average age was 2.9 years.

Group C children were cared for in a state-approved day-care home where a mother, father, and their adolescent son involved themselves in the care and the abuse of the children. The children witnessed the father having intercourse with his nine-year-old daughter. Digital, oral, vaginal, and anal penetration and physical abuse were described by the children in addition to witnessing the abuse of others. Children feared for their and their parents' well being if they told.

Memory Presentations

Somatic Memories

Somatic memories are defined as observations of physical symptoms and/or physiological arousal closely connected with trauma-specific experiences. There is generally no awareness of a physiological link to the abuse by the child or the parent. Parents report the physical complaints as a change in the child and question its medical basis, e.g., episodes of body rash with no pathophysiological basis to the symptom. The disclosure interview notes the child and other day-care children were bitten repeatedly by insects.

Disclosure interviews of all 34 children revealed somatic memories at the time of investigative interview with a progressive decline in reported physical symptoms at second and third interview. Parents, even prior to disclosure of the abuse, reported physical symptoms to include vaginal discharge, genital soreness, rashes and anal redness, bleeding, and bruises; diagnoses of herpes and clamydia were made after disclosure. Other generalized symptoms included headaches, stomachaches, and other body aches.

Example 1: Tim, age three, had initially disclosed being driven to an off-campus house, tied to a tree in a woods, and physically hit. He said that something had been pushed into his bottom. Parents recall his anus being reddened. Somatic and behavioral memories were noted in his persistent complaints of anal pain and fear that something was in his rectum. He would clench his legs, defecate and urinate on the floor and rug, and avoid using the bathroom. Abdominal pains were frequent as well as the preoccupation that something was in his rectum. He and his parents did not link this to the abuse itself, though he could recollect that he was hurt at the day-care center. On second interview, he did not draw the abuse event, but rather drew a shadow of something after him.

Example 2: Claude was cared for at the Center between the ages of six weeks and 12 months. During his day care experience parents had noted his genitals were

200

frequently red and swollen and that he came home with bruises and scratches, once with two, long, red, parallel marks, like a rope or wire mark. At the time of the second interview, Claude was five years, eight months, the parents were concerned with the bowel complaints of their child. He screamed at the mere presence of a doctor and fought any attempt to examine any part of his body. The parents feared there had been permanent damage to the rectum because of recurrent bouts of severe diarrhea. In addition to this specific somatic symptom, both parents and the child acknowledged a large number of other physical symptoms. Claude did not have any direct memories of being at the day care center nor of what was done to him there.

Behavioral Memories

Behavioral memories are defined as spontaneous expressions of trauma-linked behaviors in everyday activities, specifically sexually provocative language ("Hump on the doll"), and sexually inappropriate behavior (a girl grabbing a male's genitals). There is no awareness of the link to the abuse situation by the child or by the parent. The behavior is noted as a change in the child rather than a cue association to the trauma. For example, the child cries and is fiercely resistive to any stranger physically resembling the perpetrator. Behavioral symptoms included general expression of anxiety, such as mood swings, temper tantrums, and difficulty in peer relationships as well as sexualized behavior and language.

At the time of disclosure interviews, 28 parents reported children with behavioral symptoms and six without symptoms. Parents of children under age two reported actions classified as protest behaviors prior to their knowledge of the abuse. For example, one 21-month-old girl in the drive from her house to the day care, would pout, cling, and cry. This behavior escalated to her becoming hysterical as soon as the car door was opened, followed by her refusing to leave the car. Her mother had to physically pull her out of the car. This behavior changed within six weeks of beginning day care to a withdrawn, nonemotional, acquiescent child when left at the day care. When returning home with the mother, she would whimper, cling, and cry. Once home, she would either demand her mother's complete attention, or she would stare off into space. She withdrew from her father and did not hug or kiss him; she would wake up at night, screaming and vomiting; she refused to take a bath or remove her clothes; she would hide from males visiting in the home.

Example 3: Danny was 3.3 years old at the time of the abuse disclosure. His parents had noted change in his behavior and that of his older brother Billy (7. 9 years old). Both boys had sleep problems with night walking, nightmares, and sexualized thoughts and behavior. On second interview, while drawing, Danny spontaneously said to himself, "I need a new butt. Mine has a crack in it." As he drew his older brother, he said "I'll lick his candy stick." This is a reenactment of the adolescent perpetrator's behavior with the children. Billy reported that the adolescent offender physically hit, pinched, and bullied Danny while he was in the day program. Danny, in turn, was reported to be sexually aggressive with other children, using sexually explicit language. When alone, he was preoccupied with masturbating and, in his sleep, he cried out for someone to help him.

Example 4: Polly was 2.4 years old at time of abuse. She showed strong protest behavior when taken to the home of the day-care providers. She began to regress at home, bedwetting and urinating outside of the toilet and in strange places in the house. When her mother would change her clothes, Polly would lie on the bed staring into space; it required effort on the part of her mother to gain her attention. While in the day-care program and after disclosure, Polly began to refuse food and would not feed herself. It was known (through other children's witnessing) that she was forced to suck the adolescent offender's penis.

Verbal Memories

Verbal memories are defined as direct spontaneous verbal statements of abuse information by the child with or without questions and prompts from others. Only those children who could verbalize their abuse were validated by authorities for the civil suit as abused.

Various responses occurred when children were initially asked what happened at daycare. Children screamed and ran out of the room or whimpered they would be hurt or the parent hurt if they told. After being reassured of safety and protection, children told of having to touch the teacher's genitals or having objects pushed into their genitals.

Peripheral details of the abuse varied with children. For example, of four children who described Dracula at an empty house, three children described him having bloody teeth and one child said the "red was catsup."

On follow-up interview, 22 children's verbal statements were classified as follows.

1. **Full memory with verifiable details.** Thirteen of the 22 children had full memory of the abuse.

Evidence of verbal memory came from the school journal of Danny, age eight, who wrote about being at the babysitters with nine other children and being hit by the 14-year-old son of the caretaker who would get drunk and hit the children also. Three months after writing of the abuse experience, Danny wrote about "wanting to smoke some cigarettes, get a girl, and kiss her until she screamed he was raping her. He would go to jail; his mother would bail him out; he would find the girl, kiss her until she could not breath and was dead; and [he would have] committed murder." Also in the journal were descriptions of dreams in which a man and a teenager were threatening to kill him with an axe.

2. **Partial memory and fragmented memory traces of abuse.** Children's verbal statements meet the majority of the above criteria. Areas not accessible to memory included information about number of abuse incidents, full names of perpetrators accused, types of abuse experienced, and spontaneity. Full memory is not within the conscious awareness of the child. In some instances the child experiences the fragment as an intrusive thought about some aspect of the trauma event or the trauma setting and verbalizes it spontaneously. Behaviorally, the fragments appear as repetitive somatic preoccupations, repetition of trauma information in play or interpersonal exchanges. Parents indicate the child does not spontaneously talk about the abuse, but becomes upset (anxious, tense, crying, fighting, withdraws) around cues known by parent to be related to the event. Six of the 22 children had partial memory. Also, the case study of Jim is an example of partial memory.

One 13-year-old boy was classified as having partial memory presentation. Although he refused to talk about the abuse on second interview, he repeatedly said thinking of the Center made him feel dead. In his follow-up interview, he drew a closed casket for the event memory drawing.

3. **No memory of the abuse is present.** This category is reserved for children who despite the fact that other children witnessed their abuse have never claimed any verbal memory of the abuse. There is no indication that the child talks about it or reacts to environmental cues. Three of the 22 children expressed no memory.

Visual Memory

Visual memories are drawings or play demonstration by the child with or without questions and prompts from others that relate to the abuse environment. Again, details vary with children.

Visual memory was classified as to whether of not the children were able to draw their memory of "what happened to them at day care." Twenty or almost 60% percent of the children drew a full, fragmented, or delayed memory of their abuse at daycare.

Example 5: Alice, 8.5 years old at the time of the second interview, had full memory and made three drawings of her abuse. The first drawing is the teacher pushing a pencil into her; the second drawing is the van taking her and others to a house; the third drawing is of the devil and four children.

Example 6: Adele, 8.9 years old at time of second interview, had full memory and made eight drawings of her trauma memories. She draws being pushed off a see-saw by a teacher, three children crying with three teachers smiling, driving in a van to a house, the cellar of the house, pictures of two perpetrators naked, being scared by ghosts, being tied with another child to a tree, and being married to the devil.

Example 7: Emily, age six at time of disclosure and 11 at time of third follow-up, had full memory and used color to draw a ritualized abuse setting. A female religious figure using an open shaving razor is cutting the throat of a chained goat, blood dripping from its neck. Six children are sitting in a pew watching, and there is a piano on the stage. Emily became teary talking about the goat sacrifice. On the back of the page she pencils a church with pews, a cross on the wall, and two religious figures acting on a person with no legs, arms, neck and eyes closed; three children on stage and four in pew are watching. Outside of church is an unhappy sun looking through dark glasses.

Example 8: Pam, who was almost three at the time of disclosure interview, and eight at time of second interview, has a fragmented and delayed memory. She first draws herself, frightened and perplexed as to why she "has to wait at day care." She then draws herself waiting alone and wondering why it is taking so long for her father to pick her up after school. Three months later, her mother sent a picture she had spontaneously drawn of herself in the utility room on the washing machine. She omits the offender, but has marked recollection of peripheral details of the hanging key, bare light bulb, and curtainless window. (The drawing matched the photograph of the room).

Case Study: Jim

To return to the case study, Jim, at age 2 1/2 attended Group C for a three-month period in the spring until it closed. Jim's mother reported that her son initially seemed to like the day care, but soon began crying and clinging to his mother in the morning before leaving. He became afraid of the dark and could not be in his room alone. He had nightmares, would wake up screaming, and come into the parents bed. He would pull his pants down and say, "Look, look a game. Look mommy, it's big." He developed sleep problems and was noticeably avoidant of teenage males, especially blond-haired boys.

He came home one time with a black eye and said the teenage boy had hit him. Except for that incident, Jim did not verbalize any sexual abuse and thus, was not initially included as a validated case of abuse.

In July, Jim began attending a second day care. Staff at this facility noted a number of behavior problems. He was aggressive and nonresponsive to restrictions. In October 1989, he began biting for no apparent reason; especially in the bathroom, he would turn and bite the person. One year later in September 1990, Jim talked about a man trying to hurt his mother. He would tell the teacher that the man was in his room and wanted to hurt his mother. His behavior conformed with a change of day-care teachers. In June 1991, at age four, his class teacher changed, and his behavior escalated and became uncontrollable. The teacher noted when "Jim is placed in time-out, he laughs, runs around, or kicks the chair or me." The teacher could only control him by taking him to the director's office.

At age four, play therapy was reinstituted with his child psychologist. After becoming reacquainted and relaxed, the psychologist showed Jim pictures of the abusive day-care family and he identified the mother, father, and son. He related that the adolescent had hurt him, specifically that he had "poked him with a big magic stick that sometimes would be large and sometimes would be small." The magic stick was placed in Jim's mouth and nose. Jim also demonstrated on a doll how the adolescent manipulated his genitals.

The psychologist's opinion was that the second day-care teacher reminded Jim of the abusive day-care mother (both had blond hair). With this verbal documentation, Jim was included in the Group C and eligible for counseling.

Family history notes Jim's parents divorced in 1990, and his mother remarried in 1991 prior to a two-year overseas military tour. Jim attended kindergarten and first grade overseas. In the States, Jim had regular telephone contact and vacation visits with his father, but he had none during the two-year military tour.

Jim's behavior in first grade was continually disruptive, and it was recommended that an evaluation be done. The results ruled out attention deficit disorder diagnosis. A scheme of behavior modification was recommended for his hyperactive and oppositional tendencies.

To summarize, Jim's primary memory presentation of the day-care abuse is by visual cue association. Jim's initial acute trauma response was noted in his protest behavior while attending day care and in his repetitious aggressive and biting behavior in subsequent school settings. His verbal memory is present at age four and behavioral memory presentations are present at age seven. Dissociative defenses are noted in his unfocused school behavior. Putnam observes the critical role of dissociative defenses used to manage the overwhelming experiences of psychological trauma and abuse in the assessment of childhood trauma.[7] Painful events, write Chu and Dill,[8] may be lessened through dissociative alterations in perception (depersonalization and derealization), can be "forgotten" (psychogenic amnesia), or completely disowned as "someone else's" experience (multiple personalities).

Discussion

While childhood trauma and memory are cornerstones of efforts to understand emotional difficulties, the recoverability of early memory has been questioned by Anthony,[9] Freud,[5] Isakower,[10] Kris,[11] and Lewin.[12] Arguments suggest there is an inability of children to integrate experience from perceptions and sensations into memories, and that childhood experiences become layered with later developmental periods and are therefore often not retrievable. Although much of the psychodynamic writings report what adults remember from childhood, there is a small literature on memory retrieval from very young children. Bernstein and Blacher's case study of the recovery of a memory from three months of age supports the notion of the laying down of precise and integrated memory traces.[13] In contemporary writings, Terr's four-year follow-up study of 25 school-bus kidnapped victims was one of the first to document children's memories of a traumatic event over time.[14] A later paper by Terr advanced the understanding of verbal and behavioral presentation of childhood memories over a five-year period.[15]

Today, efforts to understand the role of traumatic events and what is learned by the child are being directed not only by conscious awareness of past events, but also by the interplay of biology and development within the context of social support. Basic research on learning and memory structures and processes are now being explored in light of traumatic life events.

Squire in his many studies on individuals with organically induced amnesic has developed a tentative memory taxonomy that consists of two divisions, (1) the declarative or explicit, and (2) procedural or implicit. Declarative is further broken down into episodic (memory for events, time sequence, cumulative events of one's life) and semantic (memory for facts, knowledge of the world).[4] Procedural memory is broken down into skills, such as priming and simple classical conditioning. This research contributes to an understanding of the relationship of memory and learning.

Trauma research is now reporting on both the psychological and biological disruption that occurs to memory structure's capacity to recollect and recall an event.[2] Of importance is the awareness that what people often request in the memory or recollection of an event can be different from what is centrally learned. Data support the notion that much of the learning that strong experiences force on an individual fall into the area of procedural memory that is not available for retrieval via language, but may manifest itself in behavioral non verbal patterns.[16, 17] Further evidence from both the study of trauma and the evolution of brain structures and processes suggests that changes occur at the most primary structures of the central nervous system, resulting in alteration of protective behaviors.[18] For example, a child is unable to think of alternatives to submitting to an abusive adult because (1) the capacity to sort and differentiate stimuli has been altered by prior assaults, and trauma and (2) the recall and spontaneous retrieval of information may be altered through the neurochemistry of learning and remembering.

The data from this day care sexual abuse study support Squire's taxonomy that somatic and behavioral memory presentations are part of procedural or implicit memory due to the lack of language and verbal and visual memory are part of declarative or explicit memory systems. The youngest children in this sample either have no memory or memory fragments of childhood sexual abuse. Terr has also suggested that children traumatized under 2 1/2 years do not have a free recall of the event, and that there will be confusion over details of memory when there are multiple events.[18] While it is understandable that with age, skills are more developed in the older children and therefore the expectation that memory will be more spontaneous and detailed, the observations divide in this sample five to 10 years after disclosure. Half (57%) of the children provide full verbal memory, while half have either fragmented memory traces or no memory.

There is research supporting this finding of fragmented verbal memory of childhood sexual abuse. Williams reports on her findings of recall of sexual abuse among 200 women who reported sexual abuse before the age of 12.[19] Seventeen years had followed the initial report made at a public hospital. In this sample, 38% of the women were amnesic for the abuse or chose not to report it 17 years later. Briere and Conte, who studied a large clinical sample of 450 adults who reported forced sexual

207

contact at the age of 16 or younger, found 267 (59.3%) reported amnesia for sexual abuse at some point before the age of 18.[20] Those who reported amnesia were younger at the time of abuse (5.8 years v. 7.3 years), were abused over a longer period of time, experienced multiple abusers, were injured, and had fear that they would have died if they said anything.

The relationship of spontaneous ability to remember traumatic events and behavioral disruption is unclear. Is the report of behavioral disruption more in the eyes of the beholder or is it a function of the activation of the abuse information itself? Is this activation in part reflecting the capacity of the parents to acknowledge behavior changes associated with the abuse experience?

It appears that different types of memory are split off at various times and possibly under various contextual conditions. Further, these types of memories may, in fact, represent different biological levels of memory structures and processes. And the dissociative states may represent a failure of the integration of these various levels of biological memory systems.

Ito, Teicher, Glod, Harper, Magnus and Gelbard, in fact, report limbic system disruption and hemispherical response differences in both physically abused and sexually abused clinic patients.[21] Further, they report greater mnemonic disturbance in those who were sexually abused and the most mnemonic disturbance in those who are both sexually and physically abused. Further support for critical limbic system disruption is found in the works assessing the biological underpinnings of post traumatic stress disorder.[17, 22,23]

In studies of abused children, memory disruptions are noted in detachment from others, constricted interpretation of social cues, aggression, and sexual acting out towards others.[24, 25,26] Ito et al infer from electrophysiological activities of the hemispheres that memory elaboration in the right hemisphere is influenced in such a manner to impact on conscious behavior and affect without awareness of the experience.[21] The repetition of trauma links of behavior noted in the children in this study suggest this level of memory disruption.

A related question is whether the social context post disclosure influences either the sustaining of abuse memories or their suppression? Kelley's work demonstrates that parents of abused children in day-care settings are themselves traumatized by the forthcoming information from their children and their own internal constructs regarding the abusive events and the future projections of how their child will develop.[27] In a secondary analysis, using simple regression equations, a pattern emerged in which it appears that the mother is most influenced by the child's and father's reactions, and the father is influenced by the wife's reactions and concerns regarding loss of income. The mother and father were specifically influenced by their intrusive thoughts related to the abuse.[28]

There is the clinical concern regarding treatment for traumatized children and their families. Bryant notes that despite the extensive literature on problems arising from childhood abuse, there are few well-controlled treatment studies of this population.[29] One clinical question raised by this project is: How do therapists clinically respect what children know when their ability to effectively communicate the information does not match adult standards based in language and conceptualization? The basic memory capacities of very young children was revealed in the persistent somatic and behavioral memory presentations in all groups over time. It is the verbal and visual memory presentations that differed in this sample. Other clinical research questions include: Is therapy that deals with the traumatic memories more successful in integrating the trauma than therapeutic strategies aimed at supporting the repression of trauma information? Are there critical developmental phases when exploration of trauma information is more appropriate and productive in resolving core symptoms of the abuse? What level of interventions best address the various memory presentations of the trauma information?

References

1. Rowan AB, Foy DW. Post-Traumatic stress disorder in child sexual abuse. *J Traumatic Stress*. 1993;6:3-20.
2. van der Kolk BA. *Psychological Trauma*. Washington, DC: American Psychiatric Press; 1987.
3. Hartman CR, Burgess AW. Information processing of trauma. *Child Abuse Neglect*. 1993;17:47-58.
4. Squire LR. *Memory and Brain*. New York, NY: Oxford University Press; 1987.
5. Freud S. From the history of an infantile neurosis. *Standard Edition*. 1918;17:3-123.
6. Ehrensaft D. Preschool child sex abuse: the aftermath of the Presidio case. *Am J Orthopsychiatry*. 1992;62:234-244.
7. Putnam, F. *Diagnosis and Treatment of Multiple Personality Disorder*. New York, NY: The Guildford Press; 1989.
8. Chu JA, Dill DL. Dissociative symptoms in relation to childhood physical and sexual abuse. *Am J Psychiatry*. 1990;147: 887-892.
9. Anthony EJ. A study of "screen memories." *Psychoanalytic Study Child*. 1961;16:211-245.
10. Isakower O. A contribution to the pathopsychology of phenomena associated with falling asleep. *Int J. Psa*. 1938;19:331-345.
11. Kris E. The recovery of childhood memories in psychoanalysis. *Psychoanalytic Study Child*. 1956;11:54-88.
12. Lewin BD. Reconsideration of the dream screen. *Psa Quart*. 1953;22:174-199.
13. Bernstein AEH, Blacher RS. The recovery of a memory from three months of age, *Psychoanalytic Study Child*. 1967;22:156-161.

14. Terr L. Chowchilla revisited: the effects of psychic trauma four years after a school bus kidnapping. *Am J Psychiatry*. 1983;140:1543-1550.

15. Terr L. What happens to early memories of trauma? A study of twenty children under age five at the time of documented traumatic events. *J Am Acad Child Adolesc Psychiatry*. 1988;27:96-104.

16. McNally RJ, English GE, Lipke HJ. Assessment of intrusive cognition in PTSD: use of the modified stroop paradigm. *J Traumatic Stress*. 1993;6:33-42.

17. Pitman R. Post-traumatic stress disorder, hormones, and memory. *Biol Psychiatry*. 1989;26:221-223.

18. Herman, J. *Trauma and Recovery*. New York, NY: Basic Books, 1992.

Horowitz MJ, Wilner N, Alvarez W. Impact of event scale: a measure of subjective stress. *Psychosom Med*. 1979;4:209-218.

19. Williams LM. Adult memories of childhood abuse: preliminary findings from a longitudinal study. *Advocate*. 1992;5(2):19-21.

20. Briere J, Conte J. Self-reported amnesia for abuse in adults molested as children. *J Traumatic Stress*. 1993;6(1):21-32.

21. Ito Y, Teicher MH, Glod CA, Harper D, Magnus E, Gelbard HA. Increased prevalence of electrophysiological abnormalities in children with psychological, physical, and sexual abuse. *J Neuropsy Clin Neurosc*. 1993;5:401-408.

22. Giller EL, ed. *Biological Assessment and Treatment of Posttraumatic Stress Disorder*. Washington, DC: American Psychiatric Press; 1990.

23. Orr SP. Psychophysiologic studies of posttraumatic stress disorder. In: Giller EL, ed. *Biological Assessment and Treatment of Posttraumatic Stress Disorder*. Washington, DC: American Psychiatric Press; 1990.

24. Friedrich W, Luecke W. Young school-age sexually aggressive children. *Prof Psychology*. 1988;19:155-164.

25. Smetana J, Kelly M. Social cognition in maltreated children. In: Cicchetti D, Carlson V eds. *Child Maltreatment*. Cambridge, MA: Cambridge University Press; 1989:620-646.

26. Dodge K, Bates J, Pettit G. Mechanisms in the cycle of violence. *Sci*.1990;250:1678-1683.

27. Kelley SJ. Parental stress response to sexual abuse and ritualistic abuse of children in day care settings. *Nurs Res*. 1990;25:25-29.

28. Burgess AW, Hartman CR, Kelley S, et al. *Child Trauma and Research*. New York, NY: Garland; 1990.

29. Bryant RA. Cognitive behavioral therapy of violence-related posttraumatic stress disorder. *Aggression Violent Behav*. 2000;5(1):79-97.

Reprinted with permission from the *Journal of Psychosocial Nursing*, Slack, Inc.
Burgess AW, Hartman CR, Baker T. Memory presentations of child sexual abuse. *J Psychosoc Nurs*. 1995;33(8):9-16.

Chapter 24 – CODIS: DNA Profiling

Stephen Niezgoda, Patricia Loftus, and Ann W. Burgess

On the morning of November 25, 1991, a masked man broke into the home of a newlywed couple in Ritchie, IL. He shot and killed the husband, Jeffrey Stephens, and then raped and shot the wife. The attacker presumed the woman to be dead and drove away in the couple's car. The woman survived, but she was unable to identify her attacker. The police were not successful in determining his identity. Two weeks later the same man raped a 17-year-old girl. This victim was able to identify him, and he was convicted of the crime. On April 6, 1993, forensic scientists at the Springfield Crime Lab were running a routine check of convicted offender DNA profiles against crime evidence in CODIS. The search produced a match between the DNA profile of the Ritchie, IL murder/rape and the man convicted of the rape of the 17-year-old girl. The offender, Arthur Dale Hickey was a neighbor of the couple in Ritchie, Illinois. Hickey was sentenced to death by a jury in Joliet, Illinois for first-degree murder, attempted murder, aggravated criminal sexual assault, and home invasion.

CODIS

The FBI's COmbined DNA Index System (CODIS) began in 1986 when DNA profiling was relatively new. The program was conceived by the Technical Working Group on DNA Analysis Methods and it has two major objectives. First, the program is to assist police investigators in the identification of suspects of violent crimes, and second, it is to increase the effectiveness of forensic laboratories by providing software tools to conduct DNA casework and perform genotype frequency calculations.

CODIS blends DNA forensic science and computer technology into an effective tool for solving violent crimes. CODIS enables state and local law enforcement crime laboratories to exchange and compare DNA profiles electronically, thereby linking serial violent crimes to each other and identifying suspects by matching DNA from crime scenes to convicted offenders. The word "index" in Combined DNA Index System is not arbitrary. CODIS is a system of pointers; the database contains only the information necessary for making matches. Profiles stored in CODIS include a specimen identifier, the sponsoring laboratory's identifier, the names of laboratory personnel responsible for the DNA profile, and the actual DNA characteristics. CODIS does not store criminal history information, case-related information, or social security numbers. When CODIS identifies a potential match, the laboratories responsible for the matching profiles contact each other to validate or refute the match.

A match occurs when two or more DNA profiles are found to be indistinguishable in genetic type. A lab will initiate a search of the CODIS database when they need to know if there are any DNA profiles in the database that match the profile with which they are working. CODIS, using user-defined parameters, looks in the specified databases to determine if there is a match.

Once a match is found, users need to compare their suspect DNA profile with a random sampling of the suspect's population. This comparison is necessary to determine how common the matching profile is in the suspect's population.

Forensic DNA profiling is an extremely important new law enforcement tool. The FBI Laboratory has therefore implemented an aggressive national forensic DNA program. It consists of four major components: 1) applied research and development, 2) technology transfer, 3) case work, and 4) development of a national index of DNA identification records (the CODIS program).

In 1990 the FBI began development of a national DNA identification, CODIS. The concept driving this development is the rarity of a DNA profile obtained from the successful analysis of body fluid stains left at crime scenes. Given the recidivistic nature of rape and other violent crimes, and the fact that body fluids of the perpetrator are left at crime scenes, a national computer-based system of storing and comparing DNA records can result in the successful application of DNA profiling in the fight to prosecute violent crimes.

The purpose of CODIS is to create a national information repository where law enforcement professionals can share DNA information. Law enforcement agencies can cross reference their DNA information with that of other agencies around the country. This "cross referencing" has the potential of producing DNA matches among previously unrelated cases.

DNA – Identification Act of 1994

Contained within the Violent Crime Control and Law Enforcement Act of 1994 was the DNA Identification Act of 1994. Major components of the DNA Act authorize the FBI Director to establish DNA indices on the following –

1. DNA identification records of persons convicted of crimes. The DNA record is the objective form of the DNA analysis test of a DNA sample. For example, the numerical representation of DNA fragment lengths, digital image of autoradiographs, and discrete assignment numbers. The DNA record comprises characteristics of a DNA sample that are of value in establishing the identity of individuals.

2. Analyses of DNA samples recovered from crime scenes.

3. Analyses of DNA samples recovered from unidentified human remains.

The DNA samples and analysis are only available to –

1. Criminal justice agencies for law enforcement purposes.

2. In judicial proceedings, if admissible according to applicable laws and rules.

3. For criminal defense purposes, to a defendant who shall have access to samples and analyses in connection with the case in which he or she is charged.

4. If personally identifiable information is removed, for a population statistics database, for identification, research, and protocol development purposes or for quality control.

Structure of DNA

Deoxyribonucleic acid (DNA) is an organic substance found primarily in the nucleus of living cells. It provides the genetic code that determines a person's individual characteristics. DNA is different for every individual except identical twins. The code is expressed by the arrangement of four basic building blocks, called nucleotides. The nucleotides are represented by the letters A (adenine), G (guanine), C (cytosine), and T (thymine). These nucleotides are linked in chain-like sequences, and their order can vary to provide an almost infinite number of possible arrangements. There are about three billion nucleotides in the entire human genetic code.

DNA is found in the chromosomes within the nuclei of cells. The DNA within any chromosome is composed of two strands wound about each other to form a double helix. The two strands associate with each other in a certain way that is governed by the chemical properties of the letter in each strand. The letter A in one strand will associate only with the letter T in the other strand. Likewise, the letter C in one strand will associate with G in the other strand. If the sequence of letters in one strand is known, the sequence in the other strand can be deduced.

DNA analysis comprises a number of specific laboratory steps. There are several different methods of DNA analysis. Currently, CODIS is designed to work with the Restriction Fragment Length Polymorphism (RFLP) and the Polymerase Chain Reaction (PCR). As DNA analysis technology advances, CODIS will be adapted to meet the needs of the forensic community.

One of the main components of the CODIS program is its Searcher and Autosearcher applications. This functionality allows law enforcement agencies to look for profiles that match the profile they are currently working with (the target profile). The CODIS system provides two separate methods for locating matches. The Searcher program searches selected indexes against target profiles. Users can perform searches on any index level. The Autosearcher program searches indexes at one level against indexes at the same level.

CODIS Performance

The FBI gauges the performance of the CODIS program by counting the crimes it helps to solve. A potential match is referred to as a "bit." "Cold hits" are unexpected matches made in cases where law enforcement agencies have no suspects. A cold hit provides police with an investigative lead that would not have otherwise been developed. "Warm hits" are expected matches based on prior knowledge. A warm hit provides police with additional evidence on an investigative lead produced from other sources.

The FBI is currently in the process of evaluating the effectiveness of CODIS as a law enforcement tool. A pilot project to interview local and state crime laboratories bagin Fall 1997. Results of this project and periodic update of CODIS success stories will be published in the *Sexual Assault Report*.

CODIS Hits

The primary purpose of CODIS is to help solve crimes in which there are no suspects. To date, CODIS has generated over 200 hits. Two examples follow.

A 1991 rape/murder in Minnesota was the first United States case solved by searching convicted offender DNA records. The Minnesota Bureau of Criminal Apprehension (MNBCA) ran the DNA profile from the crime scene specimen against approximately 1,200 convicted offender DNA records. A suspect was identified, arrested, and convicted.

In Tallahassee, FL, February 1995, the Florida Department of Law Enforcement linked semen found on a Jane Doe rape-homicide victim to a convicted offender's DNA profile. The suspect's DNA was collected, analyzed, and stored in a CODIS database while he was incarcerated for another rape. The match was timely; it prevented the suspect/offender's release on parole scheduled eight days later.

Benefits to Society

DNA typing can be used to associate or exclude biological evidence found at crime scenes with specific individuals. There are two major benefits to society. First, it will be possible to detect and identify serial offenders more quickly, thereby allowing law enforcement the opportunity to intervene in a suspect's crime spree and reduce the number of potential victims. Second, by preventing continued violent behavior of serial offenders, law enforcement will save time and effort, and courts will have fewer cases to process because investigations can be better focused and coordinated.

An additional advantage to the CODIS system is the potential for identifying suspects in unsolved cases by linking them with convicted offenders stored in the database. This may lead to criminals being charged with these crimes and being kept in prison past their initial sentence.

Implications for Healthcare Professionals

Healthcare professionals are in a unique position to assist the CODIS project. They will assume the role of collecting, preserving, and transferring the evidence. The manner in which this is done has a direct impact on the data that is input into the system. Evidence which may have once been overlooked or discarded will now be captured.

Case Examples

The following five cases illustrate ways in which CODIS worked for the apprehension of a suspect and successful prosecution.

Wisconsin: The First Interstate Match

In April 1989, a 13-year-old Caucasian girl was riding her bike in a rural area in Wisconsin within two miles of her home. A 23-year-old, unemployed, married, Caucasian male stopped in a pickup truck to ask directions. The girl answered his questions. He then held out a knife and instructed her to get into the truck. She took off on the bike. He caught her on foot, tossed the bike into the ditch, and threw the young girl into the truck. He then drove to an abandoned farm and parked behind the barn. He removed the victim's clothes, vaginally assaulted her, and ejaculated. She tried to get away again. He caught her, cut her throat, and left her for dead.

Based on a description, several suspects were investigated, including the offender. Because the victim could not pick him out of a lineup, he was let go. Since there was a similar case in Minnesota and since Wisconsin did not have the capacity to do DNA analysis at that time, the biological evidence found on the girl's clothing was sent to Minnesota for analysis. Although there was not a match with the Minnesota case, the data were entered into the CODIS system. The matched suspect was later arrested and is serving a long prison sentence in Illinois on two sexual assault charges. When the data from Illinois were entered into the CODIS system in April, 1993, there was a match with the Wisconsin case, the first interstate hit in the nation. Authorities in Wisconsin had reached a dead end in the case and doubted that they would solved this case had it not been for the CODIS cold hit. Since the alleged perpetrator is securely in prison in Illinois, the authorities in Wisconsin have not, as yet, brought the case to court.

Florida: An Unidentified Murdered Victim

In Lake County, Florida, on December 1991, the body of an unknown women was found in a state forest area by a hiker who had seen some drag marks going up to the railroad tracks. He followed these marks and noticed a body covered with dried brush. The police knew that the person had been killed recently because there had been relatively little decomposition. There was also evidence that the victim had been brutalized over an extended period of time at some other location. Foreign objects had been inserted in all of her orifices, and the medical examiner had found a partially broken bottle in her vagina. He also found sperm in the vaginal area, and this was sent in for DNA analysis.

The case was well-publicized; and profilers were brought in. They were unable to come up with leads. Nobody locally knew the victim. Blood was taken from three or four suspects, but there was no match. The police said that they felt that these exclusions resulted in the saving many man-hours and other expenses, because when the results came back negative, they stopped the investigation of that suspect. For three years, the police would look into similar cases around the state. They were then notified of the CODIS hit in February 1995.

The perpetrator in this case was a 24-year-old African-American male, who was divorced and was employed full-time in a newspaper print factory at the time of the incident. He had his first felony arrest in 1989. Since then, he had been arrested for felonies on six occasions, three times for sexual felonies. He had been sentenced to prison twice, the first time in 1993. The offense that resulted in his blood being drawn and the DNA results being entered into CODIS was committed in a different county in Florida. He was incarcerated in the jail in that other county at the time of the match. The offer of a sentence of life imprisonment, rather than the death penalty for a pleading of guilty by the perpetrator, was rejected, and the case went to a jury. While the perpetrator was charged with three counts of sexual battery and one count of first-degree murder, the jury concluded that he was guilty only of one count of sexual battery based on the DNA evidence. He was sentenced to life in prison in April 1997. Both police and prosecutor felt that the CODIS match was of primary importance in solving this case and getting a conviction. Had there not been a match, they would not have known about him. The victim was not alive to identify him, and the only other physical evidence was a bite mark on the victim, which matched up with the perpetrator once he was identified. It was speculated that since he had committed several similar crimes, he would have continued his crime spree and would have eventually been caught, but the result would have been several more victims having to suffer.

Minnesota: Rape-Murder Victim

In November 1991, a 24-year-old, single Caucasian female healthcare worker was asleep in a ground floor dwelling in Minneapolis. Her housemates were in

217

the house in other rooms. Early in the morning, the perpetrator entered through an unlocked rear door, which was near the room of the victim. The perpetrator used a ligature (bra) to put around the victim's neck. He had vaginal sex with her. The victim was found dead, lying face down on the bed. Her underwear had been pulled down around her ankles. The victim's housemates were not aware of her death until later in the day. When she did not get up, they went in and found her dead. Semen was later identified on the women's buttocks. DNA analysis was performed and the data were entered into CODIS.

The police had no suspects at the time, but they thought that it might be the male housemate. He offered a blood sample and was excluded. They were informed by the state crime lime lab that they had located the perpetrator through use of CODIS in December 1991. This 36-year-old, unemployed Hispanic male was in custody for burglary in St. Paul. He had a long history of sexual assaults and burglary, and had been deported back to Mexico on three occasions. The perpetrator was found guilty of murder and sentenced to life in prison without the possibility of parole in November 1992, a decision that was affirmed by the Minnesota Supreme Court.

Miami: Linking Jurisdictions

The CODIS system is useful as a law enforcement tool not only because it enables the identification of individuals with particular types of previous convictions based on crime scene evidence, but also because it can provide the opportunity to tie several cases in different jurisdictions together. In this example, the first of the two cases took place in Miami early one evening in September 1991. Under the pretense that he was looking for neighbors, the perpetrator had approached the victim when she was opening her apartment door early in the evening. She was a 22-year-old waitress. He forced himself into the apartment, brandishing a knife. He threatened her, telling her not to scream, and took her upstairs. Once upstairs, he demanded that she undress. He proceeded to assault her twice. The first time he ejaculated on her stomach, and then in her vagina. He then forced her into the bathroom where he ordered her to bathe. After this, he then left. The victim was taken to the hospital where a physician gathered the biological evidence using a county-standardized kit.

The victim was cooperative with police, providing them with a very accurate sketch. In spite of extensive leg work, the case remained unsolved for some time until the CODIS hit. The victim was then shown a photo of the suspect, which she identified.

Several days after the incident in Miami, a similar incident occurred in Palm Beach. A single, Caucasian flight attendant in West Palm Beach for a layover was returning to her hotel from the health club, a short distance away. It was dark. She was grabbed from behind by a man she did not know and dragged down an embankment to an alley just off a busy main thoroughfare. He forced her to have sex, including oral and vaginal penetration. Per what was later determined to be the perpetrator's method of operation, he masturbated and ejaculated on the victim. A knife was used during the crime. The DNA evidence was collected from the victim by a Sexual Assault Nurse Examiner using a state-standardized kit. The analysis that was done on the evidence was not, however, compatible with CODIS, so the results were not entered into the system.

Another person was arrested and convicted of the crime in Miami based on the description given by the victim. When the arrest was made in the Palm Beach case, his picture appeared in the paper. The father of the victim saw it and sent his daughter a copy. She identified him, and the samples from the crime were reanalyzed and entered into CODIS. A match on the actual perpetrator was made in April 1996.

The perpetrator in both cases was a single male Caucasian who worked full time as a male stripper. He was 30 years old at the time of both incidents. He was charged with burglary with assault, two counts of sexual battery with force, and kidnapping in the Miami case. He pled guilty to all charges in June 1994, in return for a 15-year sentence plus 10 years' probation.

In the West Palm Beach case, the perpetrator was originally charged with sexual battery and kidnapping. In September 1997, there was a plea bargain in the case wherein the perpetrator pled guilty to the sexual battery and the kidnapping charge was dropped. He accepted a sentence of 25 years in prison, which was to run concurrently with the 15 years he was already serving; this led to his having his blood drawn and the data entered into the CODIS system.

CODIS was particularly important in the Palm Beach case because not only was a guilty person imprisoned for a longer period of time, but an innocent person was released from jail. The police in Palm Beach had no other leads to the perpetrator. This same was true in the Miami case where they said that without the CODIS match, there would not have been a case.

Minneapolis: Excluding Suspects

In Minneapolis, MN, in November 1992, a 33-year-old, single Caucasian women who worked as a hairdresser was returning to her residence in the early morning. As she entered the residence, she was grabbed from behind and forced into her car, which was in the parking lot. The perpetrator put a stocking cap over her head at the point of abduction. He drove to an unknown location and sexually assaulted her, threatening her with a screwdriver. He then ordered her into the car, drove her to within a couple of blocks of her residence, and released her. He returned her car to the victim's parking lot. The victim told her parents who contacted the police. The victim was taken to the hospital where a Sexual Assault Nurse Examiner completed a rape exam, obtaining the biological sample using a state-standardized kit.

One suspect in the case had blood drawn, which was found not to match the DNA recovered from the victim. Police felt that this exclusion of a suspect saved them a great deal of investigative time. The suspect had been working at the time of the rape. In summary, the exclusion of suspects is just as essential in facilitating an investigation as finding a match for the DNA.

Part 3
Special Clinical Issues

Chapter 25 – Sex Crimes Against Children

Robert A. Prentky and Ann W. Burgess

The past two decades have produced a significant amount of research and clinical practice to add to the knowledge base on child victims and their offenders. The following outlines some of the contemporary knowledge: frequency, classification, roots of deviant behavior, factors that may influence sexual assault, repressed memories of abuse, complex issues, risk factors for dangerousness, pleysmographic measurement, and offender treatment. This paper highlights, in simple outline format, the major findings and conclusions that can be drawn from the clinical and empirical literature on child molesters.

Frequency

The frequency of occurrence of sex crimes against children is one of the murkiest and most debated areas of sexual violence research. More than any other type of criminal conduct, sexual offenses, in their extraordinary diversity, are likely to fade into the unfathomable abyss of human experience, never to be known by the criminal justice system.

Perhaps the single most important factor undermining our best efforts to assess reliably the frequency of sex offenses against children and women is underreporting. The assumption that sexual crimes against children and teenagers are drastically underreported is now accepted as a virtual truism. One of the strongest sources of evidence for this assumption comes from the offenders themselves, who report vastly more victims than they were convicted of. The magnitude of the problem differs considerably according to the victim age and gender. In general, underreporting is greater with sexual offenses –

- Against boys than against girls
- Against teens than against children
- Against teen boys than against teen girls

- Against known victims than against strangers
- Against adult men than against adult women

And the lower the physical injury to the victim, the higher the underreporting, particularly with adult victims.

Classification

As a group, sex offenders are very heterogeneous. The same holds true even when we consider only child molesters. As a group, child molesters are so heterogeneous that it would be impossible to come up with a single offender "profile." For child molesters, specific taxonomic constructs have yielded robust subtypes. The diversity among child molesters is as follows –

- Married men who fondle their own children
- Married men who rape their own children
- Married men who molest unknown children
- Professionals who sexually exploit children in their care
- Men with an exclusive sexual preference for children
- Men who are predatory and exploitative in their offenses
- Men whose job and social/recreational activities involve children
- Men who access/traffic/produce child pornography
- Men who abduct children
- Men who are overtly sadistic to children.

Factors that may Influence Sexual Assault

There are 10 factors that have been identified that may influence sexually aggressive behavior. These include –

1) A high degree of sexual preoccupation and sexual fantasies involving children
2) Pervasive feelings of inadequacy
3) Deficits in social and interpersonal skills
4) Impaired relationships with peers
5) Cognitive distortions involving children
6) Developmental history of abuse
7) Caretaker instability during development
8) Lifestyle impulsivity
9) Global or child-focused anger
10) 10 Substance abuse

Roots of the Deviant Behavior

The antecedents of sexually deviant behavior fall into three major categories: biological factors, sociocultural factors, and developmental factors.

Biological Factors

There is very little empirical evidence supporting a direct link between biology and sexual offenses in adults. The most interesting data comes from the treatment literature, wherein three groups of medications have had noteworthy success with certain types of offenders. MPA/CPA and LHRH/GnRH reduce testosterone, in the latter case to castrate levels, while fluoxetine enhances central synaptic transmission of serotonin. Other considerations include in utero exposure to high T levels and high T levels during early adolescence.

Sociocultural Factors

Converging evidence indicates that the social "climate" provides a powerful force for the transmission of attitudes and values that condone, and may encourage, sexual violence among those who are predisposed. In a highly complex society, transmission occurs through a variety of institutions and systems, including advertising/marketing, entertainment, and news media. These attitudes and values come to represent the "normative" response. This response is deeply ingrained and indelibly embedded in the social fabric.

Developmental Antecedents

There is compelling evidence supporting the role of childhood and adolescent attachments on criminal outcome. A history of sexual abuse appears to be complexly related to outcome for some offenders. Parental and peer role models are responsible for distorted attitudes. Impulsive, antisocial behavior in childhood and adolescence is highly related to outcome.

Repressed Memories of Abuse

The literature suggests several hypothetical risk factors for repressed memories of abuse.

1. **Close relationship to the offender.** With a high degree of betrayal and shattered trust. Where abuse is "normalized" and the child is confused about who is

responsible, and whether or not it really is abuse. Where the abuse becomes a secret that effectively insulates it from the family or where the family colludes to deny the existence of abuse.

2. **Protracted abuse.** Where the abuse is ongoing, in some cases for many years, the child must learn to "accommodate" to it and incorporate it into her/his life. That is, the abuse becomes "normalized" and the child learns "to live with it."

3. **Severity of abuse.** Perhaps the single most powerful mechanism leading to repression is traumatization. The more invasive and traumatic experience, the higher the likelihood that the child will repress the experience. This conclusion is based upon a wide range of studies pointing to various forms of repression as a consequence of some traumatic experience, such as war. It has been estimated, for instance, that a high percentage of all cases of amnesia are associated with war or combat-related experiences.

Complex Issues

There are a number of complex issues determining outcome of abuse.

- How different abusive experiences interact on childhood
- The age of onset and the duration of the abuse
- The severity and invasiveness of the abuse
- The stability of caregivers through childhood and adolescence
- The presence and role of nonabusive adults
- The quality of out-of-home and institutional placements
- Peer influences and the quality of peer role models

Assessing Risk of Dangerousness

Major advances have been made in the specification and validation of risk factors for child molesters and rapists. Risk analysis represents one of the most rigorous areas of empirical inquiry.

Risk Factors For Child Molesters

- Degree of sexual preoccupation with children, evidence of enduring relationships with children, child pornography

- Amount of interpersonal, nonsexual contact with children, e.g., spending time around children in social, recreational, or vocational activities
- Paraphilias – evidence of multiple, deviant sexual outlets
- History of impulsive, antisocial behavior
- Sex (gender) of victims
- Attitudes (distortions about children, anger at children)
- Poor social and interpersonal skills, social discomfort with peers, feelings of inadequacy

Penile Plethysmographic Assessment (PPG)

There is an ample empirical literature supporting the discriminate and predictive validity of the PPG. The PPG can easily discriminate, for instance, between extrafamilial child molesters and nonsexual offenders. The PPG, moreover, has been successful at predicting sexual recidivism, particularly in conjunction with other variables, such as psychopathy. Research is in progress on increasing the sensitivity of PPG assessments (probability of detecting deviant sexual arousal in subgroups of sexual offenders).

Offender Treatment

According to Safer Society, between 1986 and 1994, the number of programs servicing adults increased from 297 to 710, and the number of programs servicing adolescents increased from 346 to 684. Treatment is predominantly cognitive-behavioral, along with psychoeducation. Clear demonstration of treatment efficacy with different types of offenders has yet to be achieved.

Follow-up or Aftercare

Cognitive distortions. Irrational offense-justifying attitudes are important related to criminal outcome for most, if not all, sexual offenders.

Sexual Fantasies. Morbidity factors include: intrusive (distracting and preoccupying); reiterative (persistent and recurrent); interceptive is generally deemed to be essential (internally generated); vivid (endogenous occipital activity); and content.

Castration. The explicit purpose of surgical or chemical castration is to reduce sexual arousal and sexual fantasy. Thus, castration has its greatest potential usefulness with offenders whose behavior is highly repetitive and driven by uncontrollable sexual urges or where there are highly intrusive, repetitive sexual fantasies. This potential utility supposes that there is a correlation between strength of sexual desire and testosterone. This remains an empirical question. Most of the literature addresses the relationship between testosterone level and aggressive behavior, not sexual behavior. Castration should not be used indiscriminately with all sex offenders. Castration should never be used as the sole method of treatment.

Case of Sexual Homicide of a Child

There is ample evidence to suggest that there may be biological correlates of posttraumatic stress disorder, of which dissociation is one component. One criterion is amnesia for major aspects of the trauma. This was clearly apparent in the case of HK. He reported on a daily basis losing blocks of time, becoming aware that periods up to an hour would pass without his awareness. These losses of time were usually associated with "downtime" when his mind was not occupied and he could drift into the past. He was at risk for dissociation.

As a man with a long history of sexual molestation of children, he found himself increasingly associating with those who had a predilection for children. So his sociocultural group became other child molesters. His peers, his friends, and his subculture were all child molesters.

Developmental Factors

HK's biological father was a violently abusive man. He physically and sexually abused most if not all of the five children. His abuse of HK, in particular, lasted for years. During episodes of sodomy, he was restrained by his father choking him with his hands. As best is known, the mother never effectively intervened in the abuse of her children, presumably out of fear for her own safety. His mother had been sexually abused as a child and after marriage was physically abused and intimidated by her husband.

Repressed Memories

HK has no clear memories of any events that took place prior to the age of eight and at best foggy memories of things that occurred after the age of eight. When asked about the abuse, he reports that he thinks that he was sexually abused because he has been told that he was by his sisters and brother. He himself however has no recollection of sexual abuse. His brother vividly recalls many occasions when his

228

father locked him out of the house and he heard HK's screams coming from inside the house. The brother however was not immune from sexual abuse. He too was victimized on various occasions by the father. On some occasions when the father abused both boys at the same time

The three factors hypothetically related to repression of abuse are all present in HK. First, the perpetrator was his biological father. Second, the abuse was protracted. It went on for years. Third, the severity of abuse was extreme.

He reports nothing about the abuse. Detailed accounts are provided by his siblings, all of whom were abused, to lesser degrees, and have intact memories about HK's abuse.

HK

HK has the majority of risk factors for repeating a sex crime against a child. He has a longstanding history of victimization of children. The fantasy of victimizing children is ever-present. In the governing offense involving the sexual homicide of a young child, he reported highly intrusive, detailed rape fantasies of the child for up to two weeks before the murder. As far as history, although the criminal justice system was aware of only three victims, he reported having well over 100 victims. He had a collection of child pornography. He had a relatively normal life, meaning although he associated with adults, his friends and social companions were other child molesters. He did have extensive nonsexual contact with children in his capacity as a grounds keeper in a public park.

He had a high sexual drive in that he was promiscuous with adult women and children. There was hypermasturbatory behavior and a variety of paraphilic sexual acts. His victims were always female children. He had distorted attitudes and cognitions that justified his sexual contact with children. These attitudes were moreover reinforced by his peer group. He talked of the children as being sexually experienced and said that there was mutual interest in the sex. The distortion was that this was a normal heterosexual relationship.

Although he was a young, bright, reasonably attractive man with reasonably good interpersonal skills, he never held a job other than that of a maintenance and groundskeeper for a public park. In this capacity, he had almost constant contact with young children.

There are several points of discussion. First, HK received no trauma therapy for the severe childhood abuse. The trauma was sealed over and under stress, he would act on the sexually deviant fantasies. It is quite clear that the type of treatment needed to address HK's extreme pathology was not provided at any point in his life. In fact, the first treatment he ever received was as a sex offender when in prison. After prison, HK was coping until his siblings began pressuring him to talk to his mother about his early abuse. The revisiting of this trauma, without medication or support from a therapist, proved deadly. His psychological defenses were inadequate to manage the rage that was unresolved from the childhood abuse and the critical issue for him. He had been out of prison for years and was managing the deviant fantasies, and there was no evidence of reoffending. There was a major deterioration in his coping ability after the mother's visit. He almost overdosed on his roommate's antidepressant medication and from there went to alcohol abuse in an attempt to manage the rage, but was totally unsuccessful and the murder resulted.

On the day of the murder, HK reported seeing the victim on several occasions playing with her friends before she approached him and requested to play with the puppy that was inside his house. He was able to recount in first person detail all of the events of the day, leading up to moments before the murder. At some point the victim runs into him, striking him accidentally below the waist, in her pursuit of the puppy. It is at the moment of physical contact that he recounts the murder in third person. When the shift in tense was pointed out, he stated that he could see himself killing the child, but he wasn't there, implying a dissociative state.

HK stood trial. The role of dissociation could have been raised as a mitigating factor for a diminished capacity defense in a capital case. However, the only witness put on by the defense was the forensic social worker who did the investigation on the case. HK was convicted of second-degree homicide and received a death sentence. He immediately appealed and lost. He is currently on death row.

Chapter 26 – 13-Year-Old Case Example

People v. Blake 678 N.E.2nd. 761 (Ill.App.1 Dist. 1997)

A 13-year-old girl awoke to find her hands tied behind her back and 30-year-old Glennell Blake on top of her, warning her not to tell anyone about what was going to happen. Blake had known his victim since she was seven years old, and the prosecutor would later allege that he knew the girl was mentally handicapped before he raped her. Immediately after the attack, she told an adult who was staying at the house that the defendant was "messing with me." The adult advised the girl to tell the defendant to stop.

The girl returned to her room, and Blake repeated his assault. The girl again told the adult, who now asked her if the defendant had sex with her. The girl replied that he did not. The mother would later testify that her daughter's learning disability affected her ability to articulate her feelings.

One month later, the girl told a family friend about the assault. The friend told the girl's mother, who brought her to the hospital for an examination. The physician determined she had been sexually assaulted. Blake was charged with aggravated criminal sexual assault and unlawful restraint. The State alleged that Blake was aware the victim could not understand the nature of the act, and therefore the girl did not give knowing consent.

Blake was convicted. On appeal, he argued, among other things, that the prosecutor presented insufficient evidence as to the victim's capacity to understand the nature of the act and her capability to give knowing consent. In support of this argument, Blake pointed out that the girl was mentally aware enough to protest the attacks and used anatomically correct terms.

Holding: Blake's conviction was upheld. The court noted that "mere evidence the victim understood the physical nature of sexual relations is not sufficient to establish

231

that the victim comprehended the social and personal costs involved." The court emphasized that the victim's learning disability was a determinative factor in its conclusion that she was unable to understand or give consent to intercourse with Blake.

Burgess Comments: The young adolescent was bound, forced to have sex, and warned to remain silent by a person who had known her since she was a young child. She understood that what he had done was wrong, and she disclosed to a houseguest who told her to protest to the perpetrator. In essence, she was told she had to take care of the assault herself; there was no protection from adults. By insisting the girl assumes the responsibility for self defense, the houseguest negated her own accountability and responsibility as an adult. Subsequently, she was again assaulted; she again told the houseguest, who now questioned whether or not she had sex with the defendant. Such a question implied in the girl's mind that it was sex, and that she was responsible and participated in it.

The victim's negative reply called into question 1) whether she understood what sex meant; 2) whether she was frightened and confused, since the houseguest already made her responsible for the defendant's actions; or 3) whether she was able to differentiate consent (sex) from force (rape). The physician's examination, one month later, determined the girl had been sexually assaulted.

The above scenario in no way indicated consent. The girl was restrained, penetrated, and threatened to remain silent. The first person she told of the assault abdicated the role of protector; even the defendant later acknowledged that the girl protested the attack. This type of assault is classified as a Subordinate Rape, in which the relationship between victim and offender is one of status imbalance, and the offender has power over the victim. The relationship status is used to take advantage of the victim. There is callous indifference to the victim; sick, disabled, or otherwise handicapped children are vulnerable to this type of rape.[1]

This girl protested the assault and sought an adult for assistance, even though she had a cognitive handicap. Such victims respond to threats both implicitly and explicitly. The explicit threat of the defendant did not dissuade the victim, but the implicit threat of the houseguest did detour her, and she had to seek another adult, this time a family friend, who assumed the role of adult protector.

We have found that despite a mental handicap, mental illness, or cognitive or sensory deficit, victims are able to recognize and acknowledge they have been assaulted and did not consent. For example, in the Glen Ridge, NJ, case, the 17-year-old mentally retarded adolescent's desire to have a friendship with the high school youths overrode

232

her distress of what they were doing to her in a basement room with a broom, baseball bat, and stick. The lawyers for the defendants translated this misguided desire into consent. However, after the assault, she immediately attempted to protest to a friend. Her clinical symptoms of decreased appetite, crying spells, dreams about the assault, and difficulty concentrating and conducting her work indicated that she did not want to be raped by the foreign objects.

The victim did not immediately disclose the assault to authorities because she was fearful of repercussions, and she had a need for human contact in that she wanted the boys to be her friends. To quote sportswriter, Tom Junod, in a March 29, 1993 article in *Sports Illustrated*, "For the offenses she paid dearly. The boys had known her for a long time, and they knew how to treat her. They gave her dog feces to eat when they were children, and they gave her a bat and a broomstick when they were on the verge of becoming adults. They called her a whore, and in the aftermath of the assault, they told friends they were not turned on by her but rather, repulsed. They chose the bat not to make any symbolic statement as athletes, but simply because it was available, and they did not wish to touch her."

In cases not so clear cut as People v. Blake where age or force are subtle or nonexistent factors, coercive sex may be viewed as acquiescence. The person acquiesces to the will of the other in order not to lose a critical resource of the relationship and whatever they perceive that relationship to offer, such as sustenance, affection, friendship, or companionship. The assault must be understood within its context, the response of adults to the disclosure, and the victim's perception of his or her relationship to the offender. In a Pennsylvania case involving prolonged sexual abuse between a caretaker who told each victim she was very special, the women manifested their symptomatic distress by becoming dysfunctional in daily activities and on home visits, by becoming physically disruptive or aggressive, reenacting the sexual abuse, and using sexualized language.

Evaluating cases involving mentally handicapped victims will depend on the interviewer's expertise and prior experience in factoring in the handicap when the facts and circumstances of the crime are revealed. With careful interviewing, even in cases where there appears to be acquiescence to the acts, the victims usually show the protest, if not through words, then through behavior, and have evidence of clinical symptoms of the abuse.

References
1. Douglas JE, Ressler RK, Burgess AW, Burgess AG. *Crime Classification Manual.* San Francisco, CA: Jossey-Bass; 1995.

Chapter 27 – Child and Adolescent Sex Rings

Ann Wolbert Burgess

The number of reported cases of child sexual abuse is increasing. This prompts questions as to whether this increase is due to better reporting by victims, to a more responsive criminal justice system, or to increased sexual deviance. For forensic nurses, however, the fact remains that skills are needed for assessment, diagnosis, treatment, and expert testimony. This chapter will outline the phenomena of child and adolescent sex rings and the use of pornography.

Child Sexual Abuse

The study of the sexual victimization of children has primarily focused on incest or family member (intrafamilial) abuse of female children. As reports have indicated a growing number of abusers who are outside the family (extra-familial) and who abuse males and females, attention has focused on this type of sexual deviancy. Furthermore, reports from both the US, the United Kingdom, and the Netherlands emphasize the need for health professionals and law enforcement to increase their efforts concerning sex ring cases involving multiple victims of the same offender.

Sex ring crime is a term describing sexual victimization in which there are one or more adult offenders and several children who are aware of each other's participation. There are three different types of child sex rings.

The *solo sex ring* involves one or two adult perpetrators and multiple children. There is no exchange of photographs, nor are there sexual activities with other adults.

By contrast, a *syndicated ring* involves multiple adults, multiple child victims, and a wide range of exchange of items, including child pornography and sexual activities.

At a level between these two types of rings is the *transition ring*, in which the children and pornography are exchanged between adults, and money often changes hands. These three types of rings are further described in this chapter with case illustrations.

Child pornography can be defined as any visual or print medium depicting sexually explicit conduct involving a child. More simply stated, child pornography is photographs or films of children being sexually molested. Sexually explicit conduct includes sexual intercourse, bestiality, masturbation, sadomasochistic abuse, and lewd exhibition of the genitals or pubic area. The child or children visually represented in child pornography have not reached the age of consent.

Solo Sex Rings

Solo sex rings are characterized by the involvement of multiple children in sexual activities with one adult, usually male, who recruits the victims into his illicit behavior by legitimate means. This offender can be assessed by his methods for access to and sexual entrapment of the children, control of the children, maintaining the isolation and secrecy of the sexual activity, and by the particulars of ring activities. The events surrounding disclosure of the ring and the victims' physical and psychological symptoms are also important elements of the ring. Victims can be both male and female, and their ages can range from infancy to adolescence. The distinguishing factor is the age preference of the offender. Victims are found in nursery schools, babysitting and day-care services, youth groups, and camps.

Crime Scene Indicators

The crime scene is usually the offender's residence, vehicle, or group meeting hall. There can be many locations. The pornographic material is usually hidden in the residence of the offender. The most recent crime scene will usually have the camera and other equipment needed to create the pornography as well as props, collateral material, and goods used to bribe the victims.

Forensic Findings

The victimization is usually reported by a third party and little if any forensic evidence is immediately available. To obtain forensic evidence, detailed medical and psychiatric examinations of the victims is required. Medical evidence could include anal or vaginal scarring, bruises, etc.

Investigative Considerations

Obtain a search warrant for the offender's residence. Check telephone and financial records for purchases of materials needed to create the pornography. Be sensitive to props and collateral used to bribe the targeted age group. Interviews with the victims should be carefully done by an investigator specially trained for interviewing children.

Solo Ring Example

In brief, sexual encounters between adults and children usually fall into a predictable pattern: access to and sexual entrapment of the child by the adult; isolation and secrecy of the sexual activities; and disclosure of the victimization which includes short- and long-term outcomes and impact for the child and his family. In outlining these phases with the case under consideration, one notes the consistency in the patterns and phases.

Access and Entrapment. The sexual abuse of a child is a consciously planned, premeditated behavior. The adult is usually someone known both to the child and parent and who has ready access to the child. The offender stands in a relationship of dominance to the child. Ambivalence as a component of the decision-making process is a characteristic of the young person's emotional life, and the offender trades on this. The desire for domination by the adult is aimed at breaking the internal resistance of the subordinate. After gaining access to the child, the adult engages the child into the illicit activity through the power and authority that adulthood conveys to the child as well as misrepresenting moral standards.

In this case, the adult was an authority person vis a vis his position as a sports director with the YMCA. The families were supportive of their son being in the school and summer activities at the local YMCA because of its program for assisting in the positive development of young males. While in the role as sports directors, both the director and his associate became acquainted with the young boys and almost immediately began paying special attention to specific boys both at the YMCA, during the activities at summer day camp, and when the boys would be invited to their homes.

Isolation and Secrecy. When an offender is successful in abusing his victim, he must try to conceal the deviant behavior from others. More often than not, he will try to pledge the victim to secrecy in several ways. Secrecy strengthens the adult's power and control over the child and perpetuates the sexual activity. It is important to understand that the child usually keeps the secret; some children never tell anyone.

There are many reasons why the abuse is kept secret. The child may fear people will not believe such behavior; that people will blame the child for the activity; that there will be punishment for disclosure; and that the adult will carry out the threats. The child fears for the protection of the abuser.

In this case, the sports directors programmed the boys to believe that they needed to be educated about sex and that this kind of activity was practiced between men and their students. Pornographic magazines depicting heterosexual acts were shown to normalize the activity. The boys did not tell because of loyalty to their coach and a belief that they were very special to the adult. The boys were unaware of each other's involvement with the adult.

Sexual activities. There are a wide range of sexual behaviors that may occur between the adult and child in combination of psychological pressure and/or physical force. There may be a slow progression of advancing sexual acts perpetrated with the characteristics of sexual seduction, or the acts may be forceful and sudden to the child.

In this case, youths described sexual acts, including fondling, mutual masturbation, kissing, and escalating over time to oral and anal sex. Nude photographs and videos were taken of the youths without their knowledge. The boys were also shown pornographic videos.

Encapsulation Phase. As part of the isolation stage, the child is trapped in the sexual activity, having to participate yet having to be silent. Much of the psychological injury derived from the exploitation can be linked back to the manner of entrapment, the length of time of encapsulation, and nature of the sexual activity. Children are confused over the use of power and authority, and there is a disorganizing impact on their thinking. As the abuse continues, their belief about sex between adults and children shifts from wrong to right. Some think they can intervene and stop. The child often tries to protest the activity and begins to reenact and repeat the abuse, first to himself and then to others. The resistance is normal and always there if one carefully looks for it. However, there is also the component of arousal disharmony and because of the trauma learning the behavior is usually reenacted.

In this case the overt protest behaviors were noted in various of the boys in that some had minimal contact with the adults and others had extended contact. With disclosure the boys' behavior begin to deteriorate.

Disclosure. There are usually two ways child sexual abuse is discovered: accidental and purposeful. In *accidental disclosure*, a third party may observe or note symptoms in the child. In *purposeful disclosure*, a child consciously decides to tell an outsider or parent about the abuse. When there is disclosure, then the social meaning of the abuse becomes known; that is, the child must deal with the reactions of people (i.e., parents, friends, authority) to the knowledge of the abuse. It becomes important whether people believe the child, understand the confusion and fear that permeates the experience, and take protective action on behalf of the child.

In this case, after disclosure occurred, parents were notified by the police. Some of the boys continued to deny their involvement with the offenders until photographs and videotapes surfaced.

Psychological Injury. The impact of child sexual abuse will be discussed in terms of critical issues in general, specific injury, insult, and psychological damage.

The repetitive secret nature of the sexual abuse requires the victim to psychologically compartmentalize (encapsulate) the event; that is, keep it separate from the rest of his or her life. It is through this process that the coping mechanism of dissociation is derived ("I thought of other things while he was doing [it].") Inherent in the dissociation is cognitive confusion. At some level the child knows it is wrong because it has to be kept secret. Thus, he does not let the outside world know. There is a break with social ties. Commitment and social ties to values lose their color and dominance.

Further along in the dissociation is the mechanism of *splitting*. In this particular case, the real disruption is evidenced in the splitting of parental relationships. There is a strong lack of trust in people, and the attachment or bonding nonsexually to people is missing. To attach in a social way means there must be some trust and faith, and this component has been shattered and destroyed for the youths. Rather than developing a normal trusting social bond with others, the bonding was to the deviant sexual activities. The boys were trapped.

The youths were inhibited from exerting any action to protect themselves and to prevent or stop the exploitation. Self-protection was inhibited and adult protection nonexistent. Because this inhibition cut the boys off from self-assertive behaviors, the aggressive drive was compromised and displaced in its direction. Thus, anger and aggression were noted in symbolic and/or inappropriate behaviors. That several of the youths are showing anger and aggression is derived from the fact that they could not protect themselves.

Impact on Victim. The evaluation of the impact that sexual abuse has on an adolescent's life may be noted in several ways:
1. Reviewing the details and circumstances of the sexual abuse and noting any unusual or out-of-the-ordinary features;
2. Listing the symptoms that reflect the posttrauma features;
3. Citing the dynamics of the abuser's behavior.

In the first method, the details and circumstances of the sexual abuse and exploitation help to evaluate the major impact the abuse has had on the youths' lives.

The betrayal of a trusted relationship was critical in this case. The boys were programmed by the sports coachs to be overly attached to them. The youths were at a critical developmental period and vulnerable for attention from an adult male. The coach gave what appeared to the boys to be love and attention, meeting the narcissistic wish of a child to be the center of attention. The exchange for being taught about sex and to be special was secrecy of the sex. The youths' rage is over the betrayal of this special status and the humiliation of the knowledge that many other boys were so treated.

The second way to evaluate the posttrauma effects are to document symptoms that a boy develops as a result of the abuse. Symptoms, which include intrusive thoughts and phobic/avoidance behavior, evidence the major impact the abuse had, and continues to have, on the youths' lives.

In addition, the youths became unusually quiet, confused, less active, and less energetic. Behavior was of depression, moodiness, and preoccupation. Other symptoms included difficulty with sleeping (trouble falling asleep, sleeping restlessly, or sleeping more); bad dreams; nightmares; and startling easily.

Since disclosure, there is difficulty listening, not hearing people as clearly, trouble concentrating, and paying attention. Of major concern is the amount of aggression and violence felt displayed by the youths.

Symptoms noted under the age of 15 in the youths were primarily conduct behaviors: skipping school, running away, starting fights, forcing others to have sex, hurting an animal on purpose, hurting other people (other than in a fight), deliberately damaging things not their own, setting fires, lying, and stealing or robbing.

Treatment Issues. Some of the general treatment issues for the youths include the following:

- Attachment to a caring, therapeutic figure who is experienced in child and adolescent trauma. This attachment is critical to reduce the potential of the youth acting out in a self- or other-directed manner.
- Attention and assessment of the youth's thought processes. It is critical to find out what is on the youth's mind. For example, how entitled vs. disregarded did he feel in his family? Does he believe his family is uncaring? These are the premises laid down by the offender. He has been supported in transgressions by the offender. Are these thought still operant?
- The sexually abusive experience needs to be first linked with current symptoms. People can have a conscious awareness of upsetting events, but be totally incapable in connecting it to ongoing symptomatic behavior. The anger and rage is because of the violation, the exploitation, and the compromising. The defense of anger is easier to manage than to deal with the loss of innocence and the loss of the trusted coach who lied that they were special.

In conclusion, many of the youths are at a crossroad. They need to attach to a therapist in order to begin to trust and reduce anxiety. Then there can be work on the issues evolving from the traumatic experience. If the alienation from people continues, they will be at risk for acting on the aggressive and suicidal thoughts.

Transitional Child Sex Ring

The transitional child sex ring involves multiple offenders as well as multiple victims. The offenders are known to each other and collect and share victims.

Defining Characteristics

In the transition sex ring, multiple adults are involved sexually with children, and the victims are usually pubescent. The children are tested for their role as prostitutes and thus are high risks for advancing to the syndicated level of ring, although the organizational aspects of the syndicated ring are absent in transition rings. It is speculated that children enter these transition rings by several routes: (1) they may be children initiated into solo sex rings by pedophiles who lose sexual interest in the child as he or she approaches puberty and who may try, through an underground network, to move the vulnerable child into sexual activity with pederasts (those with sexual preferences for pubescent youths); (2) they may be incest victims who have run away from home and who need a peer group for identity and economic support; (3) they may be abused children who come from disorganized families in which parental bonding has been absent and multiple neglect and abuse are present; or (4) they may be missing children who have been abducted or kidnapped and forced into prostitution. It is difficult to identify clearly this type of ring because its boundaries are blurred and because the child may be propelled quite quickly into prostitution. Typically the adults in these transition rings do not sexually interact with each other, but instead have parallel sexual interests and involvements with the adolescents who exchange sex with adults for money as well as for attention or material goods.

Crime Scene Indicators

The crime scene can be the offenders' residence vehicle, group meeting hall, or hotel/motel. There are usually many locations. The pornographic material is usually hidden in the residences of the offenders. The most recent crime scene will usually have the camera or other equipment needed to create the pornography as well as props, collateral material, and goods used to bribe the victims.

Forensic Findings

The victimization is usually reported by a third party and little if any forensic evidence is immediately available. To obtain forensic evidence detailed medical and psychiatric examinations of the victims is required. In addition to the general forensic findings described above, there could be anal or vaginal scarring, bruises, and other injuries.

Investigative Considerations

Obtain a search warrant for the offenders' residences. Check telephone and financial records for purchases of materials needed to create the pornography. Be sensitive to props and collateral used to bribe the targeted age group. Interviews with the victims should be carefully done by an investigator specially trained for interviewing children.

Case Example of a Transitional Child Sex Ring

A classic case example is over 20 years old. From December 1977 to December 1978, Boston was in the spotlight regarding a male youth prostitution ring. Earlier that year, the investigation of a solo child sex ring had led an assistant district attorney and police to uncover a second generation of rings. In the apartment of a man who had an extensive history of convictions for child molesting, investigators found numerous photos of naked youths as well as pornographic films. Sixty-three of the depicted youths were located and interviewed, and 13 agreed to testify before a grand jury. From this testimony, additional men (many with professional and business credentials) were indicted on counts of rape and abuse of a child, indecent assault, sodomy, and unnatural acts.

By December 1978 the trial of the first defendant, a physician, began. Testimony from four prosecution witnesses revealed the linkages between the two types of rings. According to news reports, the first witness, a man who was serving a 15- to 25-year term after pleading guilty to charges derived from the child solo ring, admitted to having sexual relations with boys as young as 10 during the 13 years he had rented the apartment. He testified that he could be considered a "master male pimp" and that he became involved in the sex-for-hire operation after meeting one of the other defendants. He said that initially no money was involved, but after a few months, expenses increased, so the men were charged and the boys were given $5 to $10 for sexual services.

Newspapers reported that another prosecution witness, an assistant headmaster at a private boys school, admitted visiting the apartment more than 40 to 50 times over a five-year period. He denied being a partner in a scheme to provide boys for hire, but admitted to taking friends to the apartment with him and paying for having sex with the boys.

Victimology. A prosecution witness, a 17-year-old, testified to being introduced into sexual acts by the first witness, who had told the boys they could make all the money they wanted. "All we had to do was lay there and let them do what they wanted to us," he said.

Another victim testified that at age 12 he had met the third witness through friends. He received gifts of clothes and money for going to the man's apartment. While there, he would drink beer, smoke pot, and watch stag movies. He brought his younger brother to the apartment, and they both had sex with the man. At age 14 he was "turning tricks" and charging $10 for oral sex and $20 for anal sex. At that point he met the defendant.

Offender Characteristics. The defendant, a pediatrician and psychiatrist, claimed in his defense that he went to the apartment as part of a research study, which was submitted to a journal after his indictment and subsequently published in a sex research journal.

Outcome. The jury, sequestered for the 19-day trial, deliberated two- and-one-half days before reaching a verdict of guilty. The judge sentenced the physician to five years' probation on the condition he undergo psychiatric treatment. Over a year later the state's board of medicine revoked his license. The other defendants in the ring plea bargained their charges, and there were no further trials.

Syndicated Child Sex Ring

In a syndicated child sex ring, there is a well-structured organization that involves the recruitment of children, the production of pornography, the delivery of sexual services, and the establishment of an extensive network of customers.

Defining Characteristics

The syndicated ring involves multiple offenders as well as multiple victims. The syndicated child prostitution is a well-established commercial enterprise.

Crime Scene

There can be many locations. There are many levels of material created. Information and details about locations can be obtained from the pornography itself. Most recent location will have all the equipment necessary to create the material.

Forensic Findings

The victimization is usually reported by a third party and little if any forensic evidence is immediately available. To obtain forensic evidence detailed medical and psychiatric examinations of the victims is required.

Investigative Considerations

Investigation requires an understanding of typical operation of a syndicated ring. The organizational components of the syndicated ring include the items of trade, the circulation mechanisms, the supplier of the items, the self-regulating mechanism, the system of trades, and the profit aspect.

Items of Trade. Items of trade include the children, photographs, films, and tapes. The degree of sexual explicitness and activity may vary. For example, photographs range from so-called innocent poses of children in brief attire taken at public parks, swimming pools, arcades, or similar places where children congregate to carefully directed movies portraying child subjects in graphic sexual activities. In the films, the child is often following cues provided by someone standing off-camera. Also, in audiotapes the children may be heard conversing with age-appropriate laughter and noises as well as using language that is highly sexual and suggestive of explicit behaviors.

Circulation Mechanism. Various mechanisms for circulation include the mail (photographs, coded letters), tape cassettes, CB radio, telephone, and beepers. The mail is a major facilitator for circulation of child pornography. Often, a laundering process may be used. For example, buyers send their responses to another country; the mail, received by the overseas forwarding agent, is opened and cash or checks are placed in a foreign bank account; the order is remailed under a different cover back to the US. This procedure ensures that the subscriber does not know where the operation originates and that law enforcement has difficulty tracing the operation.

Suppliers. Suppliers of child pornography include pedophiles, professional distributors, and parental figures. Pedophiles with economic resources and community status may organize their own group to have access to children and to cover their illegal intentions, or they may work within the framework of existing youth organizations. The professional distributors include the pornographer, who has access to an illegal photographer, who in turn generally owns a clandestine photo laboratory and film processor. While these photo laboratories can provide services to many illegal operations, they also present some problems to the professional pornographers, who may find their photographs or films in magazines or adult bookstores without their knowledge and prior to their own distribution. The professional procurers who supply children also provide photographs and films through wholesale distributors and adult bookstores. Another source of professional distribution is photographic processing facilities. A photographic development laboratory often has a storefront business that handles photographic orders, such as holiday pictures, while its mail order business is advertised in magazines. One such facility had a mail-order division that promised, through its advertisements in "adult"" magazines, confidential photo finishing. These advertisements were also found in periodicals catering to clientele with special sexual interests.

Parental figures who supply children for pornographic and prostitution purposes include natural parents, foster parents, and group home workers. The supplier may operate a foster home as in the case of a self-acclaimed clergyman, who by his own estimates sold approximately 200,000 photos per year, with an income from this operation in excess of $60,000. The technique used by the man was to have older boys engage younger boys in sex acts. If a youth did not submit, he was beaten and abused by an older youth. After the youth submitted, he was photographed in the sexual acts, and the man would then use the boys for his own sexual purposes. In order to ensure secrecy, a pornographer often keeps a blackmail file on each boy.

Self-Regulating Mechanism. Syndicated child pornography operations do not have recourse to law enforcement or civil process for settling disputes that arise, such as theft, unauthorized duplication of photographs, or resources of supply. Thus a self-regulating mechanism develops for the elimination of members guilty of actions deemed unfair to or against the group through the grade of paper, typewriter keys, number of letters, as well as the sincerity and insistence of the correspondence. Letters are kept as a security measure. Recriminations between the offender and guilty party become extremely bitter, and support by fellow members in chastising the guilty party is solicited through immediate correspondence. Members of the syndicates are alert to law enforcement efforts against the group in general or with respect to their syndicate in particular.

System of Trade. One rule for trading is that members of the syndicate may assist each other in finding items of interest to other collectors. Through a system of trades, photographs held by syndicate members are traded, and those pictures chosen to be retained are kept by the receiving member.

Profit. The financial profit of child pornography appears to be an individual matter. Some collectors trade items for their personal use, and others trade items for personal as well as commercial purposes. The financial lure of pornography is seen in the actual cost of production and verified in the correspondence of the pornographers. Frequently collectors who sell photographs actually are selling duplicate copies of items in their collection, thereby having income to purchase additional photographs from other sources. Identification of additional victims can be made from the pornography obtained with a search warrant.

Case Example of a Syndicated Child Sex Ring

A child sex ring involved 10 boys and one girl. In October 1977, information regarding the offende, Paul, was brought to the attention of a West coast FBI office. The children involved ranged in age from eight to 16. Paul befriended a family with two boys and one girl; both parents worked. The parents grew to trust Paul and invited him to live in their house, renting out a bedroom to him. Paul kept the refrigerator supplied with food and bought toys and clothes for the children. He drove a Cadillac equipped with a telephone, and he handed out business cards advertising a 24-hour limousine service that he provided with his Cadillac. At one point, Paul made his child prostitutes wear beepers, calling the child he thought would best suit his customer's desires. Paul was constantly trying to recruit more children, and he would pick up runaways and use the children to recruit others. Paul would charge $100 or more for an hour with one of his child prostitutes, the price depending on the market, the child's age, the length of time with the child, or what the customer was going to do with this child.

Paul never gave any of his child prostitutes money, as he felt this would ruin them. Instead he provided food and clothing, bought them various toys, and took them to amusement parks, sporting events, movie shows, or roller rinks.

Offender. The offender kept an apartment in a complex with a swimming pool and tennis courts. He used this apartment as a "crash pad" for many of his child prostitutes, and they used the pool and tennis courts. The older boys were told by Paul to keep the younger ones in line.

Paul was sexually involved with several of his child prostitutes and provided Quaaludes to all of the children. He also had a sizable collection of child pornography, including eight-millimeter films and photographs.

Outcome. Because it was determined that no federal laws applied to Paul's activities, the case was turned over to local police. In November 1977, Paul was convicted on seven felony counts (19 felony counts were dismissed), and in May 1978 he was sentenced to 13 years' imprisonment and was declared a mentally disturbed sex offender.

Reprinted with permission from Burgess AW, Holmstrom LL. *Rape: Crisis and Recovery*. West Newton, MA: Awab; 1986.

Chapter 28 – Predatory on Web, Molester Tangled

US v. Reinhart 975 F.Supp, 834 (W.D.La. 1997)

Robert Reinhart and Matthew Carroll shared a trailer in which the government found a large amount of child pornography. Reinhart was arrested and indicted on 13 charges relating to acts of child molestation, possession of child pornography, and using the Internet to distribute child pornography. Carroll also faced charges, although he was only indicted on three counts. The government moved under the Bail Reform Act for the court to issue a detention order for Reinhart. Under the Act, it is not enough for the government to show that a defendant is a danger to the community. The government must also show that one of six circumstances outlined in the Act also applied to the defendant.

The government, in support of its motion to detain Reinhart, alleged that two of the factors applied: that Reinhart had committed a crime of violence and that there was a substantial risk that he would flee from prosecution. In support of its claim, the government produced evidence of a videotape showing Reinhart performing sexual acts with 13- and 14-year-old boys. Further, Carroll testified that Reinhart had engaged in improper sexual contact with boys on several occasions. The government also produced information from Reinhart's website, advising on how to maintain relationships with young boys. Additionally, the government described videos that showed Reinhart and Carroll giving direction to young boys performing sexual acts, as well as feeding them responses for use in a sexually explicit "chat room." Finally, a clinical psychologist who specialized in the field of sexual abuse of children testified that exclusive pedophiles, adults who are primarily attracted to children of the same sex, are rarely treated successfully. She likened treating an exclusive pedophile to "training a heterosexual to become a homosexual."

As for Reinhart's risk of flight, the government offered the Probation Office's Pretrial Services Reports, which showed that Reinhart had no ties to the community, no home (since the government seized Carroll's trailer), almost no assets, and no family members who would support him. The government also produced a tape containing a statement from Reinhart that he would flee if prosecuted.

The government's motion was granted. The court held that the evidence produced by the government was enough to establish that Reinhart posed a risk of danger to the community, particularly to young males; that he had committed a crime of violence; and that there was a serious risk that he would flee.

While the court granted the government's motion for pretrial detention, this case is critically important for its illustration of the use of the Internet as a tool for pedophiles and child pornographers. This case clearly links a pedophile's use of technology to access children for sexual purposes, to gain control over the child and his family, to recruit new victims, and to communicate with other pedophiles. The amount of detail, care, and compulsiveness that is demonstrated in the profile of a career pedophile is exemplified in this case.

Pedophile's social networks are other pedophiles. They socialize, telephone, write letters, e-mail, network, and share strategies for continuing their deviant relationships with children even when in prison. In Florida, one convicted child pornographer used his prison post office box number to expanded his distribution of child pornography until he was discovered.

Pedophiles can move from an isolated position of solo operator into a network of perpetrators, e.g., Reinhart had a codefendant. It is no wonder that we now see the elaborate and organized networking that is well underway on the Internet both nationally and internationally. This case emphasizes the Internet pedophile as an entrepreneur having a product line on his own home page. Reinhart provides advice to a chat room correspondent on how to build a long-term relationship with a young boy, how to manipulate parents so they do not "cause problems," and teaches his victims how to answer questions about the ongoing sexual relationship. Reinhart videotaped himself instructing his victim on how to type in responses to sexually oriented questions being sent from a chat room. His home page contained images of nude children and his victims as well as an image of his own penis; he had a minor assist in the scanning of his genitalia, an act serving as a permanent document of his sexual entrapment of the boy.

Pedophiles are totally preoccupied with their sexual interest in children. The probation office identified nine jobs Reinhart held between 1986 and 1997 in four states. His obsession with the Internet was noted in his owning several computers while living in a trailer. The reason for his job instability would answer whether the job was in the service of sexual deviation or whether his compulsion for children interfered with his work productivity.

This case reveals the inner workings of pedophiles and child pornographers. The general public can now access all dimensions of child sexual exploitation through the Internet. They can call up a pedophile's home page or talk with him in a chat room. Although Internet pedophile activities will lose their clandestine nature, it means the pedophile can be more discriminate in selecting and testing his victims by remaining anonymous.

The Internet pedophile is sophisticated in the investigative aspects and has developed ways to bypass the restrictions, e.g., the growing use of encryption. Investigators report that such coded messages are sometimes impossible to intercept.

A critical question is whether or not children can be protected from the Internet pedophile. In March 1997, Senate hearings examined the risks of victimization to children in cyberspace. The result was the March 1998 establishment of the CyberTipline (www.missingkids.com/cybertip). The tipline has been created at the National Center for Missing and Exploited Children for parents to report suspicious or illegal Internet activity online. The intent is to ensure that the Internet not be allowed to become a sanctuary for pedophiles, child pornographers, and others who prey upon children,

Reprinted with permission from the Forensic Panel, New York, NY. For subscription information write *The Forensic Panel Letter*, 58 East 79th Street, Suite 4R, New York, NY 10021or call (212) 396-3246.

Chapter 29 – Forensic Nursing and Violent Schoolboys

Ann Wolbert Burgess, RN, DNSc and Elizabeth B. Dowdell, RN, PhD

Forensic, a Latin term meaning an open or public forum, describes one of the newest and most dramatic nursing specialties. Nurses in this specialty combine healthcare with their biopsychological skills to investigate criminal activity, traumatic accidents, and treat victims of violence.[1] Within the open forum of the judicial system, nurses can serve as fact witnesses who explain findings from their nursing assessments and interventions to juries. They also serve as consulting or expert witnesses who review previously collected documents and evidence and render an expert opinion.

Many forensic nurses focus on interpersonal violence. At one time, schools – a workplace for students, teachers, and nurses – were considered safe. But there is growing alarm that violence on school grounds and inside school buildings is increasing in the aftermath of several high-profile cases of shooting homicides in these settings. School, community, emergency, and psychiatric nurses can play a better role in the prevention of violence understanding the dynamics and youth profiles behind four recent homicides.

Classifying Homicides

Just as the identification of the organism that causes pneumonia determines a pharmacological intervention, homicides classified by motive provide "why" the offender killed and can assist in prosecution, direct a legal defense, define a psychological intervention, and render information for violence prevention programs. The Crime Classification Manual[2] is the result of a 10-year project by the Behavioral Science Unit at the FBI Academy to classify violent crimes in order to standardize language for the apprehension of suspects and to encourage research among law enforcement agents and mental health professionals. Using this manual, four recent school shootings were classified as personal-cause homicides and subtyped as nonspecific, revenge, patricide/matricide, and authority homicides.

Personal-cause homicide is an act of interpersonal aggression that results in death to people who may not know each other. This homicide is not motivated by material gain or sexual intent and is not sanctioned by a group. It is the result of an underlying emotional conflict that propels the offender to kill.[2]

Nonspecific Homicide

A nonspecific-motive homicide appears irrational and is committed for a reason known only to the offender. Nonspecific homicides are usually committed during the daytime and in public; the offender wants as many victims as possible. The crime scene poses a high risk of capture to the offender. It is a disorganized crime scene with no effort made to conceal the victim. A firearm, the weapon of choice for this offender, is brought to the scene. This crime often becomes a massacre caused by guns that offer optimal lethality and an abundance of ammunition. The motive for such killings remains with the offender, who may be unable to state why he committed the killing.[2]

Case 1. On December 1, 1997, in West Paducah, KY, Michael Carneal, age 14, entered his high school and opened fire on a prayer meeting just before the start of class, killing three and wounding five. Carneal had previously warned classmates that "something big" would happen. When a friend pushed him to a wall to stop him, he said, "Kill me please. I can't believe I did that."[3,4]

The crime scene in Kentucky was disorganized, but the shooting was planned. Carneal came armed with a gun into a contained area and fired at random with no plan of escape or escape route. Victims fell where they were shot. Additional killings were contained due to the quick capture of Carneal by a peer.

Of note in this case is the prior warning and bragging about the prospect of killing. The perpetrator feels an alienation from others and little regard for the value of life, except his own. The shooting during the prayer meeting indicates knowledge of the school schedule and that students would be together as a contained target. It is unclear if there was any motive against the prayer meeting. Carneal's second statement that he be killed suggests suicide by proxy, that is, the authorizing of someone to commit the act.

Revenge Homicide

Revenge killing involves the murder of another person in retaliation for perceived wrongs, real or imagined, committed against the offender. The victim may not personally know the offender, but something in the victim's life is related directly to the offender's actions. A significant event or interaction links the offender to the victim. Multiple victims may be involved, depending on the nature of the event that triggered the act of revenge.[2]

Case 2. On March 24, 1998, at 12:35 PM, Andrew Golden, age 11, pulled a fire alarm in an elementary school in Jonesboro, Arkansas. He and Mitchell Johnson, age 13, sat on a hill 100 yards away and opened fire on students and teachers filing out of the school. In less than four minutes, they had fired 22 rounds of ammunition and wounded 15, only one of whom was male. Five were killed. Johnson's cousin was quoted as saying that Mitchell said he would kill to be in a gang and had started wearing the color red, symbol of the gang "Bloods."[3,4]

The crime scene was organized and focused from a distance. The shootings were well strategized and calculated. Instead of taking the morning school bus, the two stole Johnson's stepfather's van, which they stocked with food, camouflage, netting, ammunition, hunting knives, and survival gear. They drove to Golden's parents' home and stole three guns that were unsecured and then drove to Golden's grandfather's home, breaking in and stealing four handguns and three rifles. They next drove to an elevated site 100 yards from the school and parked the van with a clear view of the school's playground. Cover was provided by high grass and trees. Golden was observed pulling the fire alarm shortly after noon.

After the shooting, their escape was planned, but not well enough. Construction workers saw gunsmoke rising from the woods and called police, who disarmed them as they headed toward their getaway van. There was little or no remorse when arrested. They were silent during the drive to the sheriff's office. The next day when Golden was denied pizza for lunch in jail, he began to cry, begging for his mother.[3,5]

Two very different youths came together to commit this crime. Golden grew up as the little freedom fighter pictured on a Time magazine cover – a toddler in fatigues, holding a rifle.[5] He became proficient with guns and had a reputation for being "mean-spirited." He wore military fatigues and talked of hunting and shooting targets. Parents kept their sons from playing with him, and so he felt shunned by his peers.

Johnson is portrayed as a boy with a grudge, angry at many things and empowered with a gun. He had a long history of trouble. His behavior was said to deteriorate after his parents' divorce; he had charges pending of molesting a very young girl in Minnesota before he moved to Arkansas.

Patricide/Matricide Homicide

Patricide or matricide homicide, a type of domestic homicide, involves a child who kills his father, mother, or both. The killings are triggered either by a recent stressful event or by a cumulative buildup of stress. The offender is mission-oriented.[2]

Case 3. In October 1997, Luke Woodham, age 16, was charged for the stabbing death of his mother and the shooting deaths of two classmates in Pearl, MS. When restrained by the assistant principal, he said, "The world has wronged me, and I couldn't take it anymore." After he was convicted in June 1998, and given three life sentences, he said, "If they could have given the death penalty in this case, I deserve it." At trial, he testified that he had told his mother she did not love him and that she called him names and picked on him. He claimed the heartbreak of losing his girlfriend and fascination with occult rituals led to the stabbing of his mother and to his reign of terror over classmates. He told jurors he fell under the spell of 19-year-old Grant Boyette, whom he described as both a mentor and a tormentor who introduced him to the occult. Boyette and several others of the cult group, the "Kroth," were charged with conspiracy in the school shootings.[3,6]

In the Woodham case, there are two crime scenes. The mother's death by stabbing indicates a close personal killing. The triggering event is not known. The crime scene for the student shootings is disorganized in that there is no escape route and Woodham is well identified and captured at the scene. Woodham's statements are a narcissistic generalization of being wronged, unloved, and teased; the youth positions himself against the world implying he is so important that everyone is out to get him and wrong him.

Authority Killing

An authority killing involves a subject who kills people who have an authority or symbolic relationship by which the killer perceives that he or she has been wronged. The target of the assault may be people or a building, structure, or institution that symbolizes the authority. Random victims are often wounded or killed during the assault as a result of their actual or perceived association with the authority figure or institution under attack.[2]

The offender is mission-oriented and enters the crime scene with the mission as the ultimate priority. He has little or no intention to abort the plan and escape from the scene or from responsibility for the act. The offender may desire to die at the scene, either by suicide or police bullets, and thereby attain martyrdom for his acts. Because of the obsession of being wronged over a period of a time, the offender gathers and usually brings multiple weapons to the scene of the confrontation. The assault may develop into a mass or spree killing.[2]

Case 4. In Springfield, OR, on May 21, 1998, 15-year-old Kipland Kinkel was tackled to the cafeteria floor of the local high school after opening fire and shooting 22 students, two of whom died. Earlier he had shot his parents to death at home. He was stopped by a wounded student who realized Kinkel had emptied his gun of bullets. Kinkel asked the police officer who led him away to shoot him.[7]

Killing parents is a close and personal act of focused emotion, usually rage or anger. In Kinkel's case, there was a triggering event in which teachers and parents restricted him from his guns. When Kinkel killed his parents, it was focused rage. He then went to school where he killed at random. The anger was targeted at the school symbolically to include peers and teachers. The rage was unfocused. Although Kinkel was able to kill his parents and others, he couldn't quite kill himself. He wanted someone else to do it. The dynamics of murder and suicide by proxy are involved.

This domestic homicide combines the killing of both parents. When a parent is killed and then classmates and/or teachers are killed, the dynamics are compounded. Both Woodham and Kinkel killed their parents and then went after others whom they felt wronged them. The attachment to the parents was shallow, disruptive, and superficial. Parents are an annoyance. In the parent and peer shootings, somehow both become enemies.

Violent Youth Profile

Thinking drives behavior, and troubled youths live in an inner fantasy world with constant thoughts of anger, revenge, retribution, and justifiable rage. They think of violent solutions to perceived offenses against them. Although "offenses" by others can be minor, such as being told to study for class or clean a room, it involves control by authority.

Consider the neurobiology of homicidal thoughts and actions. Ages 13 and 14 are critical in boys for the shifting and onset of hormones. They experience a growth spurt and a kind of quasi-introduction to the adult male world. Anger may be very strong at this time, especially if a boy thinks he is exempt from rules and has a right to fight anyone who sets a limit, restricts, or criticizes him. This view of himself is heightened if there has been little constraint on his aggressive acts, such as killing animals or picking on younger children. If he is in the company of authority figures who use aggression exclusively to solve problems, the boy may have no one to whom he can channel or understand his frustration and angry feelings. Instead, he acts with little concern for consequences either to self or to others with a sense of justification. These youths, in essence, say, "You treated me disrespectfully; that is why I had to blow your head off."

When troubled juveniles have minimal bonding to people, are not involved in school, and lack a sense of participating and getting along with others, their increased isolation reinforces reliance on their own internal psychological worlds. In the case of these violent juveniles, that internal psychological world is filled with bitterness, resentment, and rage.

The year before the Kinkel homicides, his parents discovered he was downloading bomb-making instructions from the Internet and building bombs. His role model was Ted Kaczynski, the "Unabomber." Police found five sophisticated bombs and 15 other inactive explosive devices in the Kinkel home.[8] The parents had tried to discipline Kinkel by enrolling him into anger-management counseling, and the guns that he used were said to have been bought by his father in an attempt to redirect his fascination with weapons into a supervised hobby. But the day before the shootings, he was suspended from school for carrying a weapon onto school property and subsequently released to his parents' custody. That evening, his parents had taken away his weapons. The next day he killed them. On one hand, Kinkel's parents tried to help him by getting psychiatric care, but on the other hand, gave him a gun and materials for a bomb Ð mixed messages for their son.

Paul Mones, a criminal attorney who defends juveniles who have killed a parent, describes the profile of these juveniles: They are disproportionately white, middle-class boys, who have never been arrested. If they have a record, it is for vandalism, shoplifting, or playing hooky. They are often loners, anxious to please their peers, and overly polite to adults.[9] There are few documented cases of girls showing such violence; no one knows why.

One cause of this developmental situation in juveniles is interpersonal failure or conflict. For example, failure in school or peer relationships or rejection by a group can precipitate acting out against peers or authority. Frustration, accompanied by the inability to handle or resolve such situations, are precipitating events. Suicidal thoughts or attempts before killing are common.

Nurses Preventing Violence

Nurses can prevent youth violence in several ways. First, be educated about violent youth. Become knowledgeable about motives and dynamics of killings, injuries, or other violent events that go on around you; discuss them with colleagues. Second, if you are involved as a healthcare worker, provide careful documentation in recordings. Third, learn the early warning signs of teen violence to involve parents and teachers in working with the youth and to recommend mental health referrals. Dangerousness is always difficult to assess. Nursing staff in psychiatric hospitals, emergency departments (ED), clinics, schools, and the community have struggled with this for years. General profile characteristics exist, but no formula or observations that are totally accurate.

School and Community: School nurses have access to school children. In addition to being aware of violent youth profile characteristics that place children at risk for aggressive behavior, pay attention and listen for youths who are communicating threats. This information demands immediate referral to the school administration for a team conference to determine a strategy for addressing the threat. In case 4, Kinkel had been identified in middle school by his peers as the "kid most likely to start WW III."[7,8]

Nurses who work in community settings, such as primary care health clinics and homes, can help identify potentially violent youth. Their assessments should explore family and school life, threats or acts of aggression, and concerns by the family, peers, and teachers. Partnerships with the school team and teachers are critical. Aggressive behavior should not be normalized as "just adolescence." Also, chronic depression can manifest as excessive moodiness, anger, projecting blame to others, and aggressive acts. Over 50% of 25 homicidal children studied by one research team were found to have suicidal ideation at some point in their lives.[10] If threatened or actual violent behavior is observed, the nurse should explore further by talking with the youth and his peers and find out what is going on in his life, including positive events. Is he happy or accomplishing things? If these pieces are missing, more evaluation may be needed. These youths may be at risk of acting out, and in cases with clear warning signs, residential treatment may be necessary to protect the youth, his family and peers, and society.

ED: Emergency nurses become involved when a patient is admitted for trauma care as a result of crime-related injuries or for psychological evaluation due to behavior before committing a homicide. These cases require precise assessment and documentation of injuries to collect and preserve forensic evidence and coordinate critical data with law enforcement and crime scene officers.[11] Hospital EDs are regularly in contact with essential evidence in criminal cases. The most common types are clothing, bullets, bloodstains, hairs, fibers, and small pieces of material, such as fragments of metal, glass, paint, wood, and other substances.

Documentation is a key interfacing with the judicial system. Forensic nurses need to provide objective documentation and record significant data as dictated by the nature and extent of a situation or injury. As with any documentation, the record must hold up in court as a clear, concise presentation of the facts.

Psychiatric Nursing: Advance practice psychiatric nurses have the skills and expertise to provide psychological assessment of violent youth. For example, youths who talk about bombing, shooting, and killing; have access to weapons; or have acted in some violent manner, such as torturing animals, have the potential for expressing their anger and emotions through further violent actions. If a nurse identifies such a youth, the family needs to be notified and a referral for professional help should be made. Nurses should pay attention to the anger level of youths who are preoccupied with violent fantasies Ð ingredients for violent acts. The question is: Why is a youth thinking up angry, violent acts, rather than thinking about how to solve a math problem, build a computer, or pitch a good game? Is the youth depressed? If the family background is fraught with poor communication, abuse, or disenfranchised relationships, then chances increase that the youth will act on his emotional turmoil. Youth who are oppositional, uncooperative, and angry need professional attention. If they complain they are being treated unfairly and blame others, a professional evaluation needs to be made about how they process their experiences.

When nurses come in contact with potentially violent youths, standard information should include the nature of the visit or interaction, statements placed within quotations, and complaints and findings. Any action taken on a statement should also be in the record, as well as follow-up conversations or services that were provided for the client. For example, in case 4, services had been identified for Kinkel by his parents, including records indicating that referrals had been made and the family was in the process of following up. In fact, Kinkel's father called the director of a residential program for troubled teens. According to the director, Mr. Kinkel was honest about his son's problems, but indicated he did not feel that he would have any trouble with his son.[7] Later that evening, Kip shot and killed his parents. Investigators on the case are hopeful that the records will further assist them to understand what motivated him to kill.

Nurses are in prime positions to assess violent youths because they have access to them, their families, and their potential victims in the workplace, community, the schools, and inpatient and psychiatric settings. Nurses can hopefully intervene in a manner that not only identifies the risks, but protects others and the youth himself from violence.

References
1. American Nurses Association. *Scope and Standards of Forensic Nursing Practice.* Washington, DC: Standards Committee of the International Association of Forensic Nurses; 1997.
2. Douglas JE, Burgess AW, Burgess AG, Ressler RK. *Crime Classification Manual.* San Francisco: Jossey-Bass; 1992.
3. Lacayo R. Toward the root of the evil. *Time.* 1998;151(13):38-39.
4. Grace J. When the silence fell. *Time.* 1997;150(25):45-46.
5. Labi N. Two boys and their guns. *Time.* 1998;151(13):19-37.
6. Cloud J. When boys go bad. *Time.* 1998;151(26):58-62.
7. King P, Murr A. A son who spun out of control. *Newsweek.* 1998;130(June):32-3.
8. Hornblower M. The boy who loved bombs. *Time.* 1998;151(21:42-44.
9. Mones P. *When a Child Kills.* New York, NY: Pocket Book; 1991.
10. Myers WC, Scott K, Burgess AW, Burgess AG. Psychopathology, biopsychosocial factors, crime characteristics, and classification of 25 homicidal youths. *J Am Acad Child Adolesc Psychiatry.* 1995;34:1483-9.
11. Burgess AW. *Advance Practice in Psychiatric Nursing.* Stamford, CT: Appleton & Lang; 1998.

Reprinted from *Nursing Spectrum*, Greater Philadelphia/Tri-State edition. 1999;8(3):12-14.

Chapter 30 – Adolescent Runaways

Ann Wolbert Burgess and Carol R. Hartman

Critical perspectives on social institutions are often best obtained from exiles, that is, persons who leave those institutions.[1] This is perhaps why exiles' views are frequently disparaged as deviant and, in some cases, are conspicuously silenced. Runaways and the homeless, like high school dropouts, fit this pattern very well. Many of these adolescent males and females have been pushed out of the home; some have opted out; all are regarded as failures. Labeling runaways as "bad" or "wayward," "delinquent" or "helpless" shifts attention away from the social institution of the family or the foster home from which the youth flees.

We will use the colloquial term "runaway" throughout, with an understanding that many of these youths have been kicked out, forced out, or never allowed into the spotlight in the family. Despite many runaways' critical perspectives on family life, they are frequently portrayed as "losers." In our culture, adolescent runaways who are also homeless represent individuals who challenge the dominant belief that allegiance to family values leads to school and work success, which are employment and income guarantees.

We will argue that this image delegitimizes the runaways critique of families and the promise of achievement, and preserves the legitimacy of family as a social harmonizer. The critic is functionally silenced and maintains his or her exile, feeling "different" and "alienated" not only from their family, but from their childhood peers. They are forced, in a sense, to reconstruct their family on the street.

Before we continue, we do not wish to romanticize adolescents who run away from home. Clearly, some do feel hopeless; others may not be capable of staying in the home; there may be threats to the family. But neither can we neglect evidence that suggests a more radical potential within many of these youths. Their critical voices are rarely heard; they do not feel important in their family; they are not valued as family members; and social institutions (foster homes, group homes, detention homes) follow an equally dismal perception of the runaway seeking shelter.

Central to the analysis of adolescent runaways is the question of whether the "runaway problem" is one of individual differences and inadequacies or one of family structure. One position maintains that incapable adolescents seek their own level and drop out because of individual inadequacies. Another holds families responsible for failing to integrate their child into the family system due to family conflict. A third suggest youth maltreatment, usually by parents or caretakers.

What happens to adolescents who run away? Do they, as often prophesized, fill welfare roles, collect unemployment, and populate our prisons at disproportionate rates? If not, what becomes of them? In either case, do these outcomes result because these youths lack personal strengths or that the structure of a home environment has eroded?

The Toronto Study

Motivated by the continued debate about the nature and consequences of running away, we received permission to conduct a study of adolescents seeking shelter at Toronto's Under 21. This Canadian Covenant House provides temporary emergency shelter to runaways. Adolescents average three nights at the shelter. Staff counselors, specially trained in the objectives and protocol for the study, recruited adolescents who consented to participate.

Canadian Runaways

What emerged from the demographic data on the original 149 runaways follows. Of that number, 63% were males and 37% were females. Their ages range from 15 to 20 years with a mean of 17.9 years. The majority were white (81%); 9% were black and runaways of other racial groups (e.g., native Indian) made up the remaining 10%. At the time of running, 90 runaways (62.5%) were living with their families, and 54 (37.2%) ran away from institutional settings and/or foster homes.

There was a strong history of abuse reported by the runaways: 40% reported that they had been attacked or raped; 73% reported being physically beaten with 43% ranking physical abuse as a reason for running; 51% reported having been offered money for sex; 36% reported being forced to have sex; 31% reported having been sexually molested; and 19% reported being forced to witness sexual activity against their will as in pornographic materials. Verbal abuse was reported by 51% of the runaways as a very important reason for running. However, the most important reason for running, reported by 54% youths, was an unhappy life.

Runaways report first leaving home from four years to 19 years: 23.8% ran as a preteen; 36.4% ran as an early adolescent (age 13-15), and 39.8% ran as a late adolescent (age 16-19). Of the 34 pre-teen runaways, 85% reported physical abuse compared to 69% who left as an early adolescent and 70% who left as an older adolescent. The finding that preteen runaways are more likely to report physical abuse holds for both males and females. When looking at the incidence of sexual abuse, 59% of the preteen runners reported sexual abuse compared to 55% of the early adolescent and 44% of the older adolescents. The relationship between the reporting of sexual abuse and the age when they first left home is stronger for females than males. Preteens and females who first leave home between 13 and 15 years are much more likely to report sexual abuse than females who first left home as an older adolescent (p=.05). Runaways report leaving home from one to 110 times and almost half (46%) have left home more than three times.

Of the 110 runaways who estimated their family/household income, 41% report incomes higher than most people, 39% report incomes about the same as others, and 20% report incomes lower than most people. The percentage reporting "higher than most people" (41%) is consistent with the finding that 45% of families are supported by both mothers and fathers salaries or wages. Thirty-two percent are supported by fathers only, 15% by mothers only, and 7% by general relief.

In terms of family structure, 69% report a divorce or breakup in the family, and 45% report that one or both parents have remarried after divorce.

The majority of runaways (69%) claim that religion is of no or limited importance in family life. This is consistent with the finding that 50% of runaways claim no personal religious affiliation and 35% claim no major family religious affiliation.

The majority (77%) of runaways report having had trouble with either school officials or employers. Sixty-one percent had been suspended or expelled from school. Despite the problems with school, 87% of the runaways said there was a time they thought they could make it in school.

In terms of family relationships, almost all (94%) runaways report having had a serious argument with one or both parents, and 88% report serious arguments in the family. About one-third (32%) report that someone in their family had to go to court or had been arrested for a serious violation.

The profile derived from the demographic data suggests that a runner emerges from a family which has some economic concerns, but is more characterized as a broken home, high in conflict, with parents arguing. The runaways gave a variety of reasons for running, ranking family life intolerable and replete with physical, sexual, and verbal abuse. In turn, the youths also reported their family's dissatisfaction with them. The runners also describe a difficult history of adjustment in school, with authority figures, and with religion.

We began our study with the question: Why do urban adolescents run away from home. Running away has been described as a response to abuse. On the surface this statement makes sense. The complexity of the statement resides in the fact that those who are abused and run frequently return only to run again. This strikes a poignant cord in attempting to describe patterns of running and what factors in the child and social environment support the running phenomena. Thus, we have to ask a parallel but equally compelling question: And why do they return home? The repetitious behavior directs a model that considers how a child is attached to an abusive environment. The model derived from studying the pathways for running suggests that a cognitive style of runaways, which emerges out of the context of their family life, acts as a mediating factor in the cyclic running phenomena.

The pathways in the model represent the alternatives youths have for running. In the four pathways identified in this study, the youth can run to or from: the family, the institution, the street, and the shelter. The family represents the youth's family of origin (intact or separated) or the reconstituted family. The street represents the open environment that is unprotective, enticing, and exploitative, and includes subways, abandoned buildings, or other living arrangements. Institutions are pseudo home facilities, such as foster or group homes. They may include legal or health facilities, such as juvenile hall, mental institutions, correctional facilities, or jail. The shelter is a protective, temporary arrangement, which provides food, bed, and some form of companionship. It may be provided by a friend, church group, or other human service organization. The primary launching base for running for this sample was home (63%); a secondary launching base was an institution or group home (37%). The cycle patterns of running can be: (1) family to street to shelter to family; (2) street to institution, shelter to street; or (3) family to institution, shelter or family. Again there can be variations on this cycling.

There are two outcomes to running. The positive outcome includes social adaptation, such as work, school, or family. Some are able to break out of the cycle and work sporadically (about one-third of the sample). Some of the runaways reported on their reproductive history: 23% of the males said they had fathered a child and 30% of the females reported having been pregnant. The negative outcome, however, is the more dominant pattern. Once on the street, the outcome can be prostitution, criminal activity, drugs, or death by suicide, drug overdose, or murder.

This model of pathways and cycles of runaway youths highlights how little stands between the runaway and negative life outcomes of delinquent behavior, substance abuse and prostitution. For a ruanway caught in the cycle, the bottom line is survival. Work is not a frequent accomplishment. Shelters are turned to, but are of temporary assistance. The street and shelter become mediating factors for the youth and the family or other institutions. None of these environments are free from potential abuse and stress. The societal options are problematic in themselves and what operates in the youth that does not lead to self sufficiency and a safe productive life is equally important in contributing to the repetitious run.

The primary premise of the runaway model is that the internal beliefs of the youth regarding themselves and expectations of the parents and others plays a critical role in the cyclic phenomena. The belief that other people, such as family or caretakers, control events and that the events are unpredictable belies a seriously confused perception of others, oneself, and what can be expected. It is this cognitive confusion which plays a major role in the thinking patterns of the youths. Neither they nor their family can be held accountable for unpredictable events, yet somehow all "should" be responsible, yet are ineffective and unable to right confusing interpersonal relationships.

The expectations that things "should" be different links the youth back to the family. This works for the parents as well as the youth. The youth believes that the parent "should" change and that they "should" be able to change, also. It is suspected that exploration of the reason for "unhappy life" and the content of the "verbal abuse" would detail interpersonal experiences within the family in which there is great confusion with regard to what each member expects of themselves and others. While a belief that things "can change" is essential for productive living, a belief that things "should change" without sensing one and another's reasonable capacities for change, can only result in repeated disappointment. No change occurs; consequently, there is a repetition of nonproductive behaviors and cycles of running.

Returning home or to the unsatisfactory launching site can be expected because there is little basis for generating alternatives in the minds of these youths. One could also speculate that time away from a painful, confusing environment might be followed after a time by forgetting or disbelieving or questioning whether it was "that bad."

The runaways are highly symptomatic. They presented many symptoms of depression, anxiety, self-criticism, somatization, low energy, and self-destructive thinking. In addition, they reported physical and verbal fights among peers and confusion with their sexual identity. At the same time they report peers admire them, think well of them, believe themselves to be pleasant-appearing; they are happy, yet feel alienated and isolated in personal contacts. These findings support our notions that patterns of expectations of this youthful population tend to be inconsistent and not very operable for successful living on their own. In essence they vacillate from feeling good about themselves to feeling terrible. There is little tolerance for the frustration of learning and their ability to evaluate their performance and correct behaviors to achieve possible goals is distorted. Needless to say drugs and alcohol occupy their activities. They report little pleasure in their lives or in their lives at home.

Family life is reported to be highly stressful and one in which children are given little support, time, or attention. The child is not allowed to express feelings in an open way and the family atmosphere is laced with hostility and anger. The youth has not been encouraged to stand up for his or her own rights or to handle life problems. There has been a high emphasis on competition. The family is inflexible in its rules. It is important to note that it is not one factor alone that is detrimental to the youth but a combination of factors.

It is assumed that high levels of parental expectations, particularly expectations that are not able to be met, are delivered within a context of abuse. While a child may early recognize that the parents are wrong, because of their dependency and desire to love and be loved by the parents, they tend to strive to meet the expectations or in the face of failing rebel. Now this behavior becomes the focus of the family, and the child is blamed, getting into more trouble and being identified as the troublemaker. The stress increases and the child leaves. In those situations where the abuse is not recognized, the child begins to believe that she or he is depriving the family and they would be better off without them. For older adolescents who are asked to leave, their inability to function is usually tied in with asocial behavior, drugs, and sexual behaviors.

The gender differences in blame patterns (men internalizing blame and women externalizing blame) suggest a differential response to sexual abuse by runaway males and females implying a difference to the type of abuse, methods of psychologically controlling the victims, and family dynamics that support confusing and unreasonable expectations of runaways.

While the data collected cannot establish a causal link between this structure of thinking and sexual abuse, it supports clinical studies that suggest the control measures via the blame mechanism used by the adults to sexually exploit children impact strongly on the child's thinking and reasoning.[2] We mean by control that the child keeps the abuse secret, feels compelled to continue in the abusive relationship, and that in some way does not act against the abuser. This only occurs because the abuser selects strategies that can control a particular child. The child's sense that he or she is being exploited and abused is disqualified by the adult. Control is maintained at some level by the child believing he or she is responsible. Even though at another level the youth may not assume responsibility for the abuse, the self destructive patterns of behavior manifested in acting out, such as running, being sexually indiscriminant, and using drugs, reveals the personal disregard.

We speculate that the majority of sexually abused female runaways were victims of intrafamily sexual abuse, while the sexually abused runaway male was victimized external to the family. There is evidence that boys' experience in sex rings,[2] where they are in part held hostage in sexually abusive relationships with adults by committing predatory acts on peers causes them to hold themselves more accountable for participating in the sexual activity. When they become the victimizers, they assume the power and control (i.e., able to change the roles). The girls' experiences to the sexual entrapment in the family is to respond by running – i.e., they do not see themselves responsible (blame others) but they see abuse as unpredictable and uncontrollable. The sense of a capacity for personal change fits with existing gender differences in the socialization of males around power and control. Men blaming themselves are focused on issues of personal control as well as control of their environment. They may act out their sexual exploitation; they may hide it; they may try to reduce self blame through fantasies of sexual power and prowess.

In summary, there is no modification of expectations or development of reasonable self control for the runaway; rather the youth becomes polarized between unattainable expectations and nothing. He or she becomes cognitively confused and is unable to gain perspective of him or herself and the social world. Sexual and physical abuse compound the confusion of an unhappy, verbally abusive and intolerable family life. The outcome is the cycling phenomena and continued victimization via prostitution, criminal activity, or death. Only a few break out of the cycle to a socially adaptive lifestyle.

Assessment and Interventions

Assessment

Key questions to ask runaways focus on their belief about running. The following questions are recommended.

1) What has gone on at home that contributes to your running away? [Ask for details of events; interactions; relationships. If the youth says, "Nagging", try and get examples. Examine responses for blame, derogatory name calling, etc. Carefully interview for physical as well as verbal and sexual force.]
2) Given "event, relationship, etc.," how much control does the other or yourself have over this? How predictable is this type of behavior (yours/others); who's responsible (blame); how changeable are these behaviors/events by you/others?
3) What would have to be different for you to want to stay home? Have things even been this way in your home? If so, when? What made it change?
4) What would you need to make this happen?
5) What would other people need to make this happen?
6) How possible are these changes?
7) What do you want most for yourself?
8) What do you think you need first to get what you want?
9) If you were in my place, what is the most important thing to be said/done for a youth in your place?
10) On a scale of 0 to 10, with 10 being highest, how useful/safe is it for your return home? How safe/useful is it for you on the streets compared to home?

Interventions

Our levels of intervention are determined by the runaway's time away from home. At Level 1, the early runner who has been away from home less than a month has the strongest potential for working toward returning home. Careful assessment needs to be made concerning the youth's safety in the home, particularly if the youth is female and thus at high risk of having been both physically and sexually abused. A determination needs to be made of the reason for the youth's running away, the youth's choice of a stable environment, and the view of the family of the runaway.

At Level 2, the multiple runner who has been away from home one month to one year is not only at high risk for being physically abused in the home, but of having abuse occur while on the streets. In addition to Level 1 assessment, these runaways need to be assessed for general physical and sexual health, drug and alcohol use, and their own predatory criminal behavior while on the streets or in an institutional setting.

At Level 3, the serial runner who has been away from home for over one year is dealing with the compounded issue of homelessness. These youths are generally older and without satisfactory work experience; social expectations for the youth to be in the family home are lower. In addition to Level 1 and 2 assessment, this youth needs to be stabilized in a safe environment; mobilized around existing skills, if any, for work; helped to decrease the tremendous tension and anxiety; be detoxified (for drug and alcohol abuse); and assessed for potential aggression, especially for dangerousness to self as well as to others.

With the backdrop of levels of intervention, we offer suggestions about establishing contact with these youths. In general, the longer runaways have been away from home, the more self-demoralizing experiences they have had. Such experiences impinge on their ability to trust and to feel calm, connected, and committed to both people and places. The clinician needs to understand their heightened anxiety and their hypervigilence and impulsivity. They are oriented only to the present, and they defend against any reflection on their past. When the youth reveals abusive experiences, clinicians need to remember that this disclosure carries with it the resurrection of reactions to the trauma. This may activate a crisis reaction, which requires additional care and monitoring. A youth may even attempt to run away from the helping environment, such as the shelter, because of the intensity of his or her feelings about recounting the abuse. Emergency measures to protect the youth, measures that may go beyond the usual definition of service to the child, should be taken at this point.

Rapport is most readily established and maintained when runaways are responded to in a manner that gives them a sense of control, a sense they do not experience in their lives. Allowing the youth to feel in control of the interview imparts the feeling that he or she can make decisions and choose what will happen.

No matter how gently and skillfully directed, questions have great potential for arousing defensiveness in the youth. It is important to have a base to which both clinician and runaway can return in order to clarify why the question elicited a negative reaction. Because many runaways are inclined to blame themselves, they may interpret a question as suggesting that their views are not accurate. However, good rapport with the youth allows the practitioner to explore what the question means to the youth. Stressing that the intention of questions is to facilitate clarification is often useful in dealing with defensive reactions.

Cockiness is often used as a defense mechanism by the runaway and is perhaps best addressed by the clinician joining the self-aggrandizement, rather than by confronting the youth. Humor is another way of dealing with the runaway. These young people do not wish to experience additional painful arousal, and humor may serve to lessen the painful recounting of past experiences.

Finding out the runaways' reasons for why they ran reveals their perceptions of dilemmas at home. Physical and sexual abuse are often not easily acknowledged by the runaway, nor do runaways always realize that they have or are being sexually or physically victimized. This is particularly true of adolescents. Consequently, asking for details on what transpired and how often, how the runaway dealt with abuse in the past, and what the youths consider as contributory factors helps clinicians to sift through and identify options as well as to establish risk factors remaining in the home.

Nurses need to determine why a youth has run for several reasons. First, it must be determined whether a youngster is running from an unsafe environment. The issue of safety may not be uppermost in the minds of the youth. Instead, the youth may translate the safety issue into such issues as blame, fairness, expectations, demands, loyalty, and alienation.

Once a safe environment is provided for the runaway, clinicians can begin to address deeper problems and determine the thinking patterns and cognitive confusion of the runaway. Family work will be critical for those runaways who are able to return to a home that is safe. Group work with peer support is particularly useful in institutional settings that are known to be safe environments. Gradually, some youths can resume basic education and vocational goals.

It is important for nurses to keep several general points in mind when interviewing runaways. First, one single interview will not provide all the information needed. It may take many sessions to elicit the necessary responses. Second, nurses need to keep an open mind and to avoid taking sides. Extreme judgmental attitudes often prevail in the life experiences of these youths; judgments from the nurse will only harm rapport and shut down effective communication.

Helping runaway youth presents the nurse with many challenges. The understanding of the cognitive confusion and the determination of a level of intervention designed to correct distortions are based on what the youth does or does not tell the nurse. From this understanding decisions can be made both by the youth and the helper, with the goal to stabilize the runaway and mobilize resources aimed for positive life achievements.

References

1. Fine M, Rosenberg P. Dropping out of high school: the ideology of school and work. *J Educ.* 1983;165:257-272.
2. Burgess AW, Hartman CR, McCausland MP, Powers PA. Response patterns in children and adolescents exploited through sex rings and pornography. *Am J Psychiatry.* 1984;141:656-662.

Bibliography

Burgess AW, Hartman CR, Wolbert WA, Grant CA: Child molestation: assessment of impact. *Am J Psychiatric Nurs.* 1987;1(1):33-39.
Conte JR. Progress in treating the sexual abuse of children. *Soc Work.* 1984;May-June:258-263.
Garbarino J. Troubled youths, troubled families: the dynamics of adolescent maltreatment. In: Carlson V, Cicchette D, eds. *Research and Theoretical Advances on the Topic of Child Maltreatment.* Cambridge, MA: Cambridge Press; 1990.
Groth AN. Sexual trauma in the life histories of rapists and child molesters. *Victimology.* 1979;4 (1):10-16.
Janus MD. Juvenile prostitution. In: Burgess A, ed. *Child Pornography and Sex Rings.* Lexington, MA: Lexington Books; 1984.
Manis J. Addressing the seriousness of social problems. *Soc Problems.* 1974;22:1-5.
Reich JW, Gutierres SE. Escape/aggression incidence in sexual abused juvenile delinquents. *Criminal Justice Behav.* 1979;6:239-243.

Reprinted with permission from Burgess AW, Holmstrom LL. *Rape: Crisis and Recovery.* West Newton, MA: Awab; 1986.

Chapter 31 – Violence and Families

Ann W. Burgess and Albert R. Roberts

Violent crime is a serious concern in the US. We know a great deal about violence except how to stop it and how to do positive remedial work to reduce the consequences. The possibility that people might be injured or have their home invaded by a stranger is a frightening thought. But hundreds of Americans face an even more devastating reality when they are harmed, not by a stranger, but by someone they trusted. Victimization to these people occurs in their own home.

Families are viewed as the center of a society. To be abused by a partner, a parent, a trusted adult, or by one's own child or to witness such abuse becomes an engraved memory. Domestic violence victims wrestle with feelings not experienced by victims of strangers – feelings of fear, loyalty, love, guilt, and shame. Adults become torn between the desire to shield and help a loved one and their responsibility toward their own safety or others in the household. Children face alone the reality that those who should protect them are, in fact, a source of harm. To nonabused persons, home represents safety and security; to domestic violence , home is a place of danger.

The problem of family violence has existed for generations. Women have been battered by their partners for centuries. In 1885, the Chicago Protective Agency for Women, established to help women who were victims of physical abuse, provided legal aid, court advocacy, and personal assistance to the women. An abused woman could receive up to four weeks of shelter at the refuge operated by the Women's Club of Chicago. The agency helped women to secure legal separations, divorces, and equitable property distributions. Although between 1915 and 1920, 25 cities followed Chicago's lead in developing protective agencies for women, by the 1940s few shelters remained due, in part, to marital separations caused by World War II.

Turning to children and violence, the history of childhood is replete with suffering, well-documented from Biblical times to the present. The landmark Wilson case of

1874 pricked the American social conscience and opened America's eyes to the plight of children: Eight-year-old Mary Ellen Wilson lived with her adoptive parents in New York City. She was held there in chains, starved and beaten. The police responded, but could do nothing because it was a "family matter" and the parents held the "rights."[1] A man named Henry Berg was contacted. He was able to extricate Mary Ellen from her family torture chamber. Who was Henry Berg, and why was he called? Berg had founded a protective group the preceding year: The Society for the Protection of Cruelty to Animals.

This chapter presents definitions and current statistical trends from a developmental perspective of family violence, that of courtship abuse; partner threat and violence; domestic homicide; child abuse, neglect, and sexual assault; and elder abuse. The chapter also discusses key concepts of family violence: socialization into violence and learned socialized violence; the psychodynamics of violent behavior, including altered attachment, jealousy, guilt, and revenge; and the biology of trauma.

Developmental Aspects of Family and its Structure

Just as there are developmental tasks for the child maturing into an adult, the family may be viewed as having three developmental phases. The first phase begins with dating, courtship, and marriage; the middle phase includes partnership and work, with childbearing and parenting being an option; and the third phase continues a work focus, optional grandparenting, and retirement.

Because violence within families has only recently surfaced as a legal matter, research into the causes and consequences is limited. As a first step, definitions are provided in order to begin classification for the research process.

Family

Nowhere in the criminal law and its administration is the social construction of violent crime changing more rapidly than in what constitutes family violence and society's response to it.[2] Due to the myriad of different statutes and regulations, there is no national legal definition of a family.

Data on family violence is generated by identifications of people by their current marital status (married, separated, divorced, or single), by their spouse status (spouse/exspouse), or by relationships among members of a household (cohabitants, child/parent, sibling, or parent). With these definitions, statistics on family structure changes can be generated over time.

Family structure changes reported by the Bureau of Census include the following:

- The proportion of all households accounted for by two-parent families declined from 40% in 1970 to 26% in 1990.
- The number of unmarried-couple households almost tripled between 1970 and 1980 and grew by 80% between 1980 and 1990 from 1.6 to 2.9 million.
- The proportion of children under 18 years of age living with two parents declined from 85% in 1970 to 73% in 1990, an estimated 15 % of whom are stepchildren.
- In 1990, 19% of white, 62% of black, and 30% of Hispanic children under age 18 lived with only one parent.[3]

Trends in family violence must be interpreted against a decline in the fraction of households containing exclusively married couples and their biologic children.[2] Violence between growing numbers of same-sex and opposite-sex cohabiting partners is increasingly regarded as family violence irrespective of legal marital status as is violence between divorced or separated couples.

The National Research Council's Panel on Understanding and Preventing Violence considered all violent behavior within a household as family violence, specifically, spouse assault, physical and sexual assault of children, sibling assaults, and physical and sexual assaults of other relatives who reside in the household.[2] Missing from this list are events such as verbal abuse, harassment, or humiliation in which psychological trauma is the sole harm to the victim. This category is under consideration by the Panel on Research on Violence Against Women and will be considering such events as threat assessment and stalking behavior.

Family Violence

Just as "families" has no universal definition, such is the case with the term violence. However, one published in the report on understanding and preventing violence from the National Research Council is as that interpersonal violence is "behavior by persons against persons that intentionally threatens, attempts, or actually inflicts physical harm."[2]

Dynamic Nature of Family Violence

A number of defining characteristics distinguish family violence from stranger violence:

- There is a continuing relationship among its members similar to other relationships, such as teacher-student, employer-employee, child-caretaker, etc.
- Daily interaction and shared domicile increases the opportunities for violent encounters.
- Because they are bound together in a continuing relationship, it is quite likely there will be repeat violations by the offender.
- Unequal power relationship makes one more vulnerable to aggression and violence of the offender with power.
- The offender often threatens additional violence if the incidents of violence are disclosed.
- The victim may also refrain from disclosure, anticipating stigmatization and denigration.
- Episodes of violence often occur in private places, are invisible to others, and less likely to be detected or reported to police.[2]

Phase 1: Courtship and Marriage

The first phase of family life includes dating, courtship, and marriage. Although dating does not necessarily lead to courtship or marriage, it is instructive to review the statistics and studies on relationship problems and dating aggression.[4] Theories of both marital[5] and dating[6] aggression identify conflict as an important causal factor leading to aggression between partners.

Dating violence appears to begin as early age 15 or 16.[7,8] Violent tactics include slapping and pushing, beating, and threatening with or using weapons. Recurring and escalating episodes of violence in a relationship are not uncommon if the relationship is not terminated, and only about 50% of the victims terminate the relationship.[9-11]

As inquiry has continued, it has become evident that a large number of college students experience physical aggression within dating relationships. Estimates of the prevalence of dating aggression among college students range from 20%[9,12] to as high as 50%.[13]

Violence Within Marriage

Spouse assault may be the single most common cause of injury for which women seek emergency medical attention. From an investigation of emergency treatment of women in a metropolitan hospital, researchers report that battered women were 13 times more likely than other women receiving emergency care to be injured in the breast, chest, and abdomen, and three times as likely to be injured while pregnant.[14,15]

Beginning in 1988, the National Crime Survey (NCS) reports annual estimates of the extent of family violence for persons age 12 and older.[16] The NCS, however, lacks the necessary information to reliably determine how much of the reported violence is family-related. For example, data collection excludes violence among coinhabitants and does not collect information on children under age 12. The 1989 victimizations statistics were as follows regarding assault –

- 59% were by a spouse (41%) or ex-spouse (18%)
- 29% were by other relatives
- 7% were by parents
- 5% were by children

The Conflict Tactics Scale is the main measure of domestic violence used in surveys.[17] The scale includes verbal and aggressive acts, including violent acts ranging in severity from hurling objects to the use of a deadly weapon such as a gun or knife. Using it in an initial national telephone survey of couples in 1975[18] and in a repeat of the survey in 1985,[19] researchers found that 16 of every 100 couples reported at least one incident of physical aggression during the year before the survey. The prevalence of severe violence in both surveys was four in 100 females and five in 100 males.

These statistics are believed to be low because the sample excludes unmarried couples and misses segments of the population that do not have telephones.[2]

Phase 2: Assaults on Children

Various commissioned governmental studies have reported on assaults on children. The US Advisory Board on Child Abuse and Neglect, a governmental advisory board created by the 1988 amendments to the Child Abuse and Prevention and Treatment Act, estimates that in 1989 at least 1,200 and perhaps as many as 5,000 children died as a result of maltreatment, and over 160,000 children were seriously harmed.[20] The advisory board noted that in 1974 there were about 60,000 cases of child maltreatment reported. This figure rose to 1.1 million in 1980 and more than doubled to 2.4 million in 1988.[21]

Part of the increase is believed due to more inclusive definitions of abuse and neglect and an increase in professionals' recognition of maltreatment, rather than an increase in incidence per se.[21] However, it is also likely that cases of child maltreatment are reported to public health or educational agencies that are not known to social services agencies who provide the "countable" case figures. There are many cases of intrafamilial or third-party assaults on children that are never reported to any professionals concerned with the health or welfare of children.[2]

Using the expanded definitions of child abuse and neglect, the second National Incidence Survey, published in 1988 and commissioned by the National Center for Child Abuse and Neglect, estimated that the majority of countable cases involved the following –
Child Neglect (63%), involving 15.9 per thousand, or 1,003,600 children.
- Physical neglect (57%) of all neglected children or 157,600 children.
- Educational neglect (29%) of all neglected children or 292,000 children.
- Emotional neglect (22%) of all neglected children or 223,100 children.
Child Abuse (43%), involving 10.7 per 1,000 or 675,000 children
- Physical abuse involving 5.7 children per 1,000 or 358,000 children.
- Emotional abuse involving 3.4 children per 1,000 or 211,000 children.
- Sexual abuse involving 2.5 children per 1,000 or 155,900 children.[21]
Homicide Profile – Assessments of the risks of intrafamily homicide are more accurate than for other forms of assault and several patterns are noteworthy.[2]
- Newborns, infants, and children between ages one and four are more vulnerable to homicide than are children ages five to nine years.[22]
- Infants and small children are more likely to be killed by their mothers than their fathers, perhaps in part as a result of differential risk exposure.
- The risk of homicide for children under five is greater for male than female children, according to a recent case control study.[23]
- Although men's overall homicide risk is three times that for women, women face a greater risk of homicide by their spouse than do men.[24,25]
- Intrafamily violence accounted for 15% of all family homicides in 1989; 44% involved husbands and wives.

Child Abuse Risk Factors

In reviewing the statistics on child abuse risk factors, female children are three times as likely as males to be sexually abused: 2.9 females per 1,000 compared with 0.9 males.[24,25] One-fourth of all sexually abused children are males with a higher percentage of abused males found in day care (38%).[26] Black children were one and one-half times more likely to be physically abused than white children and five times more likely to die of physical abuse or neglect.[24,25] Social status (measured by family income) is substantially related to children's risk of injury. With children from families with incomes less than $15,000, the rate of physical abuse was three and a half times greater than for other children. A pattern noted was that physical abuse was more frequent than sexual abuse held for all income families.[24,25]

Phase 3: Assaults Against the Elderly

A major recommendation from the National Research Council is for priority to be given to the collection of more precise information about the prevalence and incidence of violence toward the elderly and its consequences.[27] Surprisingly little is known about its occurrence in families, primarily because studies do not distinguish between elder abuse and elder neglect.

In a stratified random sample study of all persons 65 and older in the Boston metropolitan area, researchers estimated that between 2.5 and 3.9 persons had experienced physical violence, verbal aggression, or neglect.[28] Similar results were found by a national survey of elder abuse in Canada.[29]

Explanations of Family Violence

Most explanations of the causes of family violence are partial in one of two ways: (1) either they attempt to explain a single type or a few types of family violence, such as partner assault, or (2) they seek to identify a particular factor or set of factors that account for some of the observed variation in behavior between violent and nonviolent persons or acts.[26] The leading explanations of family violence are described from social and cultural perspectives and the biopsychosocial perspective.

Social and Cultural Perspective: Gelles attempts an integrated theory with the following theories.[30]

Cultural and Structural Determinants and Social Learning. Feminist theory asserts that the unequal power distribution between men and women subjects women to male dominance in all spheres of life (work, family, and community life). Power extends to the sexual relationship as well as to work and social relationships.[31] The various ways in which coercion is used depend on man's use of their physical and social power to maintain a dominant position.[32]

The unequal distribution of power is also the basis for explaining parental physical and sexual abuse of children. The exercise of parental power over the child victim leads to disempowerment of the child, rending him or her helpless.[33]

Within this framework, growing up in a patriarchal society that emphasizes male dominance and aggression and female victimization, children are socialized into their respective sex roles.[34] In addition, they are said to learn through the experience in the family. This learning becomes reinforced in the larger community where male and female roles similarly rest on elements of macho culture. In this respect, male dominance and aggression and female acquiescence are said to be learned most critically in family and peer relationships.[2]

In addition, the recent changes in family organization and structure may account for some of the family aggression as well. Among those believed to be of significance are changes that affect the social and moral bonding among family members. One such change since the 1970s is deinstitutionalization of children in foster care, the mentally ill, and the disabled. Distinct subpopulations of the deinstitutionalized are at risk of violent victimization – the homeless and those cared for in homes. The temporary placement of children in foster homes and adoption, and the informal placement of children with relatives exposes them to risks of violence from caretakers for whom the constraints of parenting are less controlling.[2]

A second major change is the increase in the number of children who are not living with their natural parents. These numbers are substantial owing to serial cohabitation, divorce, and desertion.[2]

Social Isolation. Social isolation is a characteristic of some families that are at high risk of physical and sexual abuse of a spouse or children.[35,36] The isolation may be forced on the partner by the abuser or shame may prompt the visibly battered spouse to further withdrawal. They become isolated from friends, acquaintances, or anyone acquainted with what goes on within the family. Some families isolate themselves in subtle ways: unlisted telephone numbers or no telephone or they lack means of transportation and their homes may be physically shuttered from the gaze of outsiders. They lack community ties of any kind.[37] Risick and Reese suggest that violent families rarely invite others to their home, do not engage in social and recreational activities, and place less emphasis on personal growth and development.[38]

Violence Generational Transmission. The transmission of violence from one generation to the next is believed to be a consequence of family violence. One investigator reported that among adults who were abused as children, more than one-fifth later abuse their own children.[18] However, another cautions the methodological limitations in these studies, especially the retrospective design, restrict the validity of conclusions about the long-term consequences of abuse in childhood.[39]

Biopsychosocial Perspective

Child and family theorists often suggest that the structure and quality of family and social interaction, especially in the way the child perceives family members and their interactions with him and with each other, are important factors in a child's development. For children growing up, the quality of their attachments to parents and to other members of the family is most important in how these children as later adults relate to and value other members of society. Essentially, these early life attachments (sometimes called bonding) translate into a blueprint of how the child will perceive situations outside the family. Positive attachment speaks to warmth, affection, caring, protective behaviors, and accountability. It is at core of building a social human being. Through attachment, the person gets feedback for the emerging of self. Around 18 months of age there is consolidation of a sense of sense. Early development of the ability to self-soothe provides an inner core of calmness and the ability to avoid being overwhelmed by stimuli that results in an integrated sense of self.

While attachment theory was intended as a revision of psychoanalytic theory, it has been infused by biological principles, control-systems theory, and cognitive psychology.[40] Although it began with an attempt to understand the disturbed functioning of individuals who had suffered early separations or traumatic losses, it is a theory of normal development that suggests explanations for some types of atypical development.[41,42,43] Since Bowlby's preliminary formulations,[44] it has stimulated research into socioemotional development and the growth of interpersonal relationships. For example, it suggests a causal relationship between anomalies of attachment in the parent and abuse of the child.[45]

Family violence has been linked to mental illness and personality disorders, although the links have been established for clinical populations rather than by using case control methods or general population surveys. Studies of women's shelter populations report that depression is quite common among women who are repeat victims of domestic violence.[46]

People prone to depression may be more prone to violence. A number of studies report that abusive mothers as well as males who physically abuse their partners show signs of depression.[47] Yet the causal direction is not clear. While some sources of depression (e.g., repressed anger toward others) may cause the abuse, the depression may result from being labeled abusive, or other consequences of the violent act.[2]

Assaultive and Homicidal Behavior

How do we explain interpersonal violence, especially partner violence and homicide? It is difficult because there is a transgression of a basic sense of connectedness between people, and we wonder how can this kind of behavior exists. We know that early attachment disturbance and the impairment of self-regulation is a major diagnostic issue with traumatized children.[48]

Social bonding can fail or become narrow and selective. Caretakers can either ignore, rationalize, or normalize various behaviors in the developing child or, through their own problems (such as violence behavior), support the child's developing distortions and projections. An ineffective social environment can occur through aggressive or sexual behavior being ignored or by failing to intervene to correct behavior.

The child who lacks protection by a caretaker experiences tremendous anxiety, is overwhelmed, and survives through dissociating itself from emotion. This dissociation also inhibits a sense of feeling connected to the outside world. In the earliest manifestations of this numbing, we see children being cruel to animals, siblings, friends, and even parents. There is a lack of sensitivity to the pain of others or there can be a distorted association of pain. Children become isolated and disconnected from others. In a Massachusetts case, a 14-year-old youth took a seven-year-old retarded boy into the woods and beat him to death. He had told people he was going to do this and no one intervened.

This cruel and detached behavior can be noted in date abuse occurring in junior and senior high school. There can be a gang rape of a girl as happened in Glen Ridge, NJ. In that case, the five young high school men inserted objects into a retarded girl, while six other high school students watched. They had no sense of their impact on the victim.

In courtship violence, the aggressor does not want the relationship to end. There can be stalking behavior, parking outside the house, making harassing phone calls. The partner can not tolerate the separation. There are feelings of abandonment, anger, and depression. The partner may become suicidal. Rage is behind the depression. The narcissistic blow of the abandonment is that they cannot manage on their own. They numb out. The alteration is in basic biology of the limbic system. Their irritability, isolation, and avoidance of people is because they cannot handle emotion, and they are limited in thinking when they are emotional. They lack control. Fantasy calms them, but the fantasy is filled with their rage at the partner. The distorted thought is: I killed her because I love her.

In a study of murderers,[49] three factors were noted to negatively contribute to the critical formative events of childhood and adolescence. The first of these is trauma, in the form of physical or sexual abuse. The developing child encounters a variety of life events, some normative and others beyond the range of normal, usually extraordinarily negative. Within the context of the child's ineffective social environment, the child's distress caused by the trauma is neglected. The child is neither protected nor assisted in recovery from the trauma; his or her external environment does not address the negative consequences of the events.

One assumption regarding early traumatic events is that the child's memories of frightening and upsetting life experiences shape his or her developing thought patterns. This type of thinking that emerges develops structured, patterned behaviors, which in turn help generate aggressive daydreams and fantasies. The traumatized child's play remains fixed on thoughts associated with the family violence. Successful resolution of traumatic events results in an adaptive integrated and flexible patterned response. Unsuccessful resolution of trauma underscores the victim's helplessness; aggressive fantasies, aimed at achieving dominance and control missing from reality, emerge.[50,51]

A second assumption regarding early traumatic events is that manifestations of the impact of abusive events are influential in the child's social development.[50-52] Concurrent with the abusive events, the child may experience a sustained emotional physiological arousal level. When this sustained arousal level interacts with repetitive thoughts about the trauma, the child's perceptions and patterns of interpersonal relationships may be altered.

The second factor contributing to the formative events component is developmental failure. For some reason, the child does not readily attach to his adult caretaker. As a result of this negative social attachment, the caretaker has no influence over the child and later over the adolescent. If the child has been psychologically deprived or neglected, he or she may feel a diminished emotional response.

Interpersonal failure, the third factor, is the failure of the caretaking adult to serve as a role model for the developing child. There are various reasons for this failure, including the caretaker's being absent or serving as an inadequate role model, e.g., an abusive parent. The child may witness a violent home environment where he or she sees aggression such as drunken fights associated with the sexual behavior of adult caretakers.

In domestic murders, the killing may be spontaneous. For example, in June 1995, two young boys died of hyperthermia after being buckled in car seat belts for eight or 10 hours while their 20-year-old mother partied at a Tennessee motel. This case does not involve intentional killing. However, some domestic murders are staged and involve careful planning as in the case of Diane Downs. About 10:30 PM, May 19, 1983, in Springfield, OR, Downs pulled into an emergency department screaming for help and that her three children were shot. Her seven-year-old daughter was dead on arrival; her eight-year-old daughter had two small caliber bullet wounds in her left chest and a third bullet wound through the base of her left thumb; and her three-year-old son had a bullet entry to his spinal column. Downs, herself, had a gunshot wound in her arm.

Downs said she had been driving in her car when she noticed a man standing in the middle of the road. She stopped and got out, and the man pulled out a gun, reached through the window, and shot the children and herself. She said she then pushed and kicked him in the leg, jumped in her car, and sped off for the hospital. The story fell apart when her daughter Christie proved to be an eyewitness to the crime. She saw her mother go to the trunk of the car where the gun was stored, come around the car and shoot Cheryl, then her brother, and then herself. Another witness testified to seeing Down's red Nissan Pulsar creeping along the road about 10:15 PM, waiting for them to die before going to the hospital. Diaries and unmailed letters to a married letter carrier with whom she was having an affair contained such incriminating statements as, "You know I don't want a daddy for my kids...You would never be left alone with them." The motive was to eliminate the obstacle (her children) to her fantasized relationship with her lover.

A history of Downs' background reveals child abuse, neglect, and incest. Little, if any, attachment occurred with protective caretakers. The result is a flaw in human development and attachment. It cannot be denied that other environmental stressors play a role in shaping civilizing and moral development, but case after case addresses the issue of failure of attachment and how it excludes the welfare of others. The abuser imitates the behavior of others. It is not drawn out of true individuation and appreciation of the uniqueness of others.

Incest

Incest is a manifestation of inadequate bonding of the parent. There are no clear boundaries. The family member responds to the sense that "it is all right." There is a basic disregard for the humanness of child. These are people with real flaws in being able to behave in affiliative relationships.

Elder Abuse

Aggression toward the elderly is multifacted. Abuse may occur to parents who, themselves, have been abusive and exploitative. The dynamics are different between elder spousal abuse and elder abuse by their children..

Although child and spousal abuse have received increasing attention in family violence research, very little is known about the dimensions, scope, causes, or effects of elder abuse. The characteristics of individuals and families that are associated with abuse of the elderly need considerations, as do the features of interventions designed for other forms of family violence that might be adapted to this problem.

Interventions

There are no easy answers to problems of family violence. A comprehensive set of family support programs or a continuum of services for families within each of the developmental phases of family life does not exist.

Although services are needed for ongoing abuse cases, it is critical to identify families at risk for potential violence. Rather than waiting for incidents of violence, counseling and education services need to build on an integration of existing interventions and to design proactive approaches that are responsive to community needs and feasible with community resources. Other suggestions include the following.

Courtship Violence. Research continues to develop to provide an understanding of relationship problems that lead to dating violence. In Riggs' study, although aggressors reported more problems in general than did nonaggressive individuals, the difference appeared to result from specific problem areas.[4] These include jealousy; the interference of people outside the relationship, such as friends and parents; and more fighting and conflict within the couple. If one conceptualizes jealousy as a reaction to the threat of loss, it is possible that such a threat will also result in anger that could lead to aggression. Other issues that may be related to jealousy, such as possessiveness and control, may also lead to aggression.

Riggs' study results support the need to address general problem-solving issues in any educational program designed to treat or prevent dating aggression. Whether the relationship problems lead directly to the aggressor or if both the aggression and the problems reflect some third variable (e.g., aggressive personality), it appears that aggressive individuals face a greater level of conflict within their relationships. Reducing this conflict through counseling or training might be effective in reducing the occurrence of dating aggression.

Spouse Assaults. Most research has focused on testing police arrests of the abuser in preventing recurrences of domestic violence. Arrest, in replication studies, has shown to not be an effective deterrent; indeed, it may well increase the incidence of domestic violence of unemployed males with low socioeconomic status.[53] Research is recommended on police-administered treatments as well as police referrals to social service and substance abuse treatment agencies and to battered women's shelters.

The last few decades have seen programmatic efforts focused on providing shelters for battered women – residences where abused women and their children can reside safely and receive emotional support. There are now approximately 1,200 shelters offering temporary, emergency housing (typically families stay from two days to three months) to more than 300,000 women and children each year.[2]

The goal of shelters is a safe harbor. Other services are designed to provide help to women to become self-sufficient and include relocation assistance, day care for children, and welfare advocacy. Services directed at increasing self-esteem include support groups and courses on parenting, job readiness, and budgeting. Services for children who have witnessed family violence are often incorporated into shelter programs.

The Duluth Minnesota Domestic Abuse Intervention Project conducted a 12-month follow-up study in which battered women were asked their opinion of the intervention that the Project had used in an effort to have the batterer change his violent habits. Of the women studied, 60% said they felt there was improvement when the batterer took part in education and group counseling, whereas 80% of the women stated that the improvement had resulted from a combination of involvement from the police, courts, group counseling, and the shelter.[54]

Programs to reduce partner assault include public education and awareness campaigns for batterers. Education targets children to develop nonviolent ways of coping with anger and frustration. Public awareness programs emphasize that family violence is a crime and that help is available.

Courts mandate batterers to attend programs that teach alternative ways to behave. Alcohol and drug abuse programs are emphasized for batterers for whom chemical abuse is an issue.

Pharmacological intervention may be useful. Understanding that depression may affect the severity of maltreatment of children as well as lead to their neglect, the treatment of depression may be indicated. If a significant subgroup of abusive parents or caretakers suffer from affective disorders, especially major depression, then chemical and other forms of treating depression may be a means of controlling family violence. This assumes that reasonably effective means are available for controlling affective disorders, particularly any volatile mood swings associated with them.[2]

Child Abuse. Foster care placement is a major intervention in child-abuse cases. An estimated 15% of victims of child maltreatment are placed in an unrelated foster home.[55,56] Several studies note that the more changes in placement a child experiences, the greater the likelihood of adult criminality and violent criminal behavior.[57-59]

Home nurse visitation is one proactive means of detecting maltreatment of infants and preschoolers. Olds and his collaborators have studied this intervention in high-risk groups – poor, unmarried, and teenage mothers having their first child – and found it to decrease , but not totally eliminate, the incidence of child abuse in comparison with groups not receiving the intervention.[60,61] There was a 5% rate of child abuse or neglect suggesting the need for additional preventive or ameliorative interventions. However, there were additional positive effects of the home-nursing intervention. At 12 and 24 months, infants of mothers of the high-risk group showed improved intellectual functioning on development tests and there was some evidence of improved family function with less evidence of conflict and scolding and less punishment of infants. Olds and his colleagues also concluded that although the nurse can link families to community and social services – to meliorate the effects of poverty, violence, and drug use – the lack of employment opportunities in the neighborhoods where these families live poses severe constraints on their continued improvement efforts, especially when the intervention stops.

References
1. Zigler E, Hall NW. Physical child abuse in America: past, present, and future. In: Cicchetti D, Carlson V, eds. *Child Maltreatment*. Cambridge, England: Cambridge University Press; 1989
2. Reiss AJ Jr, Roth JA, eds. *Understanding and Preventing Violence*. Vol. 1, 3. Washington, DC: National Academy Press; 1993.

3. US Bureau of the Census. *Marital status and Living Arrangements: March 1990. Current Population Reports.* Washington, DC: US Government Printing Office; 1991. Series P-20, No. 450.

4. Riggs DS. Relationship problems and dating aggression. *J Interpersonal Violence.* 1993;8(1):18-35.

5. Gelles RJ, Straus MA. Determinant of violence in the family: toward a theoretical integration. In: Hill RB, Nye FI, Reiss IL eds. *Contemporary Theories about the Family.* New York, NY: Free Press; 1979:549-581.

6. Riggs DS, O'Leary KD. A theoretical model of courtship aggression. In: Pirog-Good MA, Stets JE, Eds. *Violence in Dating Relationships: Emerging Social Issues.* New York, NY: Praeger; 1989:53-71.

7. Durst M. Perceived peer abuse among college students: a research note. *Nat Assoc Student Personnel Adm J.* 1987;24:42-47.

8. Henton J, Cate R, Koval J, Lloyd D, Christopher D. Romance and violence in dating relationships. *J Family Issues.* 1983;4:467-482.

9. Cate CA, Henton JM, Koval J, Christopher FS, Lloyd S. Premarital abuse: a social psychological perspective. *J Family Issues.* 1982;3:79-90.

10. Laner MR. Courtship abuse and aggression: contextual aspects. *Sociol Spectrum.* 1983;3:69-83.

11. Roscoe B, Benaske N. (Courtship violence experienced by abused wives: similarities in patterns of abuse. *Fam Relations.* 1985;34:419-424.

12. Makepeace JM. Courtship violence among college students. *Fam Relations.* 1981;30:97-102.

13. Sigelman CK, Berry CJ, Wiles KA. Violence in college students' dating relationships. *J Applied Social Psychol.* 1984;5:530-548.

14. Stark E, Fintcraft A. Spouse abuse. In: Rosenberg M, Fenley MA, eds. *Violence in America: A Public Health Approach.* New York, NY: Oxford University Press; 1991:123-154.

15. Stark E, Flintcraft A. Medical therapy as repression: the case of the battered woman. *Health Med.* 1982;1:29-32.

16. Bureau of Justice Statistics, US Department of Justice. *Criminal Victimization in the US, 1988. A National Crime Survey Report.* Washington, DC: US Government Printing Office; 1990. Publication NCJ-122024.

17. Straus MA. Measuring family conflict and violence: the conflict tactics scale. *J Marriage Fam Living.* 1979;36:13-19.

18. Straus MA, Gelles RJ, Steinmetz SK. *Behind Closed Doors: Violence in the American Family.* Garden City, NY: Doubleday; 1980.

19. Straus MA, Gelles RJ. Societal change in family violence from 1975 to 1985 as revealed in two national surveys. *J Marriage Fam.* 1986;48:465-479.

20. US Bureau of the Census. Household and family characteristics: March 1990 and 1989. *Current Population Reports, Population Characteristics.* Washington, DC: US Government Printing Office; 1990. Series P-20, No. 447.

21. US Department of Health and Human Services. *Study Findings: Study of National Incidence and Prevalence of Child Abuse and Neglect.* Washington, DC: National Center on Child Abuse and Neglect; 1988.

22. Federal Bureau of Investigation. *Uniform Crime Reports for the US: 1990.* Washington, DC: US Government Printing Office; 1991.

23. Winpisinger KA, Hopkins RS, Indian RW, Hosteler JR. Risk factors for childhood homicides in Ohio: a birth certificate-based case-control study. *Am J Public Health.* 1991;81:1052-1054.

24. Sedlak AJ. *National Incidence and Prevalence of Child Abuse and Neglect: 1988.* Washington, DC: Westat; 1991.

25. Sedlak AJ. *Supplementary Analysis of Data on the National Incidence of Child Abuse and Neglect.* Washington, DC: Westat; 1991

26. Finklehor D, Williams LM, Burns N. *Nursery Crimes: Sexual Abuse in Day Care.* Newbury Park, CA: Sage1988.

27. National Research Council. *Understanding Child Abuse and Neglect.* Panel on research on Child Abuse and Neglect, Commission on Behavioral and Social Sciences and Education, National Research Council. Washington, DC: National Academy Press; 1993.

28. Pillemer K, Finklehor D. Prevalence of elder abuse: a random sample survey. *Gerontol.* 1988;28:51-57.

29. Podnicks E, Pillemer K. *Final Report on Survey of Elder Abuse in Canada.* Ottawa: Health Welfare; 1989.

30. Gelles RJ. An exchange social control theory. In: Finklehor D, Gelles RJ, Hotaling GT, Straus MA, eds. *The Dark Side of Families.* Newbury Park CA: Sage; 1983.

31. Russell D. *Rape in Marriage.* New York, NY: MacMillan; 1982.

32. Finklehor D. Common features of family abuse. In: Finklehor D, Gelles RJ, Hotaling GT, Straus MA, eds. *The Dark Side of Families.* Newbury Park CA: Sage; 1983.

33. Finklehor D, Browne A. Initial and long-term effects: a conceptual framework. In: Finkelhor D, et al, eds. *A Sourcebook on Child Sexual Abuse.* Newbury Park, CA: Sage; 1986.

34. Dobash RE, Dobash R. *Violence Against Wives.* New York, NY: Free Press; 1979.

35. Garbarino J, Crouter K. Defining the community context of parent-child relations: the correlates of child maltreatment. *Child Dev.* 1978;43:604-616.

36. Pike KM. Intrafamilial sexual abuse of children. Paper prepared for the National Research Council Panel on the Understanding and Control of Violent Behavior; 1990.

37. Garbarino J, Sherman D. High-risk families and high-risk neighborhoods. *Child Dev.* 1980;51:188-198.

38. Resick PA, Reese D. Perception of family social climate and physical aggression in the home. *J Fam Violence.* 1986;1:71-83.

39. Widom C.S. The cycle of violence. *Sci.* 1989;244:160-166.

40 Crittenden PM, Ainsworth MDS. (1989) Child maltreatment and attachment theory. In: Cicchetti D, Carlson V, eds. *Child Maltreatment.* Cambridge, MA: Cambridge University; 1989:432-463.

41. Bowlby J. *Attachment and Loss. Vol I: Attachment.* New York, NY: Basic Books; 1969.

42. Bowlby J. *Attachment and Loss, Vol II: Separation.* New York, NY: Basic Books; 1973.

43. Bowlby J. *Attachment and Loss, Vol III: Loss.* New York, NY: Basic Books; 1980.

44. Bowlby J. The nature of the child's tie to his mother. *Inter J Psychoanal.* 1958;39:359-373.

45. Ainsworth, MDS. Attachment and child abuse. In: Gerber G, Ross CJ, Zigler E, eds. *Child Abuse Reconsidered: An Agenda for Action.* New York, NY: Oxford University Press; 1980.

46. Frieze IH, Browne A. Violence in marriage. In: Ohlin L, Tonry M, eds. *Family Violence.* Chicago, IL: University of Chicago; 1989:163-218.

47. Zuravin SJ. The ecology of child abuse and neglect: review of the literature and presentation of data. *Violence Victims.* 1989;4(2):101-120

48. van der Kolk & Fisler, 1994

49. Ressler RK, Burgess AW, Douglas JE. *Sexual Homicide.* New York, NY: Lexington Books; 1988.

291

50. Burgess AW, Hartman MP, McCausland MP, Powers P. Response patterns in children and adolescents exploited through sex rings and pornography. *Am J Psychiatry*. 1984;141(5):656-662.
51. Pynoos RY, Eth S. Developmental perspective on psychic trauma in childhood. In: Figley CR, ed. *Trauma and its Wake*. New York, NY: Brunner/Mazel Psychological Stress Series; 1985.
52. Conte JR. Progress in treating the sexual abuse in children, Social Work, 1984;258-263.
53. Sherman LW. *Policing Domestic Violence: Experiments and Dilemmas*. New York, NY: Free Press; 1992.
54. Pence E, Paymer M. *Education groups for Men Who Batter: The Deluth Model*. New York, NY: Springer; 1993.
55. American Humane Association. *National Analysis of Official Neglect and Abuse Reporting*. Denver, CO: American Humane Association; 1979.
56. Runyan DK, Gould CL, Trost DC, Loda FA. Determinants of foster care placement for the maltreated child. *Child Abuse Neglect*. 1981;6:343-350.
57. Hensey OJ, Williams JK, Rosenbloom L. Experiences in Liverpool. *Dev Med Child Neurol*. 1983;25:606-611.
58. Lynch MA, Roberts J. *Consequences of Child Abuse*. London: Academic Press; 1990.
59. Widom CS. Research, clinical, and policy issues: childhood victimization, parent alcohol problems, and long-term consequences. National Forum on the Future of Children, Workshop on Children and Parental Illegal Drug Abuse. National Research Council: Institute of Medicine, March 8, 1990.
60. Olds DL. The prenatal/early infancy project. In: Price RH, Cowen EE, Lorion RP, Ramos-McKay, eds. *Fourteen Ounces of Prevention: A Casebook for Practitioners*. Washington, DC: American Psychological Association; 1988:9-32.
61. Olds DL, Henderson CR. The prevention of maltreatment. In: Cicchetti D, Carlson V, eds. *Child Maltreatment: Theory and Research on the Causes and Consequences of Child Abuse and Neglect*. Cambridge, MA: Harvard University: 1989:772-763.

Reprinted with permission of Crisis Intervention and Time-Limited Treatment, Harwood Academic Publishers and Dr. Albert R. Roberts, Founding Editor-in-Chief.

Chapter 32 – Infant Abduction: A Family Crisis

AW Burgess, EB Dowdell, CR Hartman, AG Burgess, CJ Dowdell, C Nahirny, and JB Rabun

The abduction of an infant from a hospital, home, or outside setting impacts on a variety of people, including the family. This chapter reports on a study of infant abductions. Consider the following case:

A 30-year-old mother of two girls had just delivered a baby boy six weeks early by caesarean section. Two days later, while the mother was holding her son, a woman dressed in white hospital scrubs entered and said she needed to take the baby to be weighed. She asked the baby's name, placed him in the bassinette carrier, and wheeled him out. Several minutes later, a nurse came in to say she needed to take the baby back to the nursery. The mother described the earlier experience with the imposter nurse.

For an hour, the hospital searched for the baby and then notified police. Thirteen days later the baby was located through a police hot line publicized on television. The abductor stole the baby from a room located next to an elevator. She carried the infant out of the hospital in her arms. The abductor was cited by police for a noisy muffler after leaving the hospital, but before the police bulletin had been broadcast. The abductor was 32 years old, had four of her own children, and had had a tubal ligation four years before. She said she wanted a baby boy for her new husband.

While not a crime of epidemic proportions, the kidnapping, by nonfamily members, of infants (birth through six months) from healthcare facilities, homes, and other locations has clearly become a subject of concern. This chapter reports on a study of 38 family members whose infants had been abducted and returned and serves to educate nurses about the family's reaction.

The Problem and its Study

The study of infant kidnapping involves where the abduction occurs and the interpersonal aspects to stealing a baby. Hospitals are newcomers to workplace interpersonal crime as are homes to stranger violence. Historically, hospitals have been a sanctuary for healing and considered an inviolate environment. The trend of making the hospital a more open environment from one of tight control has increased the danger of violent acts perpetrated onto hospital staff[1] and of strangers' ability to abduct an infant from such perceived safe places as maternity and pediatric units[2] and their own home.[3] As infant abductions began to increase from five in 1983 to a high of 19 in 1987 and 17 in 1989[4] and national media efforts focused attention on recovery of the missing baby, questions were raised about hospital security[5] and the mental health response of family and hospital staff.[6]

As part of a larger study on child abductors, we were able to interview family members who had an infant kidnapped from either a hospital, a home, or an outside location. We identified three major questions for the substudy. First, we were interested in the type of trauma and structure of the kidnapping process; second, we asked what sequence of events was experienced by parents involved in the recovery of their infant, especially parents' observations of the effect of the kidnapping over time on their child; and third, we wanted to learn about symptom responses of family members during and following the abduction of their infant, especially as to length of time or gender of family member.

Method and Subjects.

Thirty-eight family members, representing 27 stolen babies, were located for this study from a sample of 119 cases identified between 1983 and 1992 by the National Center on Missing and Exploited Children. Twenty-seven subjects were female family members (mother, grandmother, or aunt) and 11 were male family members (fathers and grandfather). Family members ranged in age from 16 years to 67 years of age.

The time between the interview and the abduction ranged from one to seven years with a mean of 2.8 years (SD of 2.0 years). The infants were missing from one day to 90 days with a mean of 9.2 days (S.D. of 18.2 days). The majority of infants (n=20) in the study were missing two days or less.

Infant Abduction as a Family Crisis

What type of crisis is an infant kidnapping? Infant abduction is a sudden, unexpected physical loss of an infant followed by uncertainty for recovery of that child. The trauma stimulates fearful, negative images; parents said they imagined their baby suffering, being sold, abused, neglected, hurt, discarded, and lying in a trash can. This is a situation where the child is in the hands of a stranger for unknown reasons. While the baby is missing, the anxiety is overwhelming. This type of abduction trauma stimulates a reconstruction of the kidnapping and holds the risk of further traumatizing the parent.

Infants in this study were kidnapped from hospitals, private homes, and outside locations. Fifteen of the 27 infants in this sample were abducted from some area within a hospital. Ten were taken from their mother's hospital room, one from a nursery, and four from a pediatric unit. In eight cases, the mother was in her hospital room when the abductor, usually disguised by wearing a nurse's uniform, entered to say she needed to take the baby for tests or to be weighed. In two cases, the mother was in the bathroom when the abductor removed the baby from its bassinet. In four cases, the infant had been hospitalized for a physical illness, such as pneumonia, meningitis, or a gastric disturbance, and the abductor took the baby out of its crib; in one case, IV tubes were removed by the abductor. One abductor posing as a medical student stole a premature twin infant from the nursery.

In seven cases, the abductor used a work or employment ploy to gain access to a family's home for the kidnapping, for example, answering a newspaper ad for a babysitter. In two of the home cases, the abductor had been introduced to the family through a third party, and in one case, the abductor impersonated a visiting nurse. Two mothers and a father were shot and killed in the process of their infant being abducted from their home. In five cases, the abductor gained access to the baby at an outside location such as at a shopping mall, while befriending the mother and using a pretense to watch the baby while the mother shopped or stood in line for food. Two mothers were killed and one injured seriously during abduction from outside locations. Verbal or physical methods are used to kidnap an infant. As was used in the case example, a confidence or verbal ploy occurred in 13 cases; physical methods were used in seven cases; and severe force was used in seven cases.

Sequence of Events Associated with Abduction

What sequence of events was experienced by parents involved in the recovery of their infant? From the descriptions provided by parents and family members, four stages of family action and emotional response to having an infant kidnapped were noted.

1. Traumatic Impact of the Abduction News

Parents describe the sudden traumatic impact that registers physiologically when they had full realization that their infant was missing. This is noted in the hyperarousal and numbing symptoms. Parents are flooded with feelings of terror and disbelief. Shock overtakes them at the news of the infant's disappearance. The bonding process is frozen and their most immediate recall is their last image of their baby. One mother, after being notified of her baby's disappearance, began to hyperventilate, experience chest constriction, felt faint, and loudly cried, "My baby is dead." Another mother, one day postcaesarean section, remembered watching out of her hospital window the people searching the grounds and feeling numb because she could not contribute to the search. Another mother who had a broken arm, cracked ribs, and a mild concussion from being injured by the abductor had to be restrained and sedated to prevent her leaving the intensive care unit to join the search for her baby.

2. Fear and Anxiety Until the Infant is Recovered

Parents have to manage their fear and anxiety over the news of the abduction while simultaneously acting, with guidance, to recover the missing baby. Added to the terror of their baby missing is the frantic anxiety of the search. This is a complicated phase because the parents are also interacting with a host of other people. Strangers come into their lives and ask questions that can even be suggestive that they are part of the baby's disappearance. Parents may even be polygraphed by law enforcement. This phase lasts until there is news that the baby has been located. The time varies in length from hours to days to months.

In the case example, the husband was asked to take a polygraph test. The parents heard rumors that the baby was not the husband's, that the parents had changed their mind and did not want the baby and that they had sold the baby. The last rumor was made by the abductor who said the baby had been sold for $1,500. All these rumors added to the stress to the parents while their baby was missing.

3. Recovery and Rebonding

Parents experience great relief over the recovery of their infant. With recovery comes the long-awaited reuniting with their baby and the identification of the baby. The bonding process, temporarily on hold, takes on a reality dimension of threat.

Hypervigilance of their child ensues. The rebonding is directed by the length of time the baby is missing and the fears of the parents as to what happened to their baby. During this period, parents view their child as special because of the abduction. They keep scrapbook and videotapes of the media coverage; the event is discussed with the entire family. During rebonding, mothers generally refused assistance in their child's care from anyone. As one mother said, "I have to keep him with me all the time. He sleeps with me, and I have to constantly touch him."

Parents scrutinize their recovered infant. Unlike other forms of child abuse where children exhibit posttrauma symptoms, the kidnapped infants, when returned, are generally found to be in good health.[4] News reports note that the babies are returned unharmed and indeed, few have obvious negative consequences of having been kidnapped. However, eight parents in the study observed upon recovery of their baby severe diaper rash, a covering of insect bites on trunk and extremities, hair lice, and a lack of body and clothes cleanliness. Five parents commented on their baby having eating problems or crying hysterically when left alone. Parents were concerned with diet and nutrition; three noted that regular milk rather than formula had been given their child. In one case where the baby was missing for three months, parents questioned whether their baby's bowlegs were due to his drinking goat's milk for the time he had been abducted.

Sleep complaints and nightmares were noted in five of the infants within the first year. One 17-year-old mother who continued with a breast pump for nine days until the baby was returned said, "Before he was taken he was a hungry and chubby baby. Since he's been back he's been a very fussy eater and would not take the breast. He won't sleep alone, and will only sleep in my bed." Six parents reported their child experiencing fears and being easily startled to ordinary noises. In the case where both parents were murdered, the grandparents said for the first year, the infant would wake up nightly around 10 PM, shaking as if from cold, screaming, and unable to be calmed. Five years later, this night terror reaction was reported to be an intermittent symptom. It was known that on the night of the homicide, the mother had finished the 10 PM feeding and was preparing to return him to bed when her husband was shot and she tried to escape. The mother was found dead in her car with two gunshot wounds in her back and chest, keys in the ignition and a burping towel on her shoulder. She had no outer clothing; it was Christmas Eve and very cold. The baby was believed to be only lightly wrapped. When recovered, the baby was hospitalized for two weeks with pneumonia.

Over time, parents sometimes linked illness and other problems to the abduction. One mother described her two-and-a-half-year-old daughter becoming critically ill with a gastrointestinal problem and believed it was related to the abduction. Another mother placed a guard on the unit when her 18 month old was hospitalized.

4. Litigation and Retraumatization

A review of the phases of the abduction is an inherent part of the criminal litigation process. It requires a detailing of the abduction and can activate unresolved post trauma symptoms. Many feelings, including anger, fear, and anxiety, surface. Family members will be involved at some level for the criminal proceedings. Out of 38 family members interviewed, 19 attended the criminal trial and 21 wrote victim-impact statements.

Sentencing of the abductor was often a difficult issue for the families. Sentences ranged from probation and psychiatric treatment to years to life in prison for those who murdered. The abductor's release date creates fear because some parents recall the abductor insisting it was her baby. Thus, families do not believe the abduction is to be minimized; rather, they feel the abductor could still be a danger to the family, especially after release.

Symptom Response of Family Members

What symptoms do family members experience during and following the abduction of their infant? Recovery of the infant indicates a chronic state of family hypervigilance. All family members report posttrauma symptoms and these are of long duration. The parents are in a double bind. In part, the symptoms reveal an underlying assumption or presupposition that if they had been more vigilant and attentive, their baby would not have been taken. They are in a bind regarding giving up these now protective but hypertense behaviors for fear that if they let down, their family can be invaded again.

Parent Symptoms

A wide variety of symptoms are experienced by parents during and following abduction. Symptoms identified by more than 80% of the family members were intrusive thoughts of the kidnapping and changes in appetite. These symptoms were followed by increased nervousness (78.9%), sleep disturbance (76.3%), nightmares (73.7%), feeling disagreeable (73.7%), abduction nightmares (71.1%), troubling daydreams (71.1%), trying to avoid thoughts of the kidnapping (71.1%), feeling irritable (65.8%), easily startled (55.3%), and trying to avoid reminders of the event (47.4%).

After the baby is recovered, while there is some decrease in this high level of posttrauma symptoms compared to during the kidnapping, the percentage of reporting symptoms remains high (more than 50%) with the exception of "being disagreeable", e.g., feeling more argumentative and confrontative. This symptom increases and relates to interactions with other than family members.

Although the baby is returned, the traumatic memories advance to fantasies of continual threat and abduction, especially that danger that can befall the child when no one is in sight. Parents feel anxious about the safety of their child and can develop beliefs and fears that their child is not safe under any condition or at any age.

Social Network Support

Family members report many changes in social network relationships. The most frequent change involves family rules (89.5%). These changes included increased vigilance, repeated checking on family member whereabouts, and increased restrictions. There is a shift in the nuclear family that leads to monitoring and a need to know where the children are at all times.

The firmer structuring of family rules is paired with the second highest change, that of interaction with children. The majority (86.8%) of family members felt a positive change toward their children, making such comments as "You never know what you have till they are gone" and "How precious they are." There is parental hypervigilance and anticipation of a dangerous unfriendly world. For example, a mother lets her son play in the back yard, but constantly imagines someone can come through the bushes and grab him.

Over 71% reported a change in their work role. Mothers stopped working to stay at home with their child; fathers changed status and role in work settings to be closer to home. Role change involved less involvement in the work world. For example, one mother whose baby was gone one day, bargained to God, "I will stay at home if the baby is returned." She has not returned to work for seven years. Another mother, whose baby was found, promised she would change her life and no longer works.

The majority (68.4%) felt their life goals changed, and this change represented some mastery over the stress. Some narrowed their life goals; rather than traveling they stayed home and became more constricted in social activities. Several fathers quit their jobs, talked of changing jobs (e.g., becoming an FBI agent), or started their own business. One father described taking more risk with career with the overall attitude being: If I could go through something as tough as this, I can manage anything. This father, more than the mother, interacted and worked with the media with the goal to recover his child. He gave and coordinated press conferences. This effort paid off with a national TV network news story leading to a telephone tip from 2000 miles away that found the child in a state two hours south of the abduction location. This new self-confidence permitted the father a sense of mastery.

The fifth highest reported change was toward the spouse with the majority (63%) saying they felt closer to the partner, for example, "My husband is the only one I can trust," and "She is the only one who knows how I feel.". Twenty-three percent felt no change with their partner. There were two divorces and one separation postabduction in the sample, and two of the three husbands whose wives had been murdered had remarried.

Sixty percent of family members felt their family disagreements decreased, and they were able to communicate with each other in a frank and open way. Parents report staying closer together and feeling frightened to be out of each others' sight. Sometimes this prompts a parent to speak up: "We have less fights; we're more cooperative," or "I used to be passive; now I speak my mind in the family."

About half of the parents (52.6%) felt a positive change toward their parents (52.6%). Some grandparents responded to the crisis by helping in the home with other children. In one-third of the cases, the mother was not married. In two cases, the grandparents were estranged until the infant was kidnapped; with the abduction they reunited and offered their support.

Change in friendships (39.5%), change toward others (21.1%) involved with increased suspicion of strangers, and change toward in-laws (18.4%) were the lowest ranked items, indicating that the majority of family members reported no change in these categories.

Family member descriptions of the posttrauma symptoms support the notion that they are biologically based. For example, the mother's report of intrusive child-danger fantasies after the baby returns overwhelms the mother with visual images. This, in turn, retraumatizes her and sustains her high level of anxiety. This same phenomenon is noted in rape victims where they are imaging or dream of the return of the rapist.[7] This condition of interpersonal violence and the realization that it can happen again remains as an active thought or fantasy that triggers the autonomic nervous system and ultimately results in biological changes in that system.[8] This reaction is vicarious traumatization in that it was a baby that was kidnapped, but the loss and the fear of what dangerous things could happen to the baby stimulate the parent and inhibit the information processing of the trauma.[9]

The mother's symptomatology, which was higher than the father's, needs to be understood within the context of the family. After the infant is found and the father returns to work, it is usually the mother who has to manage the daily activities of protecting and caring for the baby. This might be a source of sustaining the high level of intrusive and avoidant symptomatology because she has to anticipate the daily safety of the child. In one case, every time the mother saw a large woman with permed brown hair, she would begin to hyperventilate, shake, and want to run.

Additionally, the mother or primary caretaker also has to deal with the infant's post-trauma symptoms. The baby's night terrors, noted in some cases, support Parkin's concept of nonverbal encoding that is well established at birth.[10] Also, Tinnin's concept of the double-mindedness of human memory suggests implicit memory is unavilable to conscious verbal recall, but available through behavior, thus, the behavioral reenactments through nightmares.[11]

It is interesting to note that the level of concentration in parents is not as disrupted as reported in other types of crime trauma such as rape. One difference is the source of the traumatizing event, e.g., the loss of the baby, is returned to the care and protection of the mother. The baby continues to grow and develop and thus, reminders of the abduction trauma are changed and removed; also, the baby does not talk of the abduction.

Hospital Response

Nurses were key hospital personnel when an abduction occurred. Nurses (73% of 51 hospitals surveyed) generally made the discovery of the missing infant and usually (68%) notified the victim mother of the incident. In all cases, there was an immediate search of the unit followed by a call to the security department.

In gathering information about the abductor, 24% of the hospital staff believed the abductor acted "suspicious" before the abduction. The media was quickly notified, and 67% of the hospitals surveyed believed media coverage assisted in infant recovery.

The news of an abduction came as a shock to all members of the nursing staff who were interviewed regardless whether or not they were on duty at the time of the discovery. The sense of distress remained for these nurses even following the

301

recovery of the baby. Out of 36 nurses interviewed, the majority (77.7%) expressed symptoms of posttraumatic stress disorder, including recurrent and intrusive thoughts of the event, distressing dreams, avoidance of reminders of the event, irritability, mood swings, and difficulty concentrating. Initial comments included: "I will never forget that night as long as I live," "I can never forget it," and "Every time I hear of another abduction case it brings it all back." Thirty percent of the nurses assigned to care for the victim mother resigned or transferred to another unit following the incident. One nurse manager of a unit where an infant had been abducted five years before described getting a panic feeling when she "turns around can't find one [of her grandsons]...the same panic I had the night when they told me we had a missing baby." This nurse also said she had purposely discarded the interviewer's phone number saying that she did not want any reminders of that baby.

Hospitals generally provided psychological support services to both parents and hospital staff. Only a minority of hospitals (23%) indicated that no psychological support services were offered to the parents. The remaining 41 hospitals (77%) offered some combination of social services, counsel with a chaplain, and psychiatric or psychiatric nursing services.

In contrast to these parent support services, 59% of the hospitals indicated that psychological support services were provided to their employees during or after the abduction incident. Of those employees who did use hospital-provided support services, most saw a psychiatric nurse (n=11) with a smaller number of employees seen by social services (n=8), a hospital chaplain (n=7), psychiatrist (n=4), or other (n=2).

As a result of the abduction incident, nearly 80% of the hospitals interviewed made changes in security measures for the obstetrical or pediatric units. Added security items were cameras, door locks, infant tag alarms, and door alarms. Forty-two percent of the hospitals interviewed reported major physical changes, including total relocation of the unit and removal of existing entrances. The posting of a security guard on the maternity unit immediately following the determination of an abduction was common to all the hospitals interviewed; three months after the abduction 29% of the hospitals still posted a round-the-clock guard. Seventy-five percent of the hospitals initiated changes in nursing policies, including parent education, infant identification, and employee identification.

The impact of this crime has long-lasting effects on the family both in terms of posttraumatic symptoms as well as the special manner in which the child is treated.

The distress of the parent was persistent regardless of the length of time the infant was missing and produced a chronic fear-response vulnerability.

Additionally, nursing staff directly involved with the abduction process are at risk for developing posttrauma symptoms. For all hospital staff, their sense of responsibility and feelings of anger and guilt require processing and resolution. Much of the anger is from adjustments that are made to secure and control the environment and the reality that in addition to their daily work with patients, they must now monitor and report all suspicious persons. The work environment becomes less secure.

There has been a tendency by some to minimize the act of infant abductions, feeling "sorry" for the abductor and attributing the act to a postpartum reaction following the cessation of a pregnancy. The planning noted in an abduction and the boldness of the act removes it from a reaction to replace a loss to an expression of entitlement, a right to someone else's infant.

Mental health can play a valuable role in providing crisis intervention and trauma therapy to family members and hospital staff. Careful detailing of the abduction event is suggested as a critical first step in the information processing of the trauma.[12] Further study and assessment of abductors is recommended to determine abductor characteristics and issues for preventive intervention.

REFERENCES
1. Mahoney BS. The extent, nature, and response to victimization of emergency nurses in Pennsylvania. *J Emerg Nurs*. 1991;17:282-91.
2. Smock BK. IAHS survey of infant abductions: 1983-1989. *J Healthcare Protection Manage*. 1989;Fall:40-50.
3. Grant R. The new babysnatchers. *Redbook*. 1990;May:151-154.
4. Rabun JB. *For Healthcare Professionals: Guidelines on Preventing Infant Abductions*. Arlington VA: National Center for Missing & Exploited Children; 1993.
5. Webster ML. How secure is your hospital? *Nurs Life*. 1987;7:25-30.
6. Beachy P, Deacon J. Preventing neonatal kidnapping. *J Obstet Gynecol Neonatal Nurs*. 1991;21:12-16.
7. Burgess AW, Holmstrom LL. Rape trauma syndrome. *Am J Psychiatry*. 1974;131:981-986.
8. van der Kolk BA, Saporta J. Biological response to psychic trauma. In: Wilson JP, Raphael B, eds. *International Handbook of Traumatic Stress Syndromes*. New York, NY; 1993.
9. Hartman C, Burgess A. Information processing of trauma. *Child Abuse Neglect*. 1993;17(1):47-57.

10. Parkin AJ. The development and nature of implicit memory. In: Lewandowsky S, Dunn JC, Kirsner K, eds. *Implicit Memory: Theoretical Issues*. Hillsdale, NJ: Lawrence Erlbaum; 1989:231-240.
11. Tinnin L. The double-mindedness of human memory. *ISTSS StressPoints*. 1994;3.
12. Hartman CR, Burgess AW. Information processing of trauma: a case application. *J Interpersonal Violence*. 1988;3:443-457.

Reprinted with permission of Crisis Intervention and Time-Limited Treatment, Harwood Academic Publishers and Dr. Albert R. Roberts, Founding Editor-in-Chief.

Chapter 33 – Autoerotic Fatalities

Ann W. Burgess, Robert R. Hazelwood, and Park E. Dietz

This chapter concerns deaths occurring in the course of autoerotic activities in which a potentially injurious agent was used to heighten sexual arousal. Autoerotic fatalities are deaths that occur as the result of or in association with masturbation or other self-stimulating activities. Such seemingly obscure deaths, estimated to be between 500 to 1,000 reported each year, affect not only the victims, but also their survivors and those whose professional roles demand knowledge of these matters.

There are important forensic nursing considerations. The majority of autoerotic fatalities involving injurious agents are accidental, but their features sometimes lead to mistaken impressions of suicide or homicide. The fact that many autoerotic fatalities share common characteristics with suicide, such as a finding that the victim was alone in a locked room or that he died by hanging, has led to initially classifying autoerotic deaths as a suicide. Other features, such as a blindfold, a gag, or physical restraints, have led to mistaken suspicions of homicide. Thus, understanding the important features of the autoerotic death scene, the classification of such fatalities, and the family response to the untimely death of the victim, provides the forensic nurse with knowledge for advanced practice.

Autoerotic Fatalities Study

In the spring of 1978, the Federal Bureau of Investigation (FBI) issued a mandate that original in-depth research be conducted on matters relevant to the law-enforcement community. In response to this mandate, Supervisory Special Agent Robert Hazelwood requested that students at the FBI Academy submit cases for the study. One-hundred and fifty-seven suspected cases were submitted to the Behavioral Science Unit over a three-year period.

The materials submitted varied somewhat between cases. In all instances, investigative reports were submitted along with either a description or photographs of the scene of death. Additional information was obtained related to interviews with the person who found the body and statements made by relatives. Writings, drawings, photographs, or notes that had been made by the victim were submitted in a number of cases. Although this collection of cases cannot be said to be a probability sample, it appears to be the largest collection of thoroughly investigated reported cases.

Sample Characteristics

The 157 cases were classified into four types of autoerotic death: asphyxial, atypical, partner-involved, and suicide.

Asphyxial Autoerotic Death

Asphyxial autoerotic activity was the most common form of death, accounting for 132 deaths or 84% of the sample. The asphyxial techniques most commonly recognized are compression of the neck through hanging or strangulation, exclusion of oxygen with a plastic bag or other material covering the head, obstruction of the airway through suffocation or choking, compression of the chest preventing respiratory movements, and replacement of oxygen with anesthetic agents.

It is important to note the distinction between autoerotic or sexual asphyxia on the one hand and asphyxia as a cause of death on the other. Autoerotic or sexual asphyxia refers to the use of asphyxia to heighten sexual arousal, more often than not with a nonfatal outcome. Although not necessarily fatal, sexual asphyxial practices are clearly dangerous. The autoerotic-asphyxia practitioner who dies while engaged in autoerotic asphyxiation most often dies from an unexpected overdose of asphyxiation when, for one reason or another, he becomes unable to terminate his means of enjoyment. From time to time, however, someone engaged in autoerotic asphyxia may die a nonasphyxial death (for example, from a heart attack, stroke, or exposure) during this activity. Conversely, it is theoretically possible that someone engaged in nonasphyxial autoerotic activities might die an asphyxial death (for example, carbon-monoxide poisoning from a faulty heater or automobile-exhaust system).

The overwhelming majority of victims in this sample were male and white. Of 132 persons who died by asphyxiation, five were female. There were four black males, one black female, one native American male, one Hispanic male, and one Hispanic

306

female. The mean age of decedents was 26.5 years. Four victims were preadolescent, 37 were teenagers, 46 were in their twenties, 28 in their thirties, eight in their forties, six in their fifties, two in their sixties, and one in his seventies. Although 76 (67.9%) of the 112 decedents for whom marital data was known were single, 41 of the 132 decedents were under age 20. Available data on social class suggest that the decedents were more often middle class than upper, working, or lower class. This is an unusual observation for cases coming to the attention of medical examiners and law-enforcement agencies, for members of the lowest social strata usually are disproportionately represented among traumatic deaths.

Atypical Autoerotic Fatalities.

There are forms of dangerous autoerotic activity that do not involve the purposeful use of asphyxia. These activities involve a wide variety of potentially dangerous activities, such as the use of nonasphyxial sexual bondage; infibulation; electricity; insertion of foreign bodies in the urethra, vagina, or rectum; and life-threatening games.

Nonasphyxial autoerotic practices can result in a variety of causes of death. There were 16 such cases submitted, including death by electrocution (6), heart attack (4), poisoning (4), exposure (1), and undetermined (1). In two other atypical cases, autoerotic asphyxia resulted indirectly in an asphyxial death due to aspiration of vomitus. These 18 decedents comprised 16 white males and two black females.

Sexual Asphyxial Fatalities Including a Partner

Sexual asphyxial deaths also occur in the presence of a partner. Most often, these are homicides in which a male assailant strangles, smothers, or otherwise asphyxiates a rape victim (male or female). Cases in which it was obvious that this is what occurred were not requested for this study, and none were submitted. A less common occurrence is the death by asphyxia of an individual who apparently consented to engage in sexual activity. In such instances, it is likely that there will be considerable difficulty in determining willful murder from negligent manslaughter. In addition, under certain circumstances, there may be difficulty in determining whether a sexual partner was present at the time of death.

It is also possible that a person engaged in autoerotic activity may incidentally become a homicide victim. The autoerotic activity may have nothing to do with the homicide. For example, an individual may be engaged in autoerotic activity when a burglar enters his home and kills him. The autoerotic activity may have some bearing on the homicide. In one case (not from the study sample), a wife shot and killed her husband in his bed, believing him to be her husband's lover. What she did not know at the time of the shooting was that her husband was a transvestite and had fallen asleep dressed in his female clothing after engaging in autoerotic activity.

A remote possibility that must always be borne in mind is that of a homicide scene staged to appear to be accidental autoerotic death. In one unusual case from the study, the decedent's wife, who had previously observed him engaging in autoerotic asphyxia, altered the death scene to make it appear like a homicide. Her effort was singularly unsuccessful, for she left the noose within sight and inflicted a minor stab wound that was readily shown to have been inflicted after death by asphyxia.

Autoerotic Suicides

True autoerotic suicides are rare. Over the years, many autoerotic fatalities have been mistaken for suicide, largely because the investigators were unaware of the phenomenon of autoerotic asphyxia. Thus cases described as a suicide by unusual methods or a bizarre form of suicide are scattered throughout the literature.

In addition, some cases are factitious suicides in which family members or others have removed evidence of sexual activity in order to make the manner of death appear to be suicide. In one study case, for example, the decedent's wife removed the female clothing he had been wearing at death and dressed his body in a suit before calling the police.

Two study cases were autoerotic suicides that could be documented as such on the basis of antemortem behavioral indicators, such as a suicide note. There is no possible means by which to determine with certainty how often other cases may have involved clear suicidal intent. It is certainly feasible that an individual fond of dangerous autoerotic activity will include that behavior in a purposeful suicide. It is conceivable that a suicidal individual, having heard of sexual asphyxia, might chose an asphyxial method of suicide over other options in order to lessen discomfort, but this possibility remains highly speculative. Also, an individual who repetitively engages in dangerous autoerotic practices might decide to end his or her life, although there is no proof of this ever having occurred. More likely, individuals fond of sexual risk-taking might escalate the risk to their lives purposefully with full knowledge that death might ensure, but without formulating a conscious intent to die on one particular occasion. Courts deciding whether to award accidental-death benefits in asphyxial autoerotic fatalities have presumed the intent of the decedent, ruling that the fact of the insured's having engaged in an obviously life-threatening act is sufficient evidence of the intent to bring about "the natural and probable consequences of the act" quite apart from whether any particular consequence was consciously intended in a given instance.

The Autoerotic-Death Scene

As in all death investigations, the autoerotic death scene should be preserved through photographs and sketches to complement the written record. The possibility of a victim's parent or spouse legally challenging the cause or manner of death listed on the death certificate should be anticipated. There have been cases where parents have litigated cases believing their child was murdered or pressuring a local coroner to change a ruling from accident during autoerotic acts to accident due to physical exertion. And the decedent's insurance company may also contest the manner of death when accidental-death benefits are at stake. Thus, a careful investigation and documentation of the death scene is of utmost concern. The major points to attend follow.

Location

Sexual fantasies preceed and accompany an autoerotic act. Thus, the individual preparing to act out his fantasies typically selects a secluded or isolated location. The locations involved in the study sample included locked rooms; isolated areas of the victim's residence, such as attics, basements, garages, or workshops; motel rooms; places of employment during nonbusiness hours; summer residences; and wooded areas. The victim's desire for privacy is paramount in the selection of location. Such acts require concentration on the fantasy scenario and, depending on the use of props, may require considerable preparation time. Thus the individual takes precautions to avoid disruption. The location itself may play a role in the victim's fantasy.

Case: A 28-year old repairman was discovered dead by coworkers when he failed to return to the office. His repair truck was located on a rural road approximately two miles from his last service call. The body was located in a heavily wooded area 250 feet from the roadway. The victim was lying face down with the upper portion of his body resting on his forearms. Around his neck was a 3/8-inch hemp rope secured by a slipknot. The rope extended from his neck to a tree limb approximately six feet overhead. To the left front of the victim were four magazines depicting nude females. The victim's pants were undone and his underwear had been lowered sufficiently to expose the penis and scrotum. Medical authorities recorded the cause of death as asphyxiation due to constricted carotid arteries.

Victim Position

Most commonly, the victim's body is partially supported by the ground, floor, or other surface. Occasionally, the victim is totally suspended. The most common position noted in the study was one in which the deceased was suspended upright with only the feet touching the surface. In most such cases, some type of ligature was around the neck and affixed to a suspension point within the reach of the victim. The forensic specialist should not be unduly influenced in deciding whether a death is accidental or homicidal by the fact that the body position seemingly indicates the involvement of a second party. Accidental-death victims have been found sitting, kneeling, lying face upward or downward, or suspended by their hands.

Case: A 32-year-old fully clothed man was found lying on his stomach on his floor. A handkerchief was over his mouth and tied behind his head. A length of rope wound around his neck and was tied with a slipknot. The rope ran down his back and was attached to a brown, leather belt which held his ankles together. His feet were pulled toward his head by the rope connecting his neck and feet. Blood had trickled from his nose and ears. The responding officers initially thought the death to be a homicide. An examination of the decedent's head revealed no blunt-force trauma, and the ear and nose bleeding was properly attributed to asphyxiation. They also noted the victim's arms were free: had he not lost consciousness, he could have released the ligature by the slip knot at his neck or by cutting the rope with a serrated steak knife found on the floor nearby. On a table beside the body were two similar pieces of rope that had been tied with slipknots. He had probably practiced with those two pieces of rope before engaging in the lethal act.

The Injurious Agent

The forensic-nurse death investigator at the death scene is charged with the responsibility of gathering information that will allow determination of any action or lack thereof that contributed to the victim's death. That includes that the injurious agent be studied in great detail, including a careful search for and analysis of possible malfunctioning.

In the study, the most common injurious agent was a ligature of some sort that compressed the neck. Other injurious agents included devices for passing electrical current through the body; restrictive containers; obstruction of the breathing passages with gags; and the inhalation of toxic gases or chemicals through masks, hoses, and plastic bags.

In the construction or use of these devices, the individual risks miscalculation. Depending on the mechanism used, he may misjudge the amount of time, substance, pressure, or current.

Case: A 23-year-old single, white male college student was found dead clad in a pair of shorts in his apartment that he shared with another male. His hands were secured in a pillory, which rested across his shoulders. This restraining device consisted of two pieces of wood secured at one extreme by a spring-load hinge. Two holes, lined with gray rubber, held his wrists and a six-inch hole had been cut to fit the neck. Situated between the neck and one wrist aperture was a padlock. Approximately two and a half feet from the victim's body was a set of keys, one of which fit the padlock securing the pillory. He was wearing a full-face gas mask with a hose leading from the mask to a metal canister which contained 13 cotton balls saturated with chloroform, a wadded wash cloth, two sheets of toilet paper, and a small bottle containing chloroform. He apparently dropped the keys, was unable to retrieve them, and lost consciousness. He died from chloroform inhalation.

The Self-Rescue Mechanism

The self-rescue mechanism is any provision that the victim has made to reduce or remove the effects of the injurious agent. The self-rescue mechanism may be nothing more than the victim's ability to stand erect, thereby lessening the pressure about his neck, or it may be as involved as an interconnection between ligatures on the extremities and a ligature around the neck, thereby allowing the victim to control pressure on his neck by moving his body in a particular way or pulling on a key point. Any of a wide variety of items or potential actions that the practitioner had available may have been intended as a self-rescue mechanism. If the injurious agent is a ligature, a slipknot or knife may be involved; if locks are involved, a key may be present; if chains are involved, a pair of pliers may be nearby. As with the injurious agent itself, the possibility of a malfunction of the self-rescue mechanism must be carefully considered.

Case: A 23-year-old white female died as a result of ligature strangulation. The woman had used an extension cord to interconnect her ankles with her neck. She had used a slipknot as a self-rescue mechanism. Examination of the slipknot revealed that in tying it, her hair had become entangled in the knot, thereby preventing her from disengaging it.

Bondage

The terms bondage and domination are used to describe a range of sexual behaviors closely related to the features commonly associated with autoerotic deaths. Bondage refers to the physical restraining materials or devices that have sexual significance for the user. This factor is important for its involvement and is most often responsible for the misinterpretation of these deaths as homicidal rather than accidental.

Physical restraints in the study included ropes, chains, handcuffs, and other similar devices that restricted the victim's movement. Even in obvious cases, the death investigator needs to prove it was physically possible for the victim to have placed the restraints as they were discovered. It may be necessary to duplicate bindings or knots, and for that reason, the knots should not be cut or undone prior to scrutiny.

Case: A 40-year-old man was discovered dead by his wife in the basement of their home. He was totally suspended by a rope that had been wrapped several times around an overhead beam. Around his neck was a hangman's noose that had been meticulously prepared. The body was dressed in a white T-shirt, a white panty girdle with nylons, and a pair of women's open-toed shoes. His hands were bound in handcuff fashion with the wrists approximately 10 inches apart. Over his head was another girdle, and his ankles were bound with a brown-leather belt. On discovering the body, the wife assumed her husband had been murdered.

The investigators correctly assessed the death as accidental and attributed the bound wrists, ankles, and covered head to sexual bondage. They recognized that the girdle covering his head was a bondage-related feature. Bodily restraint through bondage includes not only restrictions in the movement of the body but also constriction of the body and restrictions of the organs of sensation and expression. Constrictive materials identified in this study included elastic garments (for example, girdles, support hose, and tight underwear) and other materials, such as ace bandages. In one case, a man covered himself entirely with mud prior to placing a ligature around his neck. As the mud dried, it caked and constricted the skin. Examples of restrictions on the organs of sensation and expression identified in this study include hoods, blindfolds, and gags. In addition, belts, decorative chains, and other features have been observed that were presumed to be elements of symbolic bondage for the victim, as they often are for individuals who engage in other forms of sexual bondage behavior.

Sexually Masochistic Behavior

It will sometimes be observed that the decedent had inflicted pain upon his genitals, nipples, or other areas of his body. In addition to whatever pain may be associated with bondage restraints or constrictive materials, pain may have been induced mechanically, electrically, or through self-induced burns, piercing, or frank mutilation. Cases in the study have included a belt tightened around the scrotum, clothespins affixed to the nipples, electrical wire inserted into the penis or anus, an electrified brassiere, and cigarette burns to the scrotum. The term infibulation is used to describe the passing of needles or pins through the body, most often through the scrotum, penis, or nipples, but sometimes through an earlobe or the nose. In one case, pins had been passed through each of the decedent's nipples. The self mutilation may be more extreme, as in the following case.

Case: This 31-year-old white male was found suspended from a beam by a hangman's noose around his neck. His feet were touching the floor. He was nude except for a black-leather belt around his waist. Handcuffs secured his wrists in front, and a key to the handcuffs was found in his right hand. Examination of his penis revealed a surgical-like incision around the circumference of the shaft. Inserted and tightened into the incision was a metal washer. The outer edge of the washer was flush with the penis shaft.

Attire

Sometimes the victim is attired in one or more articles of female clothing, especially undergarments. Nylon, lace, leather, rubber, or other materials that hold sexual significance for the victim are commonly part of his attire. The investigator needs to be aware the attire may have been adjusted, altered, or completely changed by family members prior to the arrival of the investigative team. In the instances where this had been done, family members said they attributed their alterations to shame, embarrassment, or impulse.

Case: A 16-year-old white male was discovered dead in his room by his father. When the police arrived, they found the victim lying on his back and wearing blue jeans, a T-shirt, jockey shorts, and wool socks. A belt looped on one end, was near his head, as were his glasses. His father informed the officers that when originally found, his son was wearing only his T-shirt and socks. The victim's underwear and pants were on the floor at the end of the bed. The father said that he did not know why his son had been undressed when first found and that he had dressed his son without thinking.

Had the adjustment in attire not been discovered, the death might have been ruled a suicide. Close examination of the body and its lividity may reveal that attire or restraints have been adjusted, altered, or completely changed, or that the body has been moved since death.

Protective Padding

Frequently, the victim will be found with soft material between a ligature and the adjacent body surface. The purpose of this protective padding is to prevent abrasions or discoloration that might prompt inquiries from family or friends. In the previous case, the parents had no idea their son was involved in such dangerous activities. His mother, however, recalled that some months prior to her son's death she had noted burn marks on both sides of his neck. When she inquired as to their cause, he had explained the marks as having occurred when he had been grabbed by his jersey while playing football. When he was discovered dead, there was no protective padding in place.

Sexual Paraphernalia

Sexual paraphernalia was found on or near the victim in many cases in the study sample. These paraphernalia included vibrators, dildos, and fetish items, such as female garments, leather, and rubber items. Often materials that are present are not recognized as having a sexual meaning for the victim because they do not appeal sexually to the investigator and are dismissed as inconsequential. All items at the scene and their proximity to the body should be noted and photographed in their original positions for later interpretation. In the case of a 51-year-old single male victim, discovered fully dressed with the exception of wearing two leather jackets, and suspended by a rope around his neck and attached to a tree limb, a search of his residence revealed the following: over 50 leather coat, ropes, chains, handcuffs, leg irons, a penis vice, scrotum weights, electrical shock devices, discipline masks, traffic cones with fecal material on them, 107 pairs of leather gloves of which 29 were determined to have seminal stains inside, a mace with chain, and spiked ball, canes, whips, and assorted padlocks.

Props

Items found at the death scene may have been used as fantasy props. Items so identified in this study included mirrors, commercial erotica, photographs. films, and fetish items. One wife volunteered that the bondage magazine found by her husband's body was open to his favorite bondage picture. She said he would replicate to exact detail every knot and tie in the picture. Magazines about women's fashions and hairstyles were also found in the possession of some cross-dressers. In one case, a movie projector threaded with a pornographic film was found, indicating the victim had been watching the film prior to or during his final autoerotic act. One man found bound and hanging, with mirrors arranged such that he could view himself, had been watching an explicitly sexual movie on cable television.

Masturbatory Activity

The victim may or may not have been engaged in manual masturbation during the fatal autoerotic activity. The presence of seminal discharge is not a useful clue in determining whether a death is due to sexual misadventure. Seminal discharge frequently occurs at death, irrespective of the cause or manner of death. To be sure, the existence of seminal stains on the victim or nearby surfaces should be noted, photographed, and collected for possible blood-type determination and comparison to the victim, but the mere presence of seminal staining is not evidence of sexual activity.

Manual masturbation may be suggested by finding the victim's hand on or near his genitals, but it is to be remembered that the extremities may twitch or move in the final movement of life. Other indicators of sexual activity include such findings as a dildo or vibrator in or near the body, the penis wrapped in cloth to prevent staining of garments, or exposure of the genitals of a victim who is otherwise dressed. Individuals committing suicide by hanging avoid nudity (except for prisoners). Complete nudity in death is presumptive evidence of an autoerotic death.

Frequently no direct evidence of manual masturbation exists. Indeed, some living practitioners of autoerotic asphyxia have reported that they did not manually masturbate while asphyxiating themselves, but rather used asphyxiation to arouse themselves sexually, after which they would manually masturbate.

Evidence of Previous Experience

Five types of information were found in the study that is useful in judging the extent of the victim's prior experience: information from relatives and associates, permanently affixed protective padding, suspension-point abrasions, complexity of the injurious agent, and collected materials.

Information from Relatives and Associates. Although family members, sexual partners, and friends sometimes have no awareness of the victim's dangerous autoerotic practices, they may nonetheless have observed behavior that gains meaning in retrospect. One father noted that his son was always tying knots. Another father knew that his son occasionally put a belt around his neck and tightened it until becoming weak.

Permanently Affixed Protective Padding. One factor indicative of prior practice is the permanent affixing of protective padding to ligatures or devices used in the activity. This suggests both the that victim has engaged in similar acts in the past and that he intended to do so in the future. The padding indicates the victim's intent to prevent leaving marks on his body.

Suspension Point Abrasions. If the victim's death involved the use of ligatures over or around suspension points, the forensic specialist should examine those areas and others like them for abrasions or grooves caused by similar use in the past. A young white male died while suspended from a braided leather whip that went around his neck and over the top of a closet door. The whip was secured to a wheel and tire on the opposite side of the door. His hands were free, but his ankles were loosely bound with leather thongs. The door top revealed several grooves and abrasions from previous use.

Complexity of the Injurious Agent. When the injurious agent is highly complex, it is likely that the apparatus became complex through repetitive experience and elaboration over time. One 26-year-old victim was discovered dead wearing a commercially produced discipline mask and had a bit in his mouth. A length of rope was attached to each end of the bit and ran over his shoulders, going through an eyelet at the back of a specially designed belt he was wearing. The pieces of rope ran to eyelets on both sides of his body and were connected to wooden dowels that extended the length of his legs. The ropes were attached to two plastic water bottles, one on each ankle. The bottles were filled with water and each weighed seven pounds. The victim's ankles had leather restraints about them. A clothespin was affixed to each of the victim's nipples. The victim's belt had a leather device that ran between his buttocks and was attached to the rear and front of the belt. This belt device included a dildo that was inserted into his anus and an aperture through which his penis protruded. His penis was encased in a piece of pantyhose and a toilet-paper cylinder. A small red ribbon was tied in a bow at the base of his penis.

Family Response

Although the forensic and law enforcement literature describes the investigative and medical components of autoerotic deaths, little exists in the behavioral or social science literature that describes this type of fatality or the response of family members and others. This absence may be attributed largely to: 1) misdiagnosis of suicide or homicide rather than accident, and thus an underreporting of this manner of death; 2) a general acceptance and encouragement of all types of consenting sexual activity and a concomitant reluctance to acknowledge or emphasize the dangerous component in certain sexual activities, e.g., sexual bondage; and 3) social stigma surrounding sexually motivated death.

Clearly there is a need to alert forensic nurses and mental health professionals about young people who engage in this type of activity in order that they and their families can be counseled. This need has been heightened through the study by learning of parents of young victims who had been shocked at the sudden death of their children and who had known nothing about the manner of these deaths. If parents who have lost children to this type of death believe it is timely to talk about the subject, not only to investigators but to the news media, then forensic nurses whose work may bring them into contact with families need accurate information also.

Traumatic News

There is no news that has so great a psychological effect upon survivors as the death of a family member or close associate. Although many factors influence the severity of a stress reaction to a traumatic grief event, the emotional response is particularly devastating when the discovery of the body is made by a family member of friend, when the death is untimely, when the decedent is young, and when the death is sexual in nature. These are the factors generally present in autoerotic fatalities.

Upon learning of a victim's death, friends and family were invariably stunned and shocked. The victim was usually described as having been in good spirits and physical health, as active and having a future orientation. There was rarely any suspicion of suicidal ideation.

A sexual death resulting from the use of an injurious agent during a masturbatory ritual is considered an unusual type of death because many people, professionals included, have never heard of it. Although many people are familiar with autoerotic practices using manual stimulation, it appears that a significantly smaller number of people are aware of techniques for reducing oxygen to the brain to achieve an altered state of consciousness and to enhance erotic sensations and fantasy. The sexually associated features of this type of death puzzle and confuse family members.

Family members may help investigators to determine if the victim had prior experience with autoerotic asphyxia. In the study, relatives made pertinent observations but, lacking the knowledge of dangerous autoerotic activity, failed to attach significance to the victim's preoccupation with tying knots, signs of red marks on his neck, bloodshot eyes, or confused behavior for short time periods.

In summary, the reaction of the family to this type of death depends on how, when, and what they are told. Clinicians skilled in this area should be called upon to assist in the grieving process.

This chapter has been reprinted with permission from sections of the book, *Autoerotic Fatalities,* by Robert R. Hazelwood, Park E. Dietz, and Ann W. Burgess. West Newton, MA: Awab, Inc; 1997.

Chapter 34 – Rape and the Prostitute

Ann Wolbert Burgess and Lynda Lytle Holmstrom

The first time we were called on a rape case where the patient was a prostitute, we both wondered what we would do. What did the woman want from the hospital? Would she talk with us or tell us to go away? What should we say to her? Since one can never be faulted for "playing it straight," we simply talked to her as we did to any other patient. As the year went on and we talked to prostitutes, such as in the opening case example, and to the staff about rape victims and prostitutes, two things became clear.

First of all, we realized that the presence of prostitutes in the emergency ward of the hospital and making complaints at the police station influences the way people perceive rape victims in general. To some people, working in hospitals and in the police system, the term "rape victim" triggers a suspicious attitude that the victim may not be telling the truth; that she may "just be a prostitute who didn't get paid." It became clear that a lot of energy is exerted by staff in asking themselves, "Is it a real rape, or is she a prostitute?"

Second, it became clear that, if one takes the time to talk to the prostitute about her problems, one will learn a great deal. The literature on prostitution, like that on rape, has tended to overlook the human predicament of the women involved. Prostitutes have important information to tell and people need to listen to and understand their perspective.

Victimization of the Prostitute

There are ways in which prostitutes are victimized because of their occupation. This became increasingly clear as we talked with the 18 prostitutes who came to the hospital emergency department with a complaint of rape. We have categorized the ways in which they are exploited as 1) rape, and 2) sex-stress situations, including nonpayment, perversion, robbery, and violence. Prostitutes are especially vulnerable to exploitation in these ways. Because the services they provide are against the law at present, it is much harder for them to obtain justice by reporting their victimization to the authorities.

Rape

For a man who wants to rape a women, the prostitute is an easy mark. She is often known by her occupation or her style of "hooking" or by her hours of work. The prostitute is often on the street in the early hours of the morning when there is minimal protection. Some prostitutes are raped because the man knows who they are and knows that the victims will have next to no chance of going to court and of bringing charges against him due to their own reputations and records with the courts.

Of the 18 prostitutes from our victim sample, three were raped. The following example illustrates how one well-known prostitute was victimized because the two men must have known what she was.

Nora, a 22-year-old attractive woman, wearing a frosted wig and wearing brown hot pants and tan jersey and a blue multicolor design blazer, was brought to the emergency service by the police at 5 AM. She was barefoot, the men having taken her black suede platform sandal shoes. She cried when describing certain parts of the experience, but was composed and in control of her reactions for most of the interview.

Nora said she was walking along the street having just left a local bar, when a small car pulled up, and a little man jumped out and grabbed her by the arm and pulled her into the car. He put his arm around her neck and said, "We want to fuck you." The man driving the car spoke in a foreign language to the other man. When they arrived at the apartment building, the man put his hand over Nora's mouth and pushed her up to a third-floor apartment. In the apartment, the men told her to take her clothes off. She said no, and one man started to pull at her clothes and jacket, and the other man slapped her in the face and punched her in the chest. The men seemed to fight with each other over who was going to go first. The big guy pushed the little man, which angered him to the point where he put all his clothes on, which he had taken off, and took Nora's shoes and money – $6 – which she had in her purse. He threatened to take everything and said, "How'd you like to go home without your clothes and hair?"

320

The big man pushed Nora on the bed and asked how much money she made a night and what she charged. Then he asked her to blow him and threatened to cut her up in little pieces and leave her in the cellar if she did not do as he said. She was quite frightened by this. The man said he wanted sex. Nora said she had her period and that she had a tampon in place. This did not matter to him, and the man continued to penetrate her. Nora told him he was hurting her, which made no difference.

The little man then came back to the apartment and the two men began shouting at each other. The little man took a candle and beat Nora with it, saying he did that because a candle would leave no marks (and it did not). Nora finally managed to get away from the men and went to a local restaurant where a security guard called the police, who in turn brought her to the hospital. The police, who knew her, said the facts indicated that she had been raped. The police were able to arrest the two men, and the case was assigned for arraignment. However, typical of the other prostitutes who were able to identify the assailant who raped, robbed, or assaulted them, this woman never appeared in court. The decision not to appear seemed to occur with the prostitutes who were known to the police and who had arrests for prostitution. It is speculated that they feel their backgrounds would be held against them. This is one reason why, in the majority of these cases, the woman does not appear for district level hearing, and the case is usually dismissed.

Sex-Stress Situations

Prostitution is basically a business transaction involving an agreement between the provider and the buyer. The prostitute offers services for a price, and the customer who obtains the services is expected to pay for them. Customers may, however, violate the contract by nonpayment, perversion, violence, or robbery. Almost all of the prostitutes we talked to at the hospital had been victims of such sexually stressful situations during the course of the night's work. It should be noted, however, that the chief complaint of these victims, as listed in the hospital record, is "rape." Societal attitudes and the law are such that one does not simply walk into the hospital and say, "I work the streets and something really upsetting happened to me tonight." Instead, the patient must make the request for help in an indirect way. Thus, for official bureaucratic purposes the chief complaint gets listed as "rape."

Nonpayment

Prostitutes are aware of the possibility they might not get paid. Some told us, for example, that as a precaution, they always tried to get the money first before providing the sex. Nevertheless, nonpayment was still a common form of exploitation mentioned by the prostitutes we saw. It seemed to occur in the following ways.

First, as in the opening example, the man persuades the woman to have sex first, then he refuses to pay. One prostitute told us she had been persuaded to provide sex first because the man had said, "The last time I paid first, the girl took the money and left and I got nothing." Or, if it is a group of men and several prostitutes, one man may say the other man is paying, and because of the circumstances of the situation, the woman never gets paid.

Second, the contract is made, and then violence is used instead of money. There may be two men, one of whom holds the woman while the other forces her to have sex and then the roles are reversed. The woman is then pushed out of the car and no money is paid. Ten of the 15 women prostitutes in sex-stress situations were assaulted by two or more men. Or, there is a weapon used after the contract is made, rather than payment.

Perversion

Prostitutes typically have a certain range of sexual services that they sell, but these do not necessarily include the full gamut of what certain men desire. Thus, the prostitute may find out only when it is too late that the customer really has much more in mind than she does. The case illustration which is presented in some detail later in this chapter provides an example of this. The two prostitutes were made to do sexual things to each other while the men watched and laughed, and, also, one prostitute was made to urinate on a drunken man's face. The women described these acts as being distasteful to them.

Robbery

Prostitutes are easy prey for robbery. They are known by their occupation and may keep their money with them until the end of the night's work. One victim complained of being robbed of $150. Another victim had been paid $80, but the young men who paid her robbed her later of this money. She was so angered that she told authorities she would press charges. She went to court. She told her story on the witness stand, saying she had prostituted herself for money and that the young men later took the money away. The judge reprimanded everybody. He said, "These boys should not be involved in such debauchery...But," he added, "no matter how she earned the money, one should not steal it from her." He ordered that the payment be made before the men could be released. Right in the courtroom, their lawyers walked over and paid her in cash what was owed. This, incidentally, is one of two prostitutes in our sample so far to actually go to court; and, although she originally wanted to press charges, she had been very ambivalent about going through with it and told both us and the police many times that she did not want to testify and that she wanted to drop the charges. The case is unusual in that it got to court at all.

Violence

Prostitutes become equally concerned when the sexual behavior of the client turns to violence. They say very explicitly that they fear for their life when this occurs. The woman from one case said that she reported one assault and not others. She said, "I'll go to court on this one. I hope they hang him. This time the guy beat me up and he's a sadist. Suppose he got a virgin sometime – it could ruin her mentally." The woman went on to describe parts of the assault:

He said he would kill me if I didn't do as he said. He called me names such as whore, slut, cunt. Then he would ask me if I was scared while he waved the gun in my face. Then he asked if I would like it if he killed himself in front of me – Would it be an experience for me? He made me blow him, and he raped me front and back. He tied me to the bed and beat me with his belts. Nothing has hurt like that.

Reactions to Victimization

A Range of Emotions

Prostitutes respond to rape, nonpayment, violence, and the other types of victimization with a variety of feelings. Some link their reaction specifically to their feelings of being exploited as a woman. The prostitute quoted at the beginning of the chapter said, "The man said I didn't have to put the police onto him. But he doesn't know how I felt as a woman. I had to get some revenge. I had to do something. He forced me to have sex."

Another prostitute said, "I feel I was used; treated like a joke; treated like an animal. It was inhuman." Such statements often come from women who have been forced to indulge in what they regard as perverse sexual acts or who have been degraded in very specific terms or sent into the street without any clothes.

It is not unusual to find the prostitute very angry and wishing to have some revenge. One woman intended to find her assailants and stated:

I am going to stand around [street walking] till I see them again. Then I am going to tell the police. I will stand around till I see them. I have already told the police the first half of the license plate, and I just need to find the rest of the number or the guys.

Revenge can take another route with a different type of weapon. One prostitute who was concerned she might have a venereal disease said, "Maybe they'll catch it. I hope they suffer. They won't notice they have it [until it is too late]. They were so out on dope."

Ambivalence about Being "In the Life"

In contrast to the prostitutes quoted above, whose concern was with the particular victimization that had just occurred, some of the prostitutes also voiced concern about their lifestyles. The prostitutes who did this tended to be ambivalent about being "in the life" and seemed to be trying to decide if prostitution was what they really wanted to do. Their comments focused not only on the exploitation aspect, but also on their own reactions to being a prostitute and the reactions of other people to their occupation. They were reacting to a more diffuse kind of victimization that results from living in a society where many people are only too willing to reward them for their services, but want also to berate them for these same services. Ambivalence was also shown in another case in which a woman contracted for sex, but then at the last moment could not go through with the act. This woman stated:

I've just arrived in Boston and I was looking for an apartment, a cheap one. Two men were on the street. I asked them if they knew of any apartments, and we talked, and then after a while they offered me a ride back to where I was staying. While in the car they propositioned me and said each would pay me $15. We went to their apartment, but I just couldn't go through with it. I told them and tried to get away. The older guy didn't care, but the younger man forced me to have sex. I couldn't get away from him.

In the following case, the woman volunteers the information about her work and reactions to it:

I had thought of going to the street for a profession. Thought about it and ended up doing it...Did it today, but it was just one of those days. But I go for my checkups; clean myself out; don't take any chances. I am living with a girlfriend. My mother said if I went into that, she might as well forget that she had a daughter. She said if she died, not to come to the funeral. I wanted my daughter to live with me, but my mother kept her, said she would understand things.

In asking this woman how she felt and how she thought she would be after tonight's incident, she said: "I will have to be more cautious. I am edgy now; nerves are bad. Get these awful sinus headaches." She also told us that she had seen a psychiatrist at another hospital the month before. She had taken an overdose of pills and had to see the psychiatrist before being discharged. It is of interest that she talked considerably of her therapist as well as her concern over her mother's reaction to her occupation. We asked if she had someone to talk to about this incident. The woman replied, "Maybe I should talk about it. Gives me a headache to keep it inside. I try to keep on the bright side and not make things seem so bad." Not only did the woman express her ambivalence about her lifestyle, but she was also aware of the tension her lifestyle created in her life. This woman talked spontaneously to us and clearly indicated a request to ventilate.

Case Illustration of Sex Stress

Two prostitutes were admitted to the emergency department two days before Christmas. Both were quite willing to talk about the incident as well as to make quite clear from the start that their business was "working the streets." The two women had been involved with four men that evening and were quite upset about the incident. We will describe the case in detail, as it encompasses all four of the methods by which we have seen prostitutes victimized by clients with whom they contracted for sex: nonpayment, perversion, robbery, and violence.

April, age 23, wore a brown pin-striped pants outfit and a tan leather, belted short coat, and tan wool tam-type hat. She was carefully made up with eye makeup, wore a medium length black-hairstyle wig; wore many rings on her fingers, and carried a multicolored shoulder bag.

Holly, age 24, wore her long black hair straight and was carefully made up. She was wearing a dark-gray turtleneck sweater, black velveteen slacks with circular multistriped stockings, and high-platform shoes. She wore gold sparkle-rimmed glasses and midi length tan-colored coat with fur-trimmed collar and hem.

Both women were quite attractive and stylish in appearance. They said they began working around 11 PM, the block next to their usual block ("It had been getting hot with police around our usual spot so we moved for that night."). It was two days before Christmas and considerable activity was going on in that downtown area of Boston.

They were soon approached by three men who began to contract with them. The women said there was a third girl they could get, "but as the men kept talking and the money kept going up, we decided to do it between the two of us – they offered $100 to go back to their place for the evening."

The men took April and Holly to a house described as old, dingy, and dirty. The men broke one of the doors down and when they did, "there was a drunk lying in the bed." There was no furniture in the room, and the women began to wonder what they had gotten into. The men separated the women – taking April upstairs and keeping Holly downstairs. They didn't like working that way and began to see the men were lying to them. For example, April said Holly had some condoms, and the man said she didn't and April knew that Holly always carried them. Then April asked where the money was – that they were to be paid first. The man kept saying it was downstairs with the others.

The women thought they were separated so each man could "do his own thing," but then they were brought together, and it became clear that there was more involved for them. April said, "I came in the room and saw one guy pulling up his pants, and I could see Holly struggling and trying to get away, so I knew something had happened. Then they said they would cut our throats; they told Holly if she put her head up they would kill her. I thought I'd go for help, but one guy pulled me back and said he would kill me if I tried that again. I really thought I would be killed. Holly was crying because they did something unnatural to her, so then they started doing things to me. Then they made us do sexual things to each other while the men sat and watched and laughed. While Holly was doing something sexual to me, someone took a broom handle, dipped it in shaving cream and stuck it in my rectum. It hurt so bad, but I didn't dare cry or scream for fear the men wouldn't like it. We had to suck the men lots of times, and they also got the old drunk in on things. They made me urinate on the old drunk's face, and the others sat around and laughed. They also made me stick a fork in the old drunk's prick."

The women were forced to do sexual acts to the men "on command." The men also had vaginal and rectal sex with the women. One man took April to the bed and just held her and said such things as "I love you and I'd like to spend the night holding you." He did not do anything sexual, and April thought this behavior was strange and it frightened her. One man was described as being oversexed, and he had to keep proving to everyone how often he could have sex with the women.

The men stripped both women and searched for money that was kept in their stockings. The men also looked for needle marks and not seeing any said, "Most of you girls are on drugs – how come you aren't on drugs?"

There was considerable conversation during the evening. The women felt they had to talk and say the things the men wanted to hear because they were afraid they would be killed. Holly asked one of the counselors whether she had ever felt like she would be killed – this seemed to be something specific the women wanted to talk about.

In exploring this line of thought, it appeared that the men had talked about death with the women and talked about what death was like saying, "What happened after the lights went out." Holly felt this was a message of some kind and that perhaps they were going to be killed.

April said, "They had quite an orgy for themselves. Two would be on us at a time, and one seemed like he was on drugs. He kept saying he liked me; that I was like his girlfriend. I was nervous then. It was dawning on me what was happening. That man must be sick. If a guy is going to rape a girl, he wouldn't talk like this. And I thought, 'What have I got myself into?' I thought I was going to pass out – it was hot and their bodies were hot. And I had to do a lot of things to keep their minds on sex and off of violence.

This orgy lasted from 11:30 PM. until 3:30 AM. The men then escorted April and Holly out of the building, saying such things as, "Look at all the fun we had. Now how much do we owe you," and then rather than pay, they just laughed. Holly said, "It was a big joke. They told us to have a Merry Christmas. One man said to another man, 'You weren't even going to come along for a beer with us tonight. See what you got.'"

After the men left them, April and Holly decided to go to the police and walked into a station which was across the street and told the officers what had happened. The officers returned to the building and arrested the drunken man who was the owner of the building. Then the police brought the women to the hospital. One of the men told April that a lot of women in Boston were looking for him because he was spreading syphilis around. The women were concerned about medical treatment and specifically asked for that. They also requested their mouths be examined, as April complained of soreness and also knew the possibility of contracting venereal disease through oral contact.

In talking with the women about other reactions, they said that the men had called them degrading names and that upset them. When asked how it felt sexually to them, one woman answered, "I didn't feel anything. I thought, 'I'll play it cool' and maybe we'll get out. You had to laugh to participate to keep it going; to fake it."

In asking their reasons for pressing charges, April said, "Oh, definitely. These guys might take a girl who is not in this business. It might make her go into a mental state. Even we could. But especially someone else. They might even take a woman coming out of her home – even a married woman with children."

In asking how they planned to handle their feelings about the incident and who they might talk to about it, they said, "We'll tell our friends – tell them to be on the lookout for these guys. And I think I'll be more skeptical of men. I'll only go to places I know."

Holly said, "I never thought it would happen to me. Girls have told me about such things. But it was like being in prison. I felt guilty – I thought if I hadn't been so eager [for the money] I wouldn't have gone there."

In asking their feelings about going to court, April said, "There was a judge who once said that regardless of who you are, no one has the right to assault you." However, Holly felt the courts would give them a very hard time.

On follow-up, the police said that the women did not show up in court for the arraignment, and so the case was dismissed against the one man who owned the building.

In summary, these two prostitutes were able to discuss their occupation and their victimization. They stated a medical and police request for intervention. They expressed concern over wishing to protect other women against such a situation, and they also expressed fears and reactions to the violence of the incident.

Reprinted with permission from Burgess AW, Holmstrom LL. *Rape: Crisis and Recovery*. West Newton, MA: Awab; 1986.

328

About the Author

Ann Wolbert Burgess, RN, DNSc, CS, FAAN, is van Ameringen Professor of Psychiatric Mental Health Nursing at the University of Pennsylvania School of Nursing. She received her bachelor's and doctoral degrees from Boston University and her master's degree from the University of Maryland.

Dr. Burgess, with Lynda Lytle Holmstrom, cofounded one of the first hospital-based crisis-intervention programs for rape victims at Boston City Hospital in 1972. From that program, Dr. Burgess established rape trauma syndrome as a nursing diagnosis, published in the *American Journal of Psychiatry* in 1974. The admissibility of rape trauma syndrome in legal proceedings has been referenced in over 300 appellate court decisions. Her clinical research on rape victims has advanced knowledge of psychosocial concepts of trauma, human behavior, and nursing care. One current development of the work with rape victims has been the forensic-nursing role of Sexual Assault Nurse Examiner (SANE). States, including Massachusetts and New Jersey, passed legislation in 1995 to permit these nurses to practice independently in this role, to testify in court as a fact witness, and to be reimbursed for services rendered.

Following initial unfunded research on rape victims, Dr. Burgess has conducted many funded projects. She has been principal investigator of research projects on the use of children in pornography; heart attack victims and return to work; sexual homicide and patterns of crime scenes; possible linkages between sexual abuse and exploitation of children, juvenile delinquency, and criminal behavior; children as witnesses in child sexual abuse trials; AIDS, ethics, and sexual assault; and infant kidnapping. She has written nine textbooks in the fields of psychiatric nursing and crisis intervention and 10 books on assessment and treatment of child, adolescent, and adult sexual assault victims and serial offenders, including rapists, murderers, child molesters, and abductors. She has coauthored more than135 articles and chapters in the field of rape victimology and coauthored six monographs for the Department of Justice on child sex rings, adolescent rape victimization, adolescent runaways, child molesters and abductors, juvenile prostitution, and infant abductions. Her current research is on patterns of trauma in elderly and handicapped rape victims and testing interventions for reducing post-trauma symptoms in rape victims.

Dr. Burgess has maintained a private clinical practice since 1966 in Massachusetts. In addition, she serves as an expert witness in criminal and civil suits for the government, plaintiff, and defense. Through her writings, lectures, and leadership at the national level, Dr. Burgess impacts on the delivery of care for traumatized populations in need of psychiatric services.

Dr. Burgess has served on the ANA Council of Specialists in Psychiatric Mental Health Nursing Executive Committee, the ANA Cabinet of Nursing Research, and the American Academy of Nursing's Governing Council. She has served as chair of the first Advisory Council to the National Center for the Prevention and Control of Rape of the National Institute of Mental Health (1976-1980). She was a member of the 1984 US Attorney General's Task Force on Family Violence and was a member of the planning committee for the 1985 Surgeon General's Symposium on Violence. She served on the National Institutes of Health National Advisory Council for the Center for Nursing Research (1986-1988) and was a member of the 1990 Adolescent Health Advisory Panel to the Congress of the US Office of Technology Assessment. She was chair of the National Institutes of Health AIDS and Related Research Study Section (ARRR 6) (1992-1994). She was elected to the National Academy of Sciences Institute of Medicine in October 1994 and chaired the 1996 National Research Council's Task Force on Violence Against Women and the 1998 Institute of Medicine's Committee on Lesbian Health Research Priorities.